GCSE
PHYSICS

Michael Shepherd
Formerly Head of Science
Malvern College, Worcestershire
and
Ian Lovat
Director of Science and Technology
Ampleforth College, York

Letts
EDUCATIONAL

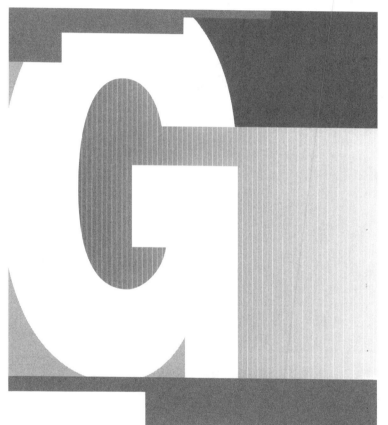

Letts Educational
Aldine House
Aldine Place
London W12 8AW

Tel: 020 8740 2266
Fax: 020 8743 8451
E-mail: mail@lettsed.co.uk

First published 1979
Revised 1981, 1983, 1986, 1987, 1989, 1994
Reprinted 1988, 1991, 1993, 1995, 1996, 1999, 2000, 2001
New edition 1997

British Library Cataloguing in Publication Data
A CIP record for this book is available from the British Library.

ISBN 1 85805 436 2

Printed in Great Britain by Bath Press Colourbooks, Glasgow

Letts Educational Ltd, a division of Granada Learning Ltd. Part of the Granada Media Group.

Contents

3 Questions and answers

Introduction

Knowing how to prepare for an examination can be difficult. This book will make it easier by providing you with a revision course. It contains not only the necessary topics, and questions on these topics, but also an extensive selection of sample examination questions with answers. To get the best from the study scheme in this book you are advised to follow the procedure outlined below.

How to use this book

Turn to pages 3 to 8 for the Analysis of Physics Syllabuses. The book covers all GCSE and Scottish Physics syllabuses. Find the Examining Group, the syllabus and the tier applicable to your Physics course and examinations (if you are not sure ask your teacher). The Analysis of Physics Syllabuses shows you:

- which grades are awarded for your tier.
- the number of examination papers you will have to take and their length.
- the percentage of the total mark awarded to the external examination and to teacher internal assessment.
- the address of your Examining Group. You may wish to contact the Group for past examination papers or a copy of the syllabus.

The tables on pages 3 to 8 show which topics are applicable to each GCSE syllabus, the Standard Grade in Scotland and the International GCSE. If a topic is followed by the letter H, this means that the material covered in it is required for the Higher Tier only. In preparing for the examination you should concentrate on the topics which correspond to the tier for which you are entered.

You are advised to work through as many of the required chapters as possible. You may find it helpful to consult your Examining Group's syllabus, as it may give valuable additional information as to what you need to know.

When you feel that you have mastered as many topics as you can, you should test what you have learned. A few questions are included at the end of each chapter for this purpose. If you can not do these or get any wrong go back to the appropriate topic(s) and revise more thoroughly. Then test yourself again before revising more topics.

A large selection of sample examination questions has been included to give you maximum practice in answering questions. For convenience these questions have been grouped by chapter.

The National Curriculum and GCSE

The National Curriculum deals with the period of compulsory education between the ages of 5 and 16 in four Key Stages. At the end of each Key Stage (at ages 7, 11, 14 and 16) attainments in specified subjects are tested. At the end of Key Stage 4 (KS 4) at age 16, assessment is made through the General Certificate of Secondary Education (GCSE).

The GCSE is administered by groups of Examining Boards. There are four groups in England (London, Midland, Northern and Southern), one in Wales and one in Northern Ireland. Different arrangements apply in Scotland (see page 7).

In Physics, as in other subjects, the Examining Groups offer assessment at two levels. The Higher Tier is intended for candidates who are attempting to gain grades A* to D, and the Foundation Tier for those who are likely to gain grades C to G.

For all Physics syllabuses in the GCSE examination 25% of the marks are awarded for teacher assessment of practical work carried out during the two years of the course. This takes the form of periodic assessment by your teacher of a number of pieces of practical work, some of an investigative nature.

The GCSE examination places emphasis on understanding and applying topics in the syllabus as well as recalling information. The examination papers are designed to measure positive achievement, that is to find out what you know and understand rather than what you do not. A significant proportion of the questions will be concerned with the applications and implications of Physics.

Assessment objectives

The Assessment objectives describe the intellectual and practical skills which you will need to acquire and demonstrate, and which will be assessed in the examination.
You must be able to:

- **Carry out experimental work and investigative work in which you plan procedures, use precise and systematic ways of making measurements and observations, analyse and evaluate evidence and relate this to scientific knowledge and understanding.**

  This means that, when you are given a practical problem to solve, you must be able to determine and write down the quantities you will need to measure in order to solve it, exactly how you are going to measure them, the apparatus you will use to do so and how you will arrange (set up) the apparatus. You will need to show that you make and write down your measurements or observations in a logical, rather than random order. If, for example, you are taking readings at different temperatures, then the results should be written down with the temperatures in numerical order (usually the lowest temperature first) rather than with the temperatures in a random order.

  You must be able to spot any pattern in your measurements or observations (conclusion). This may involve plotting a suitable graph or just looking carefully at them. Then, you must be able to decide how much importance to attach to any pattern you note. For example, do all the points lie close to the graph line (strong evidence) or are some (or all) of them well spread (weak evidence)? Finally, you must relate your conclusion to any knowledge and understanding of Physics that you may have; that is to any 'theory' you know.

  There is more detailed discussion of this assessment objective in the section on Coursework on *page 217.*

- **Recall, understand, use and apply the scientific knowledge set out in the syllabus.**

  This means that you must learn and remember everything in your syllabus. More than this, you must understand what it means, rather than simply memorizing it. You must also be able to use and apply your knowledge to different problems. This really means being able to select from your knowledge those parts of it which are relevant to the question you are answering and then to use these parts to accurately and successfully answer the question.

- **Communicate scientific observations, ideas and arguments using a range of scientific and technical vocabulary and appropriate scientific and mathematical conventions.**

  This means that you must be able to write down your scientific knowledge and understanding, accurately and concisely, using, where necessary, the correct scientific and technical words and the correct scientific and mathematical symbols.

- **Evaluate relevant scientific information, and make informed judgements from it.**

  This means that you must be able to weigh up any scientific information and decide how far the evidence given justifies the conclusion reached.

Analysis of Physics syllabuses

Find your Examining Group and syllabus in the following tables. The relevant table lists the topics you will need to know and understand. It also gives details of the papers you will have to sit, such as their length. H = Higher tier topic only.

MEG

Midland Examining Group

1 Hills Road, Cambridge CB1 2EU
Tel: 01223 553311

Syllabus A

Syllabus topic	Covered in unit number	✓
1 Electric circuits	20.2, 20.3, 20.4, 20.5, 20.6, 26.1	
2 Energy and particles	4.2, 9.1, 9.2, 10.1, 10.3, 10.5, 11.0, 11.1, 12.1, 12.2, 12.3, 12.4, 26.1	
3 Forces	2.1, 2.2, 2.3, 2.5H, 2.6H, 3.1, 3.3H, 3.5, 3.7H, 3.8H, 4.1, 4.3H, 4.4H, 4.5, 5.1, 5.2, 5.3, 5.5, 7.0, 7.1, 7.2, 8.1, 10.1	
4 Wave properties	13.1, 13.2, 13.3, 13.4, 13.5, 14.1, 14.2, 15.1, 16.1, 16.2, 17.0, 17.1, 17.2, 17.4, 17.5, 23.5	
5 Using waves	14.2, 15.1, 15.2, 15.3, 15.4, 15.5, 16.2, 17.1, 17.2, 28.6H, 31.1H	
6 Radioactivity	27.1, 27.2, 27.3H, 27.4, 27.5H, 27.6, 27.7	
7 The Earth and Universe	14.1, 28.1, 28.2, 28.3, 28.4, 28.5, 28.8, 28.9, 28.11H, 28.12H	
8 Using electricity	19.0, 19.1, 20.0, 20.1H, 21.1, 21.2, 21.3, 22.1, 22.2, 22.3, 22.4, 24.2	
9 Electromagnetism	4.2, 18.0, 18.2, 23.0, 23.1, 23.2, 23.3, 23.6, 23.7, 24.1H, 24.2, 24.3, 24.4	
10 Electronics and control	20.5, 23.2, 26.4H, 26.6, 26.7	

All candidates complete a Coursework Assessment on Sc1 25%

Foundation tier – Two written papers of structured questions. No choice of question. Targeted at grades C–G.

Paper 1	90 minutes	50%
Paper 3	45 minutes	25%

Higher tier – Two written papers of structured questions. No choice of question. Targeted at grades A*–D.

Paper 2	105 minutes	50%
Paper 4	60 minutes	25%

Syllabus C (Salters)

Syllabus topic	Covered in unit number	✓
Electricity and magnetism	18.0, 18.2, 19.0, 19.1, 20.0, 20.1H, 20.2, 20.3, 20.4, 20.5, 20.7, 21.2, 21.3, 22.2, 22.3, 22.4, 22.5, 23.1, 23.5, 23.6, 23.7, 24.1, 24.2, 24.3H, 24.4, 26.1H, 26.3H, 27.8	
Forces and motion	2.1, 2.2, 2.3, 3.1, 3.2, 3.3H, 3.4, 3.5, 3.9, 5.3, 5.4, 5.5, 7.0, 7.1, 7.2, 8.1, 10.1H	
Waves	13.1, 13.2, 13.3, 13.4, 13.5, 14.2, 15.1, 15.2, 15.3, 16.1, 16.2, 17.0, 17.2, 17.3H, 17.4, 28.6H, 29.4, 31.1H	
The Earth and beyond	3.6H, 4.2, 28.1, 28.2, 28.4, 28.5, 28.7, 28.8, 28.10, 28.11, 28.12	
Energy resources and energy transfer	3.5, 4.1, 4.2, 4.3H, 4.4H, 4.5, 5.1, 5.2, 11.0, 12.0, 12.1, 12.2, 12.3, 12.4, 24.3H	
Radioactivity	27.1, 27.3, 27.4H, 27.5, 27.7	
Extension	19.2H, 19.3H, 20.0, 20.6, 25.1, 25.2, 25.3, 25.4, 25.5, 26.1, 26.2, 26.3, 26.4, 26.5, 26.6, 26.7	

All candidates complete a Coursework Assessment on Sc1 25%

Foundation tier – One written paper. Targeted at grades C–G.

Paper 120 minutes 75%

Higher tier – One written paper. Targeted at grades A*–D.

Paper 135 minutes 75%

Syllabus D (Nuffield)

Syllabus topic	Covered in unit number	✓
Forces, energy and motion	2.1, 2.2, 2.3, 3.1, 3.5, 4.1, 4.5, 5.1, 5.2, 7.0, 8.1, 10.1	
Electricity and magnetism	18.0, 18.2, 20.0, 20.2, 20.3, 20.4, 20.5, 20.7, 23.0, 23.1, 23.2, 23.3, 26.1, 26.7	
Waves	13.1, 13.2, 13.3, 13.4, 13.5H, 14.2, 15.1, 15.2, 16.1H, 16.2, 17.1, 17.2, 17.3H, 17.4	
Electricity in buildings	19.0, 19.1, 20.1H, 21.1, 21.2, 21.3, 22.1, 22.2, 22.3, 22.4	
Energy in buildings	4.2, 9.1, 12.1, 12.2, 12.3, 12.4, 26.1	
Waves in health physics	16.2, 17.0, 17.1, 17.2, 27.4	
Radioactivity in health physics	27.1, 27.3, 27.4, 27.5, 27.6, 27.7	
Waves and radioactivity; an investigation of the Earth	27.5, 28.6H	
Our place in space	4.3H, 4.4H, 28.2, 28.3, 28.4, 28.5, 28.7, 28.8, 28.9, 28.11H, 28.12H	
Force and energy in transport	2.1, 2.2, 2.4, 3.1, 4.4H, 7.1, 7.2	
Electricity in transport	4.2, 23.6, 23.7, 24.1, 24.2, 24.3, 24.4	
Extension	1.1, 1.2, 1.3, 1.4, 2.5H, 3.3, 3.7, 3.8, 3.9, 4.6, 6.0, 8.1, 9.2, 10.2, 10.3, 11.0, 11.1, 17.5, 23.4, 23.5, 25.1H, 25.2H, 25.3H, 25.4H, 25.5H, 27.5, 29.2H, 29.4, 29.5H, 30.1, 31.1	

All candidates complete a Coursework Assessment on Sc1 25%

Foundation tier – Two written papers of structured questions. No choice of question. Targeted at grades C–G.

Paper 1 90 minutes 50%
Paper 3 45 minutes 25%

Higher tier – Two written papers of structured questions. No choice of question. Targeted at grades A*–D.

Paper 2 105 minutes 50%
Paper 4 60 minutes 25%

SEG

Southern Examining Group

Stag Hill House, Guildford, Surrey GU2 5XJ
Tel: 01483 506506

Syllabus topic	Covered in unit number	✓
Electricity and magnetism	18.0, 18.2, 19.0, 19.1, 19.2, 19.3, 20.0, 20.1H, 20.2, 20.3, 20.4, 20.5, 20.7, 21.1H, 21.2, 21.3, 22.1, 22.2, 22.3, 22.4, 23.0, 23.1, 23.2, 23.3, 23.6H, 23.7H, 24.1, 24.2, 24.3, 24.4, 25.2, 25.5, 26.1, 26.4, 26.7	
Forces and motion	2.1, 2.2, 2.3H, 3.1, 3.2, 3.3H, 3.5, 3.7, 3.8H, 3.9H, 5.1, 5.2, 7.0, 7.1, 7.2, 8.1, 10.1H	
Waves	13.1, 13.2, 13.3, 13.4, 13.5H, 14.1, 14.2, 15.1, 15.2, 16.1H, 16.2, 17.0, 17.1, 17.2, 17.3H, 25.5, 28.6, 31.1	
The Earth and beyond	28.1, 28.2, 28.3, 28.4, 28.5, 28.8, 28.9H, 28.10, 28.11H, 28.12H	
Energy resources and energy transfer	4.1, 4.2, 4.3, 4.4, 4.5, 9.1, 9.2, 10.1, 10.2, 10.3, 10.4, 10.5, 11.0, 11.1, 12.1, 12.2, 12.3, 12.4, 16.1, 16.2	
Radioactivity	27.3, 27.4, 27.5H	

All candidates complete a Coursework Assessment on Sc1 25%

Foundation tier – Two written papers. Targeted at grades C–G.

Paper 2 90 minutes 50%
Paper 3 60 minutes 25%

Higher tier – Two written papers. Targeted at grades A*–C.

Paper 4 90 minutes 50%
Paper 5 60 minutes 25%

NEAB

Northern Examinations and Assessment Board

12 Harter Street, Manchester, M1 6HL
Tel: 0161 953 1180

Syllabus topic	Covered in unit number	✓
Electricity and magnetism	18.0, 18.2, 19.0, 19.1, 19.2H, 19.3H, 20.0, 20.1H, 20.2, 20.3, 20.4, 20.5, 20.6H, 20.7, 21.1, 21.2, 21.3, 22.1, 22.2, 22.3, 22.4H, 23.0, 23.1, 23.2, 23.5, 23.6, 23.7, 24.1, 24.2, 24.3, 24.4H, 25.2, 26.1, 26.2H, 26.3, 26.4H, 26.7, 27.1H	
Forces and motion	2.1, 2.2, 2.3, 2.4, 2.5H, 3.1, 3.2, 3.3H, 3.6, 3.7H, 3.8H, 5.1, 5.2H, 5.3, 5.4, 5.5H, 7.0, 7.1, 7.2, 8.1, 10.1H	
Waves	13.1, 13.2, 13.3, 13.4, 13.5H, 14.2, 15.1, 15.2, 15.3, 15.5, 15.6, 16.1H, 16.2, 17.0, 17.1, 17.2, 17.3H, 28.6H, 31.1	
The Earth and beyond	28.1, 28.2, 28.4, 28.5, 28.9, 28.10, 28.11H, 28.12H	
Energy resources and energy transfer	4.1, 4.2, 4.3, 4.4H, 4.5, 12.1, 12.2, 12.3, 12.4	
Radioactivity	27.1, 27.2, 27.3, 27.4, 27.5H, 27.7H	

All candidates complete a Coursework Assessment on Sc1 25%

Foundation tier – One written paper of structured questions. No choice of question. Targeted at grades C–G.

Paper F 120 minutes 75%

Higher tier – One written paper of structured questions. No choice of question. Targeted at grades A*–C.

Paper H 135 minutes 75%

EDEXCEL (London Examinations)

London Examinations – Edexcel Foundation (formerly ULEAC)

Stewart House, 32 Russell Square, London WC1B 5DN
Tel: 0171 331 4000

Syllabus topic	Covered in unit number	✓
Electricity and magnetism	18.0, 18.2, 19.0, 19.1, 20.0. 20.1H, 20.2, 20.3, 20.4, 20.5, 20.7, 21.1, 21.2, 21.3, 22.1, 22.2, 22.3, 22.4, 23.0, 23.1, 23.2, 23.3, 23.5, 23.6, 23.7, 24.1, 24.2, 24.3H, 24.4H, 26.1H	
Forces and motion	2.1, 2.2, 2.3, 3.1, 3.2, 3.3H, 3.5, 3.9H, 6.0, 7.0, 7.1, 8.0, 8.1, 9.1, 9.2, 10.1H	
Waves	13.1, 13.2, 13.3, 13.4, 13.5H, 14.2, 15.1, 15.2, 16.1H, 16.2, 17.0, 17.1, 17.2, 17.3H, 17.4, 28.6H	
The Earth and beyond	28.1, 28.2, 28.3, 28.4, 28.5, 28.8, 28.9H, 28.11H, 28.12H	
Energy resources and energy transfer	4.1, 4.2, 4.3H, 4.4H, 4.5, 9.1H, 12.1, 12.2, 12.3, 12.4	
Radioactivity	27.1, 27.2, 27.3, 27.4, 27.5	
Extension	3.6H, 10.3, 23.4, 23.5, 25.1, 25.3, 25.4, 25.5, 26.1, 26.3, 27.1, 27.2, 27.3, 27.7, 27.8H, 28.10, 29.1, 29.2, 29.3, 29.4H, 29.5, 30.1, 30.2, 31.1, 32.1, 32.2H, 32.3	

All candidates complete a Coursework Assessment on Sc1 25%

Foundation tier – Two written papers of structured questions. No choice of question. Targeted at grades C–G.

Paper 1F 90 minutes 50%
Paper 2F 60 minutes 25%

Higher tier – Two written papers of structured questions. No choice of question. Targeted at grades A*–C.

Paper 3H 90 minutes 50%
Paper 4H 60 minutes 25%

WJEC

Welsh Joint Education Committee

245 Western Avenue, Cardiff CF5 2YX
Tel: 01222 265000

Syllabus topic	Covered in unit number	✓
Electricity and magnetism	18.0, 18.2, 19.0, 19.1, 20.0. 20.1, 20.2, 20.3, 20.4, 20.5, 20.7, 21.1, 21.2, 21.3, 22.1, 22.2, 22.3, 22.4, 22.5, 23.0, 23.2, 23.6, 24.1, 24.2, 24.3H, 24.4, 26.1H, 26.7, 27.1	
Forces and motion	2.1, 2.2, 2.3, 2.4H, 2.5H, 3.1, 3.2, 3.3H, 3.5, 3.7H, 3.8H, 3.9, 4.6, 6.0, 7.0, 8.1, 9.1, 9.2, 10.1H	
The Earth and beyond	28.1, 28.2, 28.4, 28.5, 28.7H, 28.8, 28.9, 28.10, 28.11H, 28.12H	
Waves	13.1, 13.2, 13.3, 13.4, 13.5H, 14.2, 15.1, 15.2, 16.1H, 16.2, 17.0, 17.1, 17.2, 17.3H, 28.6H, 31.1	
Energy resources and energy transfer	4.1, 4.2, 4.3H, 4.4H, 4.5, 9.1, 11.0, 12.1, 12.2, 12.3, 12.4	
Radioactivity	27.1, 27.3, 27.4, 27.5H, 27.6	

All candidates complete a Coursework Assessment on Sc1 25%

Foundation tier – One written paper. Targeted at grades C–G.

Paper 120 minutes 75%

Higher tier – One written paper. Targeted at grades A*–C.

Paper 150 minutes 75%

CCEA

Northern Ireland Council for the Curriculum Examinations and Assessment

Clarendon Dock, 29 Clarendon Road, Belfast BT1 3BG
Tel: 01232 261200

Syllabus topic	Covered in unit number	✓
Energy	4.1, 4.2, 4.3H, 4.4H, 4.5H, 12.1, 12.2, 12.3, 12.4	
Forces	2.1, 2.2H, 2.3H, 2.4H, 3.1, 3.2, 3.3H, 3.5, 3.6H, 3.7, 3.8H, 5.1, 5.2H, 5.3H, 5.4H, 6.0, 7.0, 7.1, 7.2, 8.1	
Waves, sound and light	13.1, 13.2, 13.3, 13.4, 13.5, 14.1, 14.2, 15.1, 15.2H, 15.3, 15.4H, 15.5H, 15.6, 16.2, 17.0, 17.1, 17.2, 17.4, 17.5H, 31.1	
Electricity and magnetism	18.0, 18.2, 19.0, 19.1, 20.0. 20.1H, 20.2, 20.3, 20.4, 20.5, 20.7, 21.1H, 21.2H, 21.3, 22.1, 22.3, 22.4, 23.0, 23.1, 23.2, 23.3, 23.5, 23.6, 23.7, 24.1H, 24.2H, 24.3H, 26.1H	
Radioactivity	27.1, 27.2, 27.3, 27.4H, 27.5, 27.6, 27.7H	
Earth in space	28.1, 28.2, 28.3, 28.4, 28.5H, 28.10H, 28.11H	

All candidates complete a Coursework Assessment on Sc1 25%

Foundation tier – Two written papers. Targeted at grades C–G.

Paper 1 60 minutes 30%
Paper 2 90 minutes 45%

Higher tier – Two written papers. Targeted at grades A*–C.

Paper 1 105 minutes 37.5%
Paper 2 105 minutes 37.5%

SQA

Scottish Qualifications Authority (formerly SEB)

Ironmills Road, Dalkeith, Midlothian EH22 1LE
Tel: 0131 663 6601

Syllabus topic	Covered in unit number	✓
Telecommunication	13.0, 13.5, 14.1, 14.2, 15.2, 16.2, 17.0, 17.1, 17.3, 17.4, 23.4, 23.5, 25.1, 25.2, 25.3, 25.4, 25.5, 28.10, 29.1, 29.2, 29.4, 31.1, 32.1, 32.2	
Using electricity	19.0, 20.0, 20.2, 20.3, 20.4, 20.5, 20.6, 20.7, 21.1, 21.2, 21.3, 22.1, 22.2, 22.3, 22.4, 22.5, 23.0, 23.3, 23.6, 23.7	
Health physics	15.1, 15.2, 15.3, 15.6, 16.2, 17.0, 17.2, 17.4, 27.3, 27.4, 27.5, 27.6	
Electronics	19.2, 19.3, 23.4, 25.5, 26.1, 26.3, 26.4, 26.7	
Transport	1.4, 2.1, 2.3, 2.4, 2.5, 3.1, 3.2, 3.3, 3.4, 3.5, 4.1, 4.3, 4.4	
Energy matters	4.2, 9.1, 11.0, 11.2, 12.1, 12.2, 12.3, 12.4, 21.1, 24.1, 24.2, 24.3, 24.4	
Space physics	2.6, 3.1, 3.5, 3.7, 3.8, 3.9, 4.1, 11.0, 15.1, 16.2, 28.1, 28.2, 28.3, 28.5, 28.10	

All candidates complete a Coursework Assessment 33.3%

General tier – One written paper. Targeted at grades 3, 4 and 5.

Paper 90 minutes 66.7%

Credit tier – One written paper. Targeted at grades 1 and 2.

Paper 105 minutes 66.7%

IGCSE

International General Certificate of Secondary Education

University of Cambridge Local Examination Syndicate, 1 Hills Road, Cambridge, England CB1 2EU
Tel: 01223 553311

Syllabus topic	Covered in unit number	✓
General physics	1.1, 1.2, 1.3, 1.4, 2.1, 2.2H, 2.3, 2.5, 3.1, 3.2, 3.3H, 3.5, 3.6H, 3.7H, 3.8H, 4.1, 4.2, 4.3H, 4.4H, 4.5, 4.6, 5.1, 5.2H, 5.3, 5.4, 6.0, 7.0. 7.1, 7.2, 8.1, 27.7H	
Thermal physics	9.1, 9.2, 10.1, 10.2, 11.0, 11.1H, 11.2H, 12.1, 12.2, 12.3, 12.4	
Waves, light and sound	13.1, 13.2, 13.3, 13.4, 13.5, 14.2, 15.1, 15.2, 15.3, 15.4H, 16.2, 17.0, 17.1, 17.2, 17.4	
Electricity and magnetism	18.0, 18.1, 18.2, 19.0, 19.2, 19.3, 20.0, 20.1H, 20.2, 20.3, 20.4, 20.5, 20.6, 20.7, 21.1H, 21.2H, 22.2, 22.3, 23.0, 23.1, 23.3, 23.6, 23.7, 24.1, 24.2, 24.3, 24.4, 25.1, 25.2, 25.3, 25.4, 25.5, 26.1	
Atom physics	27.1, 27.2, 27.3, 27.5, 27.6	

Core curriculum – Two written papers of multiple choice, short answer or structured questions with an option of a coursework, practical test or further written component designed to test familiarity with laboratory practical procedures. Targeted at grades C–G.

Paper 1	45 minutes	40%
Paper 2	60 minutes	40%
Options:		
Paper 4	coursework	20%
Paper 5	75 minutes	20%
Paper 6	60 minutes	20%

Extended curriculum – Three written papers of multiple choice, short answer, structured or free-response questions with an option of a coursework, practical test or further written component designed to test familiarity with laboratory practical procedures. Targeted at grades A–G.

Paper 1	45 minutes	80% (Papers 1–3)
Paper 2	60 minutes	
Paper 3	105 minutes	
Options:		
Paper 4	coursework	20%
Paper 5	75 minutes	20%
Paper 6	60 minutes	20%

Studying and revising

Successful students are those who can organize their work. In particular, they must be able to work effectively on their own. If you are to be successful you need determination to succeed, a work plan fitted to a time schedule and the determination to keep to that schedule.

This section contains some advice that will help you to succeed in school. It also gives reasons for this advice. There are five steps in the learning process as shown in Figure A. The first three are planned by your teacher, who knows the sort of examination you will be sitting and plans accordingly. Where many students needlessly fail is at stage 4 (revision) because they do not know how to go about it.

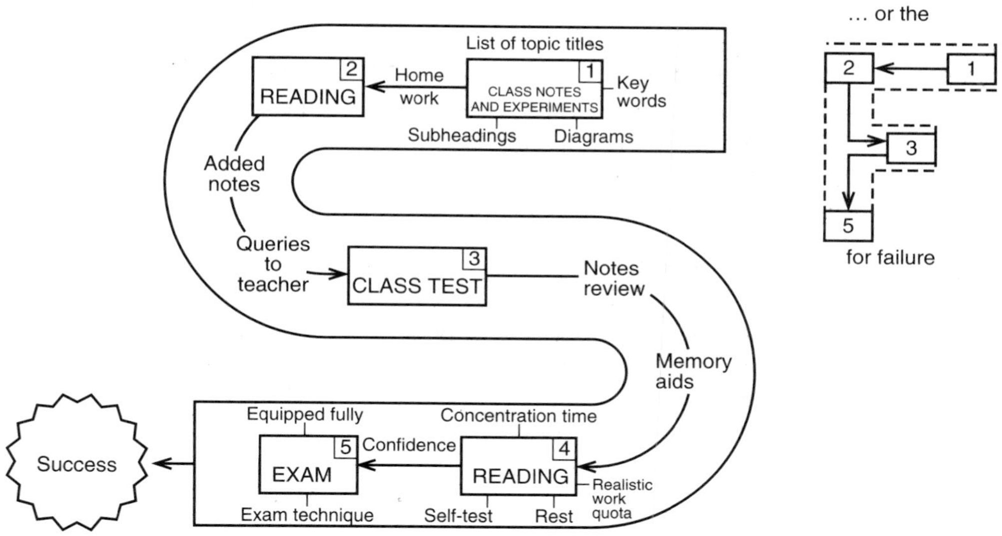

Fig. A The 'S' for success … or the 'F' for failure

Studying

In science you learn from experiments – your own or those reported by others. It is well known that students tend to remember far better the 'facts' they have learned by doing experiments themselves. Unfortunately it is not practicable to learn everything this way, either through shortage of time or because a topic is not suitable for school experiments. So the rest has to be learned by reading, listening and seeing visual aids.

Experiments: Usually you are personally involved in doing these and use several senses, such as seeing, hearing, feeling and smelling. At the end you must arrive at a conclusion, which requires some reasoning. The whole process requires *understanding* – understanding the **aim** of the experiment, the **method** to be used and how to record the **results** in a meaningful way. And, at the end, the **conclusion** requires reasoning from what you have already understood. During this process you will have built up a pattern of knowledge, like a jig-saw. In other words **learning requires patterns to be built up in the mind.** If you relate what you have just learned to what you already know, then the facts will stick because you *understand*.

Reading: In contrast to experimenting, when you read you are using only one of your senses – sight – and, unless you make a mental effort, you are *not involved*, as you are in an experiment. You have to concentrate hard to pick out and retain the facts, even if they do form patterns, as in the case of well-written textbooks. To help you in this, try 'highlighting' key words or phrases or making summary notes as you go.

Practise improving the speed of your reading. Try moving back from the page and reading several words at a time, rather than one. After a while you will find that you can absorb several words at once, whilst still grasping their meaning, and you will be able to absorb information faster.

Pictures and diagrams: Pictures and diagrams, like words, require eyes to detect them. But pictures build up patterns in the brain more readily and understanding is quicker. Similarly, if you learn to draw simple diagrams, you will help to reinforce both your memory and your understanding. Try!

Teachers: By showing films and slides, by drawing diagrams or asking your opinion and by giving you definite learning objectives, they try to activate more senses than just your hearing and try to keep you personally involved. But, in order to learn from this, you must respond positively. You must grasp the pattern of facts that the teacher explains. At the beginning, the teacher normally explains what the *whole* lesson is to be about. Listen hard to this outline as it will make the rest of the lesson easier to absorb. The outline is the basic skeleton upon which the teacher will build up the flesh and features of the subject, as the lesson proceeds.

Class notes: For easy revision these should include:

- a reference to the relevant numbered pages in your textbook.
- clear underlined titles and subtitles.
- underlined or 'highlighted' key words.
- clear labelled diagrams, where necessary.

Class tests: These are designed to:

- help you to recall facts and to reason from them.
- help you to assess your progress.
- help you to focus on the key parts of each topic.
- help your teacher to identify and clear up your difficulties.
- give you exam practice.

Revising

This is the vital last stage in the learning process, the stage when you are on your own. Time is precious so make sure that you use it well. A good method is to plan a revision timetable – make a list of all the topics that you have to study and divide up your time accordingly. Be realistic about the total time that you will be able to spend on revision.

Revision is, to a great extent, a matter of technique. It is not good enough to simply read through your notes or textbook time and time again. There are various methods which you can use to help you revise. No one method is better or worse than any other. It really depends on which you find easiest. Here are a few things for you to consider.

- **Underline or highlight important words and phrases.**
- **Make lists of key words.**
- **Write out important definitions.**
  Writing notes will help you to remember key points.

- **Draw diagrams to summarize important topics.**
  Label the diagrams and write notes at the side. Many people find it easier to remember things from pictures than from words.
- **Summarize important ideas and explanations.**
- **Keep all your notes and diagrams** so that you can look at them again. Diagrams and notes that you have made yourself will jog your memory and your understanding very quickly. Concise and well-organized notes and diagrams will increase your long-term knowledge and understanding significantly.
- **Answer the sample examination questions** as well as those at the end of each chapter, and check your answers. Answering examination questions is one of the best ways to prepare for an examination.
- **Ask your teacher if you still do not understand something.**

Whichever method of revision you choose, develop it and persevere. A good revision technique can make all the difference to your final examination performance.

Looking after yourself: Keeping fit and well during revision and the examination period is at least as important as making sure that you know and understand your work.

- Do not try to do too much revision. Set aside a realistic time for revision each day and stick to it. If you are intending to work in the evenings, start work as early as possible.
- Study for a short period of about 30 to 40 minutes, then take a short break of about 10 minutes. Then continue revising for another 30 to 40 minutes before taking another break or finishing.
- During breaks try to think of something entirely different. Relax!
- Try to work in a quiet, well-lit, well-ventilated room.
- While revising avoid distractions from family, friends, radio and television.
- Make sure that you have regular meals, that you get enough sleep and that you take regular exercise.
- Do not try to do much revision the evening before an examination. Just quietly read through the brief notes you have already made to reassure yourself.

Chapter 1
Measurements

All measurements in Physics are related to the three chosen fundamental quantities of **length**, **mass** and **time**. For many years scientists have agreed to use the metric system; the particular one used now is based on the metre, the kilogram and the second.

1.1 Length

The unit of length is the metre. Various multiples or submultiples are also used. Thus

1 kilometre (km) = 1000 metres (m)

1 metre = 100 centimetres (cm) = 1000 millimetres (mm)

1 centimetre = 10 millimetres

For day-to-day work in laboratories metre and half-metre rules are used – graduated in centimetres and millimetres. For more accurate measurement vernier calipers or a micrometer screw gauge may be used. Details of both these instruments will be found in any standard textbook. A metre rule is accurate to the nearest millimetre, calipers to the nearest 0.1 mm and a micrometer gauge to 0.01 mm.

1.2 Mass

The mass of a body measures the quantity of matter it contains. The unit of mass is the kilogram. A body will have the same mass in all parts of the universe.

1 kilogram (kg) = 1000 grams (g)

1 gram = 1000 milligrams (mg)

1.3 Area and volume

The area of a surface is measured in units of metres times metres (m^2) or cm^2 or mm^2. The volume of a substance is usually expressed in units of m^3 or cm^3 or mm^3.

The volume of a liquid is often measured in litres or millilitres.

1 litre (l) = 1000 millilitres (ml)

but 1 millilitre = 1 cm^3

therefore 1 litre = 1000 cm^3

In Physics the measuring cylinder is most commonly used for volume measurements of liquids. When reading the value it is important to look at the bottom of the curved liquid surface (meniscus).

1.4 Time

The scientific unit of time is the second (s) which is $\frac{1}{24 \times 60 \times 60}$ part of the time the Earth takes to revolve once on its own axis.

In the laboratory, time is normally measured using a stopclock or stopwatch. In some cases more accuracy is required, as, for example, when measuring the acceleration of a trolley moving on a ramp. A tickertape vibrator (also known as a 'ticker timer'), or a centisecond or millisecond timer should then be used. The sensitivities of these four instruments are as follows:

stopwatch or stopclock	1/10 s
tickertape vibrator	1/50 s
centisecond timer	1/100 s
millisecond timer	1/1000 s

In some experiments it may be appropriate to use a stroboscope to measure time. A description of the hand-operated stroboscope and its use is given at the end of Unit 13.2.

Examiner's tip

Make sure you know your units and always remember to use them in every answer.

Chapter 2

Speed, velocity and acceleration

2.1 Speed

Speed is defined as the distance moved in one second.

$$\textbf{Average speed} = \frac{\textbf{distance moved}}{\textbf{time taken}} \text{ (m/s)}$$

2.2 Velocity

The velocity of a body measures its speed and the direction in which it travels.

$$\textbf{Average velocity} = \frac{\textbf{distance moved in a particular direction}}{\textbf{time taken}}$$

(m/s in a particular direction – north for example)

Uniform velocity means that both the speed and the direction remain constant, as shown in Fig. 2.1(b).

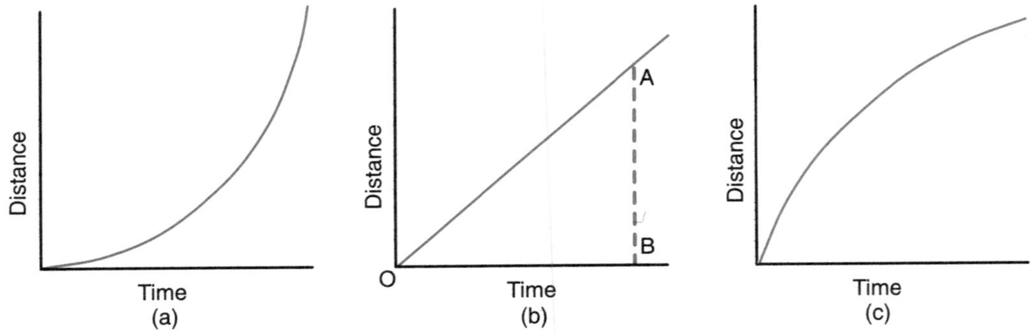

Fig. 2.1 Variation of distance moved in a straight line with time: (a) increasing velocity; (b) uniform velocity; (c) decreasing velocity

In Fig. 2.1(b) AB represents the distance travelled in the time represented by OB, thus

$$\text{Velocity} = \frac{AB}{OB}\text{; this is called the slope or gradient of the graph}$$

In Fig. 2.1(a) and (c) the gradients vary. Thus they represent bodies whose velocities have different values at different times.

2.3 Acceleration

Examiner's tip

Deceleration is simply acceleration in the opposite direction to motion and has the same unit as acceleration: m/s^2.

If the velocity of a body is changing, the body is said to be accelerating. Acceleration is defined as the change in velocity per second.

$$\textbf{Acceleration} = \frac{\textbf{change in velocity}}{\textbf{time taken for this change}}$$

For example, suppose a car travelling along a straight road increases its speed from 10 m/s to 20 m/s in five seconds.

$$\text{Change in velocity} = (20 - 10)\text{ m/s} = 10\text{ m/s}$$

$$\text{time taken for this change} = 5\text{ s}$$

Hence using the formula above:

$$\text{acceleration} = 10\text{ m/s in } 5\text{ s} = 2\text{ m/s in } 1\text{ s}$$

$$\text{thus acceleration} = 2\text{ m/s}^2$$

In this example the acceleration resulted from a change in the magnitude (size) of velocity (speed). However, velocity can change in either magnitude or direction (circular motion). A change in either means the body is accelerating.

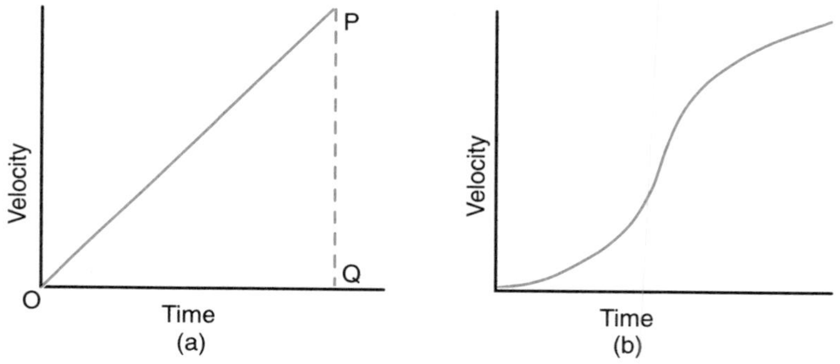

Fig. 2.2 Acceleration: (a) uniform acceleration; (b) non-uniform acceleration

In Fig. 2.2(a) the velocity is increasing with time at a steady rate, and the acceleration is said to be uniform. PQ represents the change in velocity in time OQ.

$$\text{Acceleration} = \frac{PQ}{OQ}\text{; the gradient of the velocity–time graph}$$

In Fig. 2.2(b) the acceleration is not constant. The acceleration at any moment is found by calculating the gradient of the graph at that time.

2.4 Uniformly accelerated motion

The body whose motion is represented by Fig. 2.3 is moving with a velocity u when timing starts. It has a **uniform acceleration** of a m/s^2 which means that each second its velocity increases by a, and after t (seconds) its velocity will have increased by at. Hence at the end of this time its velocity $\boldsymbol{v = u + at}$.

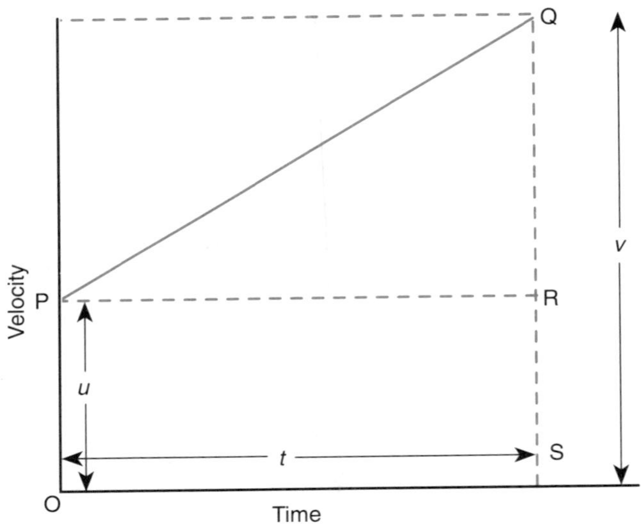

Fig. 2.3

Alternatively, Acceleration $a = \dfrac{\text{change in velocity}}{\text{time taken for this change}}$

$$= \frac{v - u}{t}$$

therefore $v - u = at$

and $\boldsymbol{v = u + at}$ (2.1)

2.5 Distance travelled

The average velocity of the object whose motion is shown in Fig. 2.3 is equal to half the sum of its initial velocity u, and final velocity v.

Average velocity $= \dfrac{u + v}{2}$ (this only applies to an object accelerating uniformly)

The distance s moved can be found using the equation:

$$\text{Velocity} = \frac{\text{distance moved}}{\text{time taken}}$$

hence distance moved = average velocity × time taken

$$s = \frac{(u + v)}{2} \times t \qquad (2.2)$$

but $v = u + at$ (2.1)

therefore $s = \dfrac{(u + u + at)t}{2}$

or $\boldsymbol{s = ut + \frac{1}{2}at^2}$ (2.3)

In Fig. 2.3, ut is the area of the rectangle $OPRS$. The area of the triangle PQR is

area $PQR = \frac{1}{2} \times$ base × height

$= \frac{1}{2} \times t \times (v - u)$

but $v - u = at$ from equation (2.1)

thus area $PQR = \frac{1}{2}at^2$

area of $OPQS$ = (area of rectangle $OPRS$) + (area of triangle PQR)

hence area of $OPQS = ut + \frac{1}{2}at^2$

but $s = ut + \frac{1}{2}at^2$ (2.3)

The area under the velocity–time graph in Fig. 2.3 is therefore equal to the distance travelled by the body. This is true for all such graphs, even when the acceleration is non-uniform.

A third equation for uniformly accelerated motion may be obtained by eliminating time t between equations (2.1) and (2.3). The resulting equation is

$$v^2 = u^2 + 2as \quad (2.4)$$

2.6 Projectiles

So far we have only considered objects travelling in a straight line. In this unit we shall study objects which are being accelerated by the force due to gravity, and at the same time, are moving horizontally at a constant speed. One example of such motion is the path of a ball which is projected horizontally over the edge of a table. This ball continues to move with the same horizontal speed as it had just as it left the edge of the table (if we ignore the small effect of air resistance). In addition the ball falls under the influence of gravity.

It can be shown that the ball takes the same time to reach the ground as another ball dropped from the same height at the moment the first ball leaves the edge of the table. This shows that the horizontal motion of the first ball in no way affects its vertical acceleration; that is, it falls in exactly the same way as it would if it were not moving sideways. The horizontal and vertical motions of the ball can be treated entirely separately.

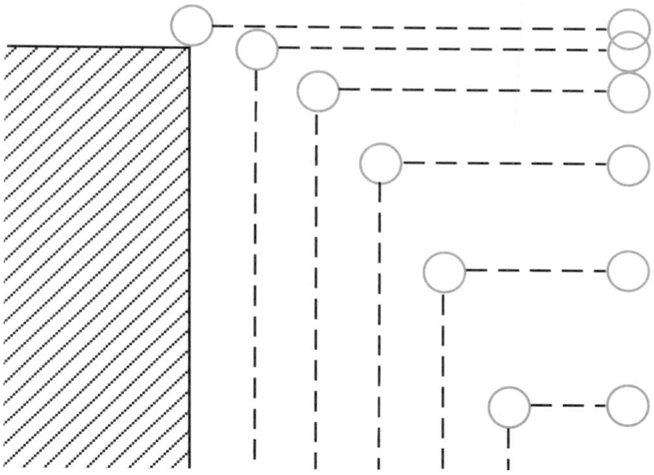

Fig. 2.4
Projectable motion

Figure 2.4 represents the motions of the two balls already mentioned. The paths of the two have been photographed at regular intervals. It can be seen that in equal time intervals both balls fall an increasing but equal distance (they undergo the same vertical acceleration). In the same equal time intervals the first ball moves equal distances horizontally. The motion may also be demonstrated using the pulsed water drops experiment. Another example of projectile motion is that of a ball thrown from one person to another.

Summary

1 **Average speed** $= \dfrac{\textbf{distance moved}}{\textbf{time taken}}$ (m/s)

2 **Average velocity** $= \dfrac{\textbf{distance moved in a particular direction}}{\textbf{time taken}}$

(m/s in a particular direction – north for example)

Velocity is a vector quantity (i.e. it has magnitude **and** direction). It may increase, decrease or remain constant.

3 **Acceleration** $= \dfrac{\textbf{change in velocity}}{\textbf{time taken for this change}}$ (m/s^2)

Acceleration is a vector quantity. It may increase, decrease or remain constant – uniform acceleration.

4 For uniform acceleration, the following equations may be used.

$$v = u + at$$

$$s = \frac{(u + v)}{2}\,t$$

$$s = ut + \tfrac{1}{2}at^2$$

$$v^2 = u^2 + 2as$$

where u is the initial velocity, i.e. at time $t = 0$
v is the velocity at time t
s is the distance travelled
a is the acceleration

5 In projectile motion the horizontal and vertical motions may be treated separately. The horizontal velocity is constant. The vertical acceleration is also constant and equal to that due to gravity.

Quick test 2

1 The graph below shows how the velocity of a moving object, starting from rest, changes with time.

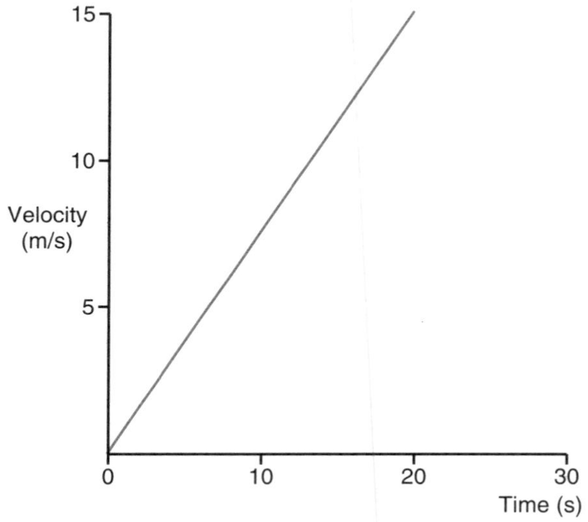

Draw graphs which show how (a) the acceleration of the object and (b) the distance travelled by the object change with time.

2 What is the unit of acceleration?

3 An object with an initial speed of 3 m/s begins to accelerate uniformly at 2 m/s^2. What will be its speed 5 s later?

4 A body accelerates uniformly from rest at 4 m/s^2 for 5 s.
(a) How far does it travel in 5 s?
(b) Calculate its average velocity in this time.

5 An object falls from an aircraft flying horizontally at a height of 180 m with a speed of 100 m/s. Ignoring the friction of the air, calculate
(a) the time the object takes to hit the ground;
(b) the horizontal distance it travels in this time.

Chapter 3

Force and momentum

3.1 Newton's Laws of Motion

The majority of the work in this chapter can be summarized by Newton's Laws of Motion:

1. **Every object remains at rest or continues to move in a straight line at a constant speed if no resultant (total) force acts on it.**
2. **When a force does act on an object, the object will accelerate or decelerate (slow down) or change its direction of motion. The value of the acceleration (or deceleration) is proportional to the resultant force.**
3. **To every action there is an equal and opposite reaction.**

The word force means a push or pull, that is something which changes an object's state of rest or constant speed in a straight line. When an object at rest is acted on by a force it tends to move. If a force acts on an object which is already moving it will change its velocity, either by altering its speed or its direction or both.

If an object has no resultant force acting on it, the object will remain at rest or it will continue to move with a constant speed in a straight line (constant velocity).

It is the **resultant** (**total or net**) force acting on the object which is important. For example, when an object is moving there is likely to be friction acting against it. A car will accelerate only when the forward force from its engine is greater than the total frictional forces from its moving parts, such as the axle bearings, and the flow of air over its surface. The frictional force, due to the air flowing over the surface of a car body when it is moving, increases greatly as the speed of the car increases. Eventually the frictional forces equal the force that the car's engine is producing and the car stops accelerating, as the resultant or total force on the car is now zero.

When the brakes of a car are applied the car slows down but the distance it travels before it stops depends on how fast it is travelling and how hard the brakes are applied. Table 3.1 gives the **minimum** braking distances for cars travelling at different speeds. They assume that the brakes are in excellent condition and that the weather is good (no rain, ice or snow). It can be seen that if a car is travelling **twice** as fast its braking distance will be **four** times as great, i.e. the braking distance depends on the square of the speed of the car. The braking distance is not the total stopping distance. To obtain this we must add the distance the car travels in the time it takes the driver to react to an emergency (thinking distance). The figures given in Table 3.1 are for an average alert driver and are proportional to the speed of the car.

Table 3.1

Speed of car (m.p.h.)	20	30	40	50	60
Thinking distance (m)	6	9	12	15	18
Braking distance (m)	6	14	24	38	56
Overall stopping distance (m)	12	23	36	53	74

It should be emphasized that in poor weather and/or if the driver is tired the total stopping distances are much greater. Therefore, cars should be driven at a speed which takes account of the surroundings, weather and visibility.

A free-fall parachutist accelerates for some while after leaving an aircraft. Eventually the force upwards due to the air flowing over the parachutist's body is equal but opposite to his weight acting downwards and he no longer accelerates. His velocity is then called his **terminal velocity**. When he opens his parachute the air resistance becomes much greater, due to the large surface area of the parachute, and he slows down. Eventually, due to his reduced speed, the force of air resistance becomes equal to his weight and he floats to earth at a gentle steady speed.

3.2 Measuring force

A spring balance marked in newtons is suitable for measuring force in a laboratory. The balance consists of a spring whose extension is proportional to the force applied to it. The spring is contained in a case and is calibrated by applying known forces to it, usually in the form of weights (Fig. 3.1).

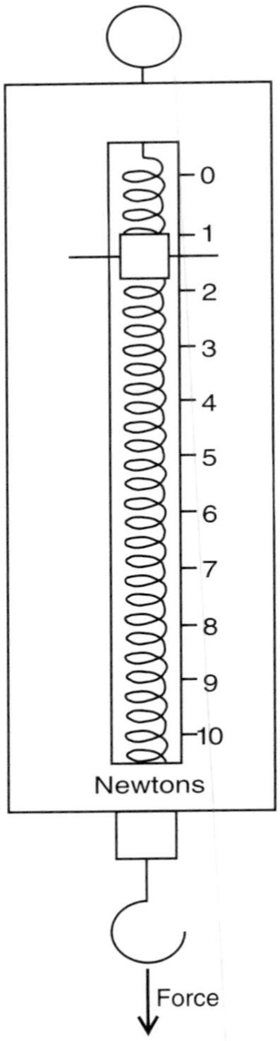

Fig. 3.1 A spring balance for measuring force

3.3 The acceleration produced by a force

The relationship between a force and the acceleration it produces can be investigated using a trolley, ramp and ticker-timer (see Fig. 3.2). The ramp has to be raised sufficiently at one end to compensate for friction in the trolley and ticker-timer. The slope should be such that when the trolley with tape in place is nudged, it moves slowly down the ramp at constant speed.

A tape is then obtained by towing the trolley down the ramp with a constant force. This can be provided by either an elastic band stretched a known amount, or by weights hung over a pulley as shown in Fig. 3.2. The experiment is repeated using twice the original force and again using three times the force.

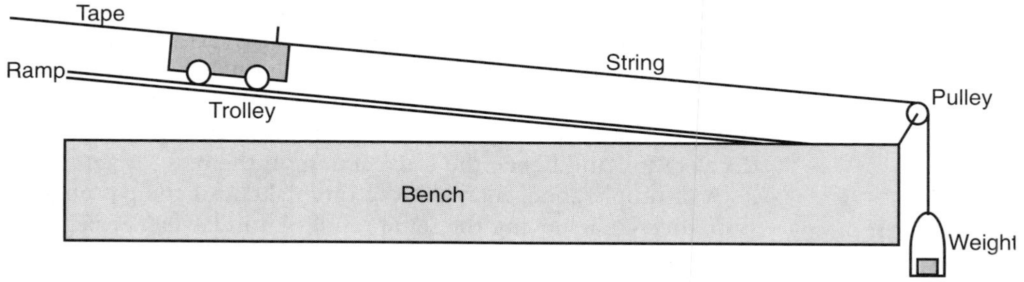

Fig. 3.2

Instead of a ticker-timer a light gate can be used to determine the velocity of the trolley near the end of the ramp. A card 10 cm or 20 cm wide is attached to the trolley so that it prevents the light falling on the photo-transistor while it is passing through the light gate. The time for which the light is cut off is recorded. The velocity of the trolley is found by dividing the width of the card by the time recorded on the electronic timer attached to the light gate. The acceleration of the trolley is calculated by dividing this velocity by the time it took the trolley to reach the light gate, which can be measured using an electronic stopclock.

Histograms can be made if tapes are used. A typical set of results is shown in Fig. 3.3.

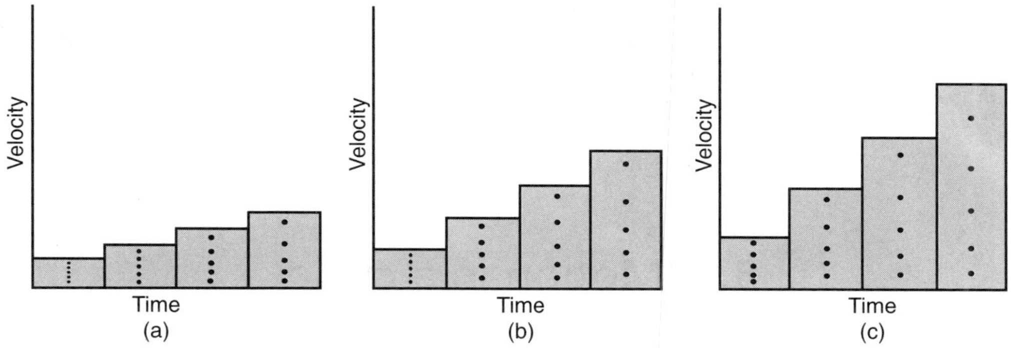

Fig. 3.3 (a) Original force; (b) twice the force; (c) three times the force

It is clear that if the force doubles, the acceleration doubles, etc., that is

$$\frac{F}{a} \text{ is constant, provided the mass is constant} \qquad (3.1)$$

The same apparatus may be used to show how the acceleration a depends on the mass m of a trolley, when a constant force is used. The force is applied in turn to one, two and three trolleys of similar mass stacked on each other. It is found that if the mass is doubled the acceleration is halved, etc., that is

$$m \times a = \text{a constant} \qquad (3.2)$$

The relation

$$\boldsymbol{F = ma} \qquad (3.3)$$

will be seen to include both statements (3.1) and (3.2). The unit of force is the **newton (N)** which is defined as the force which gives an acceleration of one metre per second^2 to a mass of one kilogram.

An object which has a large mass requires a large force to accelerate it as can be noted from equation (3.3). Such an object is said to have large inertia; it is difficult to move.

Examiner's tip

Make sure you can rearrange the equation to give $a = \frac{F}{m}$

3.4 Deceleration

When a person lands on the ground after falling from a considerable height, they will experience a large force and stop suddenly. If they land on their feet after, for example, jumping off a wall or parachuting, they can lessen the force acting on them by bending their knees when they hit the ground. This increases the time they take to stop, thus reducing the size of their deceleration and hence reducing the force on them ($F = ma$).

The same applies when a car crashes. Wearing a seat belt prevents someone from continuing forward and hitting the steering wheel or windscreen. However, it would be no use if it stopped the person instantly as the resulting force would crush them. A seat belt 'gives' a little thus lengthening the time taken to stop the person. This reduces the deceleration and hence the force acting on them.

A 'crumple zone' increases the time taken for the passenger compartment of a car to stop, thereby achieving the same result. An inflatable air bag in front of the driver works in a similar way.

All the above can be explained just as well in terms of rate of change of momentum using equation 3.7 in Unit 3.8.

3.5 Weight

The acceleration produced by the Earth when a body is falling freely is written as g, which is therefore called the acceleration due to gravity. It is also known as the gravitational field strength. The force on a body due to the Earth's attraction is found by using equation (3.3) which becomes $F = mg$, where F is in newtons.

The value of the force acting on a body due to the Earth's attraction is mg, or its weight. This force acts downwards, that is towards the centre of the Earth.

The strength of the Moon's attraction is about one seventh of the value of the Earth's attraction. A mass m on the Moon's surface would therefore experience a force of only one seventh the value it experiences on the Earth's surface. Its weight on the Moon would be about one seventh of its weight on the Earth.

3.6 Motion in a circle

When a body is moving in a circle its direction of motion, and hence its velocity, is continually changing. A force is needed to achieve this.

If you attach a mass to one end of a length of string, hold the other end and whirl it steadily round in a horizontal circle, you can feel that a force is required to make the mass move in a circular path. The force acts along the string and increases if the mass is whirled faster.

If any object is to move in a circle a force has to be continually applied to the object at right angles to its direction of motion at any instant; that is towards the centre of the circle. This is called the centripetal force. It does not alter the speed of the object, but it does alter its direction of travel and hence its velocity. The force produces an acceleration towards the centre of the circle.

Consider an object of mass m moving with a constant speed v in a circle of radius r. By calculating the rate of change of *velocity*, as the object continually changes direction, the acceleration a can be shown to be given by the equation:

$$a = \frac{v^2}{r}$$

but $$F = ma$$

thus $$F = \frac{mv^2}{r} \qquad (3.4)$$

The force required to keep an object moving in the arc of a circle increases greatly as the speed of the object increases. Also it is larger if the radius of the arc is smaller. It is larger for an object of greater mass.

A car or train going round a corner are everyday examples of motion in a circle. Friction between the tyres and the road provides the centripetal force in the case of a car cornering. If the corner is too sharp (r very small), the speed too high, or the road wet, the frictional force may not be large enough to keep the car moving in a circle, and it will slide off the road. The outer rail provides the centripetal force in the case of a train.

Another example of centripetal force is the gravitational force of the Sun on the planets, including the Earth.

3.7 Momentum

A lorry which is fully laden requires a larger force to set it in motion than a similar lorry which is empty. Likewise more powerful brakes are required to stop a heavy goods vehicle than a family car moving with the same speed. The heavier vehicle is said to have more **momentum** than the lighter one. Momentum is a measure of how difficult it is to alter a body's motion; it is more basic even than velocity.

The momentum of a body is defined as the product of its mass and its velocity.

Momentum = mass × velocity

Momentum has units of kg m/s.

By studying the linear motion of a trolley down a ramp it has been shown experimentally that the following equation is valid:

$$F = ma$$

but $$a = \frac{v - u}{t}$$

Thus $$F = \frac{m(v - u)}{t}$$

so $$F = \frac{mv - mu}{t} \qquad (3.5)$$

or $$\boldsymbol{Ft = mv - mu} \qquad (3.6)$$

Equation (3.5) can be written thus:

$$\textbf{Force} = \frac{\textbf{change of momentum}}{\textbf{time taken for this change}} \qquad (3.7)$$

All the equations just discussed concern momentum change and hence, by the definition of momentum, velocity change. They are therefore valid for changes in the direction of motion of an object as well as for changes in its speed. They apply to circular motion as well as linear, and are summed up in Newton's second law of motion (see Unit 3.1).

3.8 Conservation of momentum

When two objects collide the force one exerts on the other is equal in size but opposite in direction to the force the second one exerts on the first. As the time of contact is the same for each, both experience the same change in momentum, but in the opposite direction. The **total** momentum of the two is therefore unaltered by the collision. This is known as **the principle of conservation of linear momentum**.The principle always applies provided no forces, other than those due to the collision, act on the objects.

This principle can be verified experimentally, for a simple case, using two trolleys and a ticker-timer, on a friction-compensated ramp. Fig. 3.4(a) shows the arrangement.

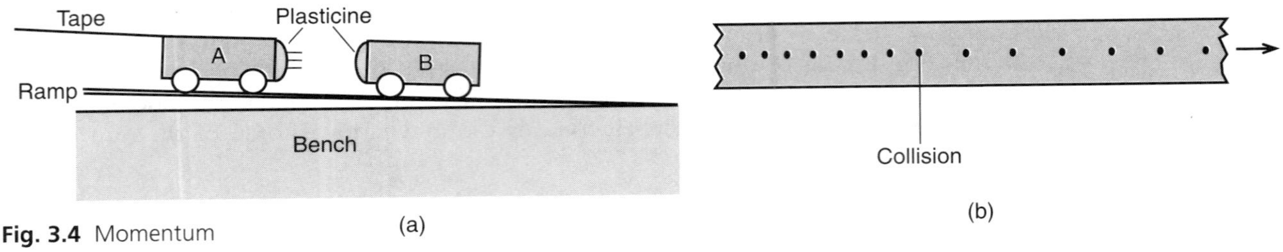

Fig. 3.4 Momentum

Some plasticine is placed on the surface of the two trolleys which will come into contact. Drawing pins are embedded in the plasticine on the front of trolley A, and tickertape is attached to the rear of this trolley. Trolley A is given a push so that it travels with uniform velocity and collides with trolley B. The trolleys stick together and move off with a common velocity. A typical tape is shown in Fig. 3.4(b). The spacing of the dots changes suddenly on collision. The velocity of A before the collision and the combined velocity of the two trolleys after the collision are found from the spacing of the dots. In this experiment the tape is **not** being used to show acceleration. Alternatively two light gates may be used, one to determine the velocity of trolley A before collision, the other to determine the combined velocity of the two trolleys after collision. The precise method is described in Unit 3.3. The results show that:

$$\text{Total momentum before collision} = \text{total momentum after collision} \qquad (3.8)$$

Alternatively

$$m_1u_1 + m_2u_2 = m_1v_1 + m_2v_2 \qquad (3.9)$$

where m, u and v represent the masses and velocities of the colliding objects. In some collisions one of the velocities may be zero or two velocities may have the same value. For example, in the experiment just described $u_2 = 0$ and $v_1 = v_2$ as the trolleys stick together after collision. Equation (3.9) then becomes simpler.

Suppose that in the above experiment $m_1 = 1$ kg, $m_2 = 3$ kg and $u_1 = 1$ m/s. Then substituting in equation (3.9) we obtain:

$$1 = v_1 + 3v_2$$

but $v_1 = v_2$

thus $1 = 4v_1$

hence $v_1 = 0.25 \text{ m/s} = v_2$

This is the value we would record from the tape after the collision, thus verifying **the principle of the conservation of linear momentum**.

3.9 Rockets

The principle of the conservation of momentum holds in the case of an explosion as well as a collision. When one object pushes on another both experience the same size force but in opposite directions (Newton's Third Law). An example is when a spring is released between two trolleys. Both experience the same size force and it does not matter to which trolley the spring is attached.

A rocket works in the same way. It is the force between it and the burnt fuel it ejects at the back which results in the force which accelerates it. The rocket gains forward momentum equal in size to the momentum of the gases it expels backwards. While accelerating its rate of ejection of fuel remains constant (constant force) but, as it gets higher, its mass gets less (less fuel left) and therefore its acceleration increases (equation 3.3).

Summary

1 When a body is in motion it obeys Newton's laws of motion.

2 The acceleration a produced when a mass m experiences a force F is given by

$$a = \frac{F}{m} \text{ or } F = ma$$

3 When a body of mass m moves at constant speed in a circle of radius r, the centripetal force F is given by

$$F = \frac{mv^2}{r}$$

4 **Momentum = mass × velocity (mv)** and is measured in units of kg m/s.

5 The law of conservation of momentum states that when two bodies collide the total momentum in a given direction after collision is equal to the total momentum in the same direction before collision.

6 The change of momentum which occurs when a force acts on a body for a certain time is given by

$$\textbf{Force} = \frac{\textbf{change in momentum}}{\textbf{time taken for this change}}$$

Force is measured in newtons (N).

Quick test 3

1 Write down the unit of (a) force and (b) momentum.

2 In your own words write down what is meant by Newton's First Law of Motion.

3 (a) A car with a mass of 600 kg is accelerated by a force of 1200 N. Calculate the acceleration of the car, ignoring any frictional force.
(b) Repeat the calculation in part (a), assuming that a frictional force of 300 N acts on the car.

4 Explain the purpose of a car seat belt. How does it work?

5 Your weight is 500 N. What is your mass?

6 Calculate the force necessary to keep a mass of 2 kg moving in a circle of radius 0.5 m at a constant speed of 1.5 m/s. In which direction does this force act?

7 What is the momentum of a 50 kg girl running at a speed of 8 m/s?

8 Explain what is meant by the law of Conservation of Momentum.

9 A boy of mass 60 kg jumps horizontally out of a dingy of mass 15 kg at a speed of 3 m/s. What happens to the dingy? Give as detailed an answer as you can.

Chapter 4
Work, energy and power

4.1 Work

The term 'work' is associated with movement. If a railway engine pulls a train along a track with a steady force the work done by the engine depends on the size of the force it provides and the distance it pulls the train with this force. Work is calculated by definition from the relation:

Work done = force × distance moved in the direction of the force

The unit of work is the **joule (J)**. One joule is the work done when a force of one newton moves through a distance of one metre in the direction of the force.

No work is done in circular motion as the force is at right angles to the distance.

4.2 Energy

Energy is transferred when work is done. All forms of energy are measured in **joules**.

The world we live in provides energy in many different forms but the Sun is the ultimate source of all these. Chemical energy is perhaps the most important. The use of chemical energy from coal and oil has been a major factor in the development of our civilization. The presence of electricity, light and heat as forms of energy in our homes is something we take for granted. Most of this energy comes from the chemical energy stored in coal, oil or gas or from nuclear energy. In each case the fuel produces heat which, in the form of steam, is used to drive turbines. In turn, these drive generators (see dynamos – Unit 24.2) to make electricity. Coal, oil and gas are fossil fuels and are **non-renewable** forms of energy. Also, oil is used to make plastics and it should not be squandered by burning it.

In the last 30 years there has been considerable research into **renewable** forms of energy such as energy directly from the Sun or from the wind, the tides and waves.

Solar energy can be harnessed by the use of solar panels on the roofs of buildings. Such panels are black so as to absorb the radiant energy from the Sun most efficiently. Normally, the energy absorbed heats water flowing in pipes just behind the black surface. There are few solar panels in the United Kingdom due to lack of sunshine, particularly in winter. Solar panels are a common sight in tropical countries.

Making use of wind energy involves the building of many windmills in windy areas, which are often areas of outstanding natural beauty. There are environmental problems, such as noise, to be sorted out as well as economic and engineering problems.

Tidal barriers have been built, the nearest one to the United Kingdom being on the Rance estuary, near St. Malo, in Brittany. The barriers control the inflow and outflow of water as the tide rises and falls. The flow of water drives turbines which generate electricity. For many years there have been plans to build a similar barrier across the Bristol Channel.

The engineering problems in producing large quantities of energy economically from wave motion are severe and have not yet been overcome.

Food has chemical energy stored in it, which is released by chemical reaction inside our bodies. Food provides us with energy to keep warm and to do work.

Energy can be neither created nor destroyed, though it may be changed from one form to another. This is **the law of conservation of energy.**

Although energy may change from one form to another, the second form may not be measurable or useful. Most energy transformations end up with the formation of a large proportion of heat. This is usually spread (dissipated) amongst an extremely large number of molecules and it is not economic to harness it and change it into other types of energy. It is no longer 'useful' energy and can be said to have been 'lost'. The 'efficiency' of any energy change is defined as follows;

$$\text{Efficiency} = \frac{\text{Useful energy output}}{\text{Total energy input}} \times 100\ \%$$

4.3 Potential energy

If an object is to be raised from a bench, an upward vertical force equal to the weight of the object must be provided. Suppose the force applied (mg) raises the object a vertical distance h.

$$\text{work done} = \text{force} \times \text{distance moved in the direction of the force}$$

thus $$\text{work done} = mg \times h = \boldsymbol{mgh}$$

Once the object has been raised it is said to have increased its **potential energy** by this amount. All the work done has been used to increase the potential energy of the object.

Potential energy is the energy an object has by reason of its position.

4.4 Kinetic energy

Examiner's tip

Energy is transferred when work is done so Energy transferred = Force × distance moved in the direction of the force.

If the object is now allowed to fall it will steadily lose the potential energy it has gained. By the time it has fallen a distance h it will have lost all the potential energy it previously gained. As it falls its velocity increases and it is said to possess an increasing amount of **kinetic energy**. The kinetic energy it has at any instant will equal the potential energy it has lost.

Kinetic energy is the energy a body has by reason of its motion.

As the object falls it is accelerated by the force of the Earth's attraction on it. Suppose it falls a distance h, in time t, as its velocity increases uniformly from zero to v.

$$\text{force} = \frac{\text{change in momentum}}{\text{time taken}}$$

thus $$F = \frac{mv - 0}{t}$$

and $$\text{distance} = \text{average velocity} \times \text{time}$$

that is $$h = \frac{v}{2} \times t$$

$$\begin{aligned}\text{work done} &= \text{force} \times \text{distance moved in the direction of the force}\\ &= \frac{mv}{t} \times h\\ &= \frac{mv}{t} \times \frac{vt}{2}\\ &= \tfrac{1}{2}mv^2\end{aligned}$$

The work done by the gravitational force results in an increase of kinetic energy of $\frac{1}{2}mv^2$, and a loss of potential energy of mgh.

Suppose an object, mass 5 kg, falls through a vertical distance of 5 m near the Earth's surface where its acceleration due to gravity (g) is 10 m/s^2.

$$\begin{aligned}\text{potential energy lost} &= mgh = 5 \times 10 \times 5 = 250\ \text{J}\\ \text{kinetic energy gained} &= \tfrac{1}{2}mv^2 = 250\ \text{J}\\ \text{thus}\quad \tfrac{1}{2} \times 5 \times v^2 &= 250\ \text{J}\\ v^2 &= 100\\ \text{and}\quad v &= 10\ \text{m/s}\end{aligned}$$

4.5 Power

Power is defined as the work done per second, or the amount of energy transformed per second.

$$\textbf{Average power} = \frac{\textbf{work done}}{\textbf{time taken}} = \frac{\textbf{energy change}}{\textbf{time taken}}$$

It is measured in units of joules per second (J/s). One joule per second is called a **watt (W)**.

1 kilowatt (kW) = 1000 watts

A rough estimate of a pupil's power can be made by asking him or her to walk or run up a staircase. If the height of the staircase is measured in metres, the pupil's weight calculated in newtons, and the time taken recorded on a stopwatch, the power can be calculated. The result will normally be about 200 W if walking or 500 W if running.

4.6 Scalar and vector quantities

A **scalar quantity** is one which has only magnitude (size), such as money and number of apples. A **vector quantity** is one which has both magnitude and direction, such as velocity, force and momentum.

Vectors can be represented by straight lines drawn to scale. If a number of forces all act in the same straight line, their resultant is found by addition or subtraction.

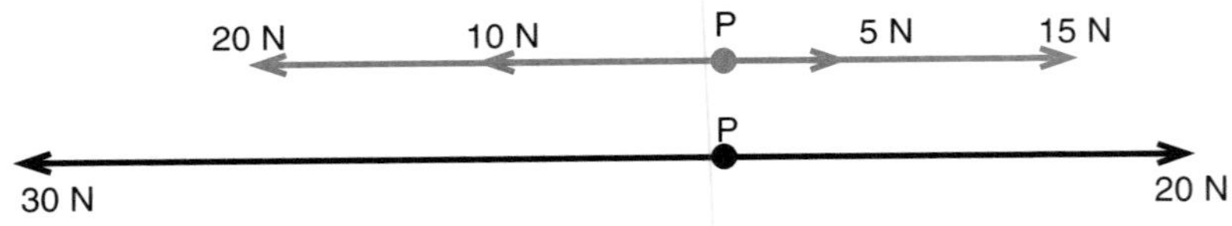

Thus if forces of 20, 15, 10 and 5 newtons all act at a point P, as shown in Fig. 4.1, we have:

total force acting towards the left = 10 + 20 = 30 N

total force acting towards the right = 15 + 5 = 20 N

resultant force = 30 – 20 = 10 N acting to the left

Summary

1 **Work done (or energy transformed) = force × distance moved in the direction of the force.**

2 The Sun is the source of all energy.

3 The change in potential energy (or energy of position) when a mass m is moved through a vertical height h is given by the equation

$$\textbf{Change in potential energy} = mgh$$

where g is the gravitational field strength.

4 The kinetic energy (or energy of motion) of a mass m moving at a velocity v is given by

$$\textbf{Kinetic energy} = \tfrac{1}{2}mv^2$$

5 Power is the work done per second or the rate at which energy is transformed:

$$\textbf{Average power} = \frac{\textbf{work done}}{\textbf{time taken}} = \frac{\textbf{energy change}}{\textbf{time taken}}$$

6 Energy is measured in joules (J) and power in watts (W). One watt is one joule per second.

7 A **scalar** quantity has only size. A **vector** quantity has size and direction.

Quick test 4

1 Name four forms of energy.

2 Write down what you understand by the law of Conservation of Energy.

3 Explain what is meant when energy is said to be 'lost'.

4 A book with a mass of 1 kg is lifted from a desk and placed on a shelf 1.5 m above the desk.
(a) Calculate the increase in potential energy of the book.
(b) The book now falls from the shelf onto the desk. Calculate the speed with which it hits the desk.

5 An object is dropped from a tower 50 m high. When it is 10 m from the ground what is the ratio of its kinetic energy to its potential energy above ground level?

6 Which unit would you use to measure the rate at which a machine is doing work?

7 A motor lifts a mass of 2 kg through a height of 3 m in 5 s. Calculate the average power produced by the motor.

8 Name (a) two vector and (b) two scalar quantities.

Chapter 5
Turning forces

5.1 Moments

When we open a door, turn on a tap or use a spanner, we exert a **turning force**. Two factors determine the size of the turning effect: the magnitude (size) of the force and the distance of the line of action of the force from the pivot or **fulcrum**. A large turning effect can be produced with a small force provided the distance from the pivot is large. The size of the turning effect is called the **moment**.

Moment of force = force × perpendicular distance from the pivot

The units of a moment are newton metres (Nm).

5.2 Experiments to study moments

Examiner's tip

The pivot does not have to be in the middle of the lever; it can be at one end and as long as the lever does not have a big mass, you can use the law of moments without worrying about the weight of the lever.

A thin uniform strip of wood, for example a metre rule, is balanced on a pivot. A weight is placed on the rule to one side of the pivot and a second weight is added on the other side and its position carefully adjusted until balance is restored (Fig. 5.1). Within the limits of experimental error it will be found that:

$$w_1 \times d_1 = w_2 \times d_2$$

Balance can be restored using more than one weight, in which case:

$$w_1 \times d_1 = (w_2 \times d_2) + (w_3 \times d_3)$$

This principle can be extended if further weights are used. **When an object is in equilibrium, the sum of the anticlockwise moments about any point is equal to the sum of the clockwise moments about the same point**. This is known as the **law of moments**. The force the fulcrum exerts on the object equals the sum of the weights on the object.

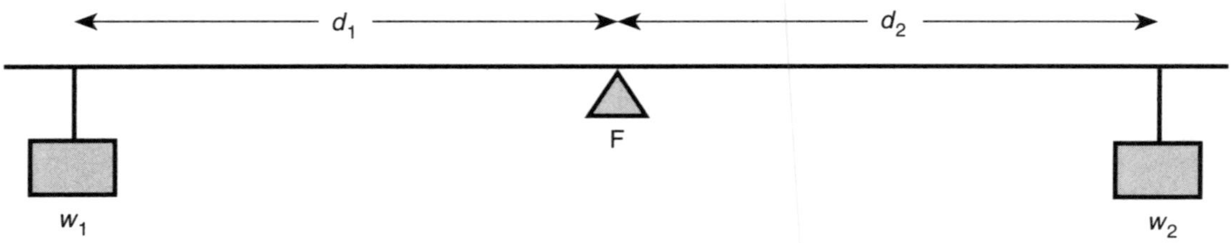

Fig. 5.1 Moments

Suppose, in Fig. 5.1 above, w_1 = 300 N, w_2 = 100 N, d_1 = 0.4 m and d_2 = 0.5 m, then we can calculate where a weight of 700 N must be placed to balance the rule.

$$w_1 \times d_1 = (w_2 \times d_2) + (w_3 \times d_3)$$

hence $$300 \times 0.4 = (100 \times 0.5) + 700d_3$$

and $$d_3 = \frac{(300 \times 0.4) - (100 \times 0.5)}{700} \text{ m}$$

$$= \frac{120 - 50}{700} = 0.1 \text{ m}$$

This weight must be placed 0.1 m to the right of the pivot.

5.3 Centre of mass

The weight of an object is defined as the force with which the Earth attracts it. This says nothing about the point of application of this force. An object may be regarded as made up of a large number of tiny particles, each with the same mass. Each of these particles is pulled towards the Earth with the same force. The Earth's pull on the object thus consists of a large number of equal parallel forces. These can be replaced by a single force which acts through a point called the **centre of mass**.

The centre of mass of an object is defined as the point of application of the resultant force due to the Earth's attraction on the object. Thus we may regard the centre of mass as the point at which the whole weight of the object acts.

5.4 Location of the centre of mass

The centre of mass of a long thin object such as a ruler may be found approximately by balancing it on a straight edge. The same method may also be used for a thin sheet (lamina). In this case it is necessary to balance it in two positions as shown in Fig. 5.2.

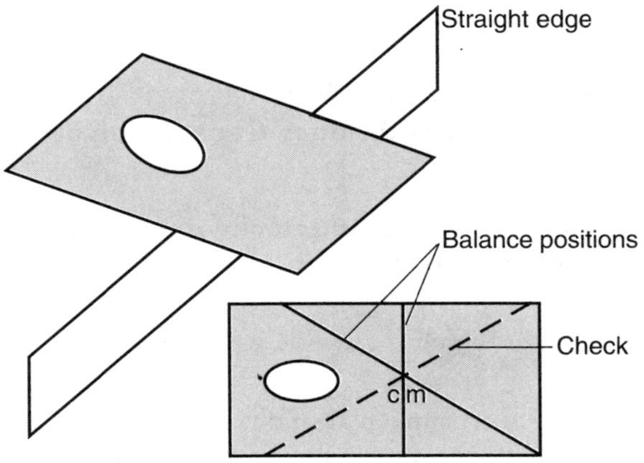

Fig. 5.2 Locating the centre of mass

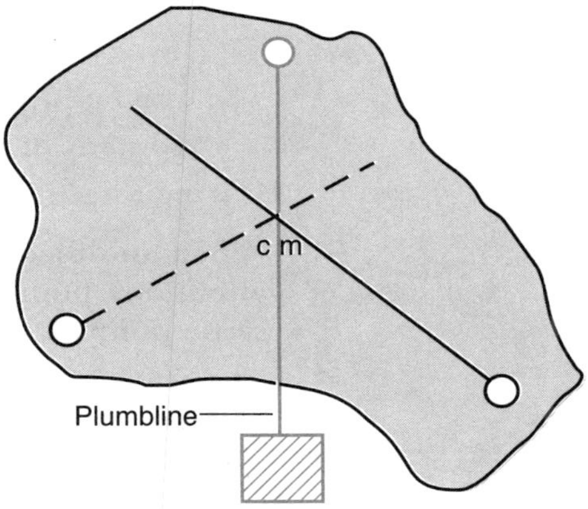

Fig. 5.3

One good way of finding the centre of mass of a lamina is to use a plumbline. Three small holes are made at well spaced intervals round the edge of the lamina, and the lamina and plumbline suspended from each in turn (Fig. 5.3).

The position of the plumbline is marked on the lamina and the point of intersection of these three lines gives the position of the centre of mass.

5.5 Stability

The position of an object's centre of mass affects its stability. For example, the centre of mass of a vehicle should be as low as possible, and its wheelbase as wide as possible, if it is to be stable.

When a vehicle corners fast there is a tendency for it to tilt on the outer wheels. It will turn right over when the vertical line through the centre of mass falls outside these wheels. If the conditions stated above are satisfied, the centre of mass has to rise a larger distance for this to happen. This requires more potential energy and it is less likely to occur.

5.6 Work done by a machine: efficiency

A machine is any device by means of which a force (effort) applied at one point can be used to overcome a force (load) at some other point. Most machines, but not all, are designed so that the effort is less than the load. They can be regarded as force multipliers; the force that the effort exerts is multiplied by the machine to be equal to the force that the load exerts.

The ratio of the useful work done by a machine to the total work put into it is called the **efficiency** of the machine. Usually the efficiency is expressed as a percentage.

$$\textbf{Efficiency} = \frac{\textbf{work output} \times \textbf{100\%}}{\textbf{work input}}$$

In a perfect machine no work would be wasted and the efficiency would be 100%. In practice, work is wasted in overcoming friction and, in the case of pulleys, in raising the lower pulley block. The efficiency is then below 100%.

Summary

1 The turning effect of a force about a pivot is called its moment.

Moment of a force = force × perpendicular distance from the pivot

It is measured in newton metres (Nm).

2 **When an object is in equilibrium, the sum of the anticlockwise moments about any point is equal to the sum of the clockwise moments about the same point.**

3 The centre of mass of an object is the point at which the whole weight of the object seems to act.

4 A machine is any device by which a force (effort) applied at one point can be used to overcome a force (load) at some other point. Most machines are designed so that the effort is less than the load.

The efficiency of a machine is given by

$$\textbf{Efficiency} = \frac{\textbf{work output} \times \textbf{100\%}}{\textbf{work input}}$$

Quick test 5

1 Write down the **law of moments**.

2 A girl weighing 600 N sits 6 m away from the pivot of a see-saw, as shown below. What force *F*, 9 m away from the pivot, is needed to balance the see-saw?

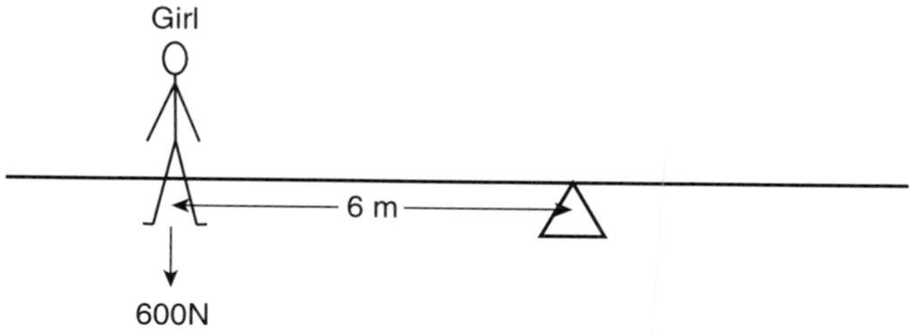

3 What do you understand by the term **centre of mass**?

4 Write down what you understand by the **stability** of an object.

5 Calculate the percentage efficiency of a machine which requires an energy input of 20 J to lift a mass of 1 kg through 1.2 m.

Chapter 6
Density

Equal volumes of different substances vary considerably in their mass. For instance aircraft are made chiefly from aluminium alloys which, volume for volume, have a mass half that of steel, but are just as strong. The 'lightness' or 'heaviness' of a material is referred to as its **density**.

$$\textbf{Density} = \frac{\textbf{mass}}{\textbf{volume}} \ (\text{kg/m}^3 \text{ or g/cm}^3)$$

6.1 A regular solid

The mass of the solid is found by weighing, either on a chemical balance, if great accuracy is required, or on a spring balance. If the latter is used the result must be converted to mass units; that is if the balance is calibrated in newtons, the value recorded must be divided by 9.81 to obtain the mass in kilograms.

The volume of the solid is found by length measurement, using a ruler, vernier calipers or a micrometer screw gauge, depending on the accuracy required. This method can be used for cuboids, spheres, cylinders and cones amongst other regular shapes. The formulae giving the volume of such shapes in terms of their linear dimensions can be obtained from textbooks. For example, metals are often in the form of turned cylinders whose volume can be calculated from the formula:

$$\text{Volume} = \pi r^2 h$$

where r is the cylinder radius and h is its height.

6.2 An irregular solid

The mass is found in the same way as for a regular solid. In order to find the volume it is necessary to partly fill a measuring cylinder with water. The reading is taken and the solid then lowered into the water on the end of a length of cotton, until it is completely immersed, and the new reading taken. The difference between the two readings gives the volume of the solid. This method cannot be used if the solid dissolves in water.

6.3 A liquid

A measuring cylinder is first weighed empty using, for example, a top-pan balance. Some of the liquid to be tested is poured into the cylinder, and the cylinder reweighed.

The difference between the two readings gives the mass. The volume of the liquid is found by direct reading of the measuring cylinder. If a more accurate value is needed a specific gravity bottle can be used. Details may be found from a textbook.

Summary

1 **Density** $= \dfrac{\textbf{mass}}{\textbf{volume}}$

It is measured in kg/m^3 or g/cm^3.

Quick test 6

1 Define density.

2 What measurements would you need to make in order to calculate the density of a regular solid?

3 A metal cube, with each side 2 cm in length, has a density of 8 g/cm^3. What is the mass of the cube?

4 A stone has a mass of 480 g and a volume of 160 cm^3. What is the value of its density?

Chapter 7
Pressure

The word **pressure** has an exact scientific meaning. It is defined as the force acting normally (perpendicularly) per unit area.

$$\textbf{Pressure} = \frac{\textbf{force}}{\textbf{area}}$$

For example, the pressure exerted on the ground by an object depends on the mass of the object and on the area of the body in contact with the ground. A boy wearing ice skates will exert a far greater pressure than if he were wearing shoes. The pressure exerted on the ground by a brick depends on which face is in contact with the ground (Fig. 7.1). However, the weight of the brick and thus the force it exerts on the ground is about 22 N, whichever face is in contact.

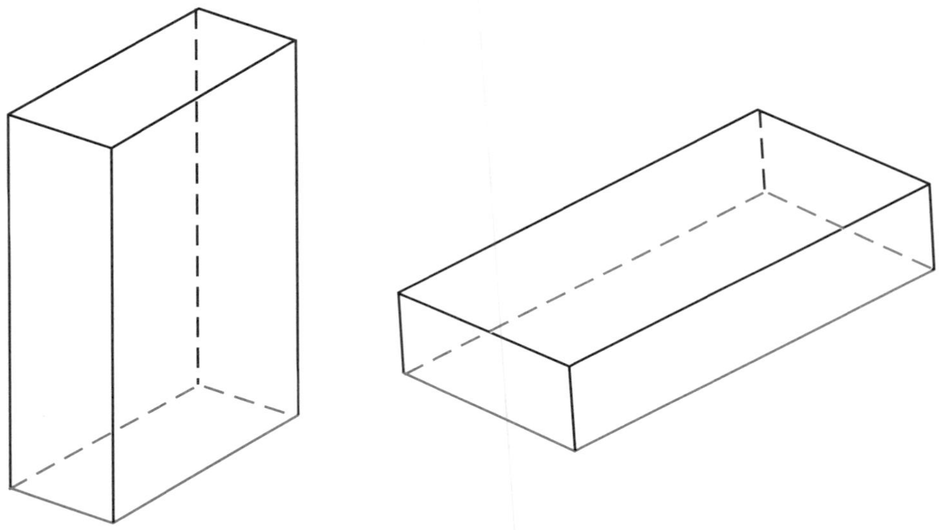

Fig. 7.1

One does not have to use a very large force when using a needle. As the area of the point is very small, a relatively small force produces a large pressure and the needle pierces the material.

7.1 Pressure in a liquid or gas (a fluid)

The pressure in a fluid increases with depth. This may be shown by using a tall vessel full of water with side tubes fitted at various depths (Fig. 7.2).

The speed with which the water spurts out is greatest for the lowest jet, showing that pressure increases with depth. This demonstration also shows that pressure acts in all directions in a fluid – not just vertically. The pressure responsible for these jets is acting horizontally. A sealed plastic bag full of water may be used to show the same effect.

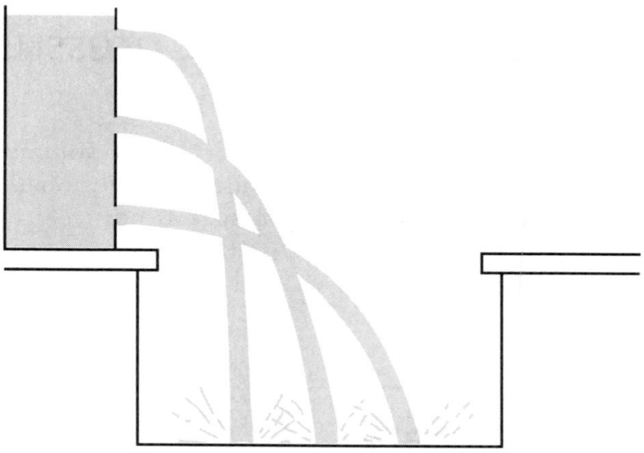

Fig. 7.2

Suppose we consider a horizontal area A at a depth h below the surface of a liquid of density d. Standing on this area is a vertical column of liquid of volume hA, the mass of which is hAd. The weight of this mass is $hAdg$.

$$\text{Pressure} = \frac{\text{force (weight)}}{\text{area}} = \frac{hAdg}{A}$$
$$= hdg$$

The usual units are newtons per metre^2, often called pascals (Pa). The area does not appear in the final expression for pressure in a liquid.

The property of liquids to transmit pressure to all parts is used in many appliances. Some car jacks consist of an oil-filled press used for lifting (Fig. 7.3).

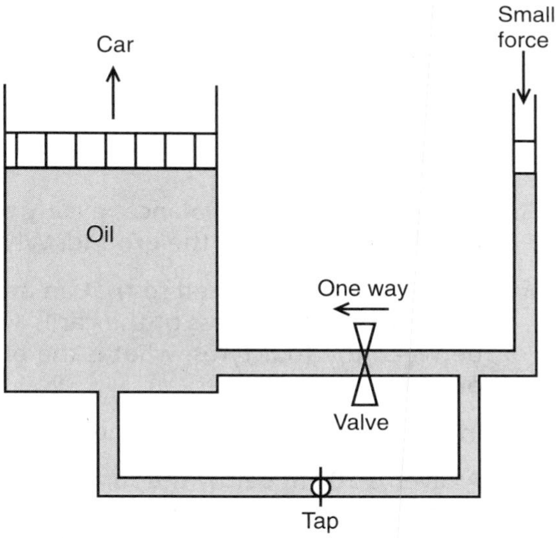

Fig. 7.3 Hydraulic car jack

The pressure exerted on one side of the press is transmitted through to the other side. Thus a small force applied over a small area on one side can result in a large force over a large area on the other side. A large mass, such as a car, may thus be raised by application of a small force.

Mechanical diggers and bulldozers use hydraulic principles to power the blade or shovel. Cars require a braking system which exerts the same pressure on the brake pads of all four wheels to reduce the risk of skidding. Each brake consists of two brake shoes which are pushed apart by hydraulic pressure in a cylinder and press on the brake drum. When the brakes are applied the increased pressure on the pedal is transmitted through oil to the cylinders in each wheel and the shoes applied. Because the total area of the brake shoes is much greater than the area of the piston at the end of the brake pedal, the force applied to the brakes is much greater than the driver applies to the brake pedal.

7.2 Atmospheric pressure

On Earth we are living under a large volume of air. Air has weight and as a result the atmosphere exerts a pressure not only on the Earth's surface but on objects on the Earth. **Atmospheric pressure** is normally expressed in newtons per metre^2 or pascals (Pa). The average value is 100 000 Pa approximately. It gets less as one goes up through the Earth's atmosphere until it becomes virtually zero at a height of about 8 km.

Summary

Examiner's tip

You can measure pressure in N/cm^2 or 'atmospheres' as long as you keep the same units for pressure throughout the calculation.

1 The word 'pressure' has a precise meaning.

$$\textbf{Pressure} = \frac{\textbf{force}}{\textbf{area}}$$

It is measured in N/m^2 which is often called a pascal (Pa).

2 The pressure a distance h below the surface of a liquid which has a density d is

$$\textbf{pressure} = hdg$$

where g is the gravitational field strength.

3 A pressure applied at one point in a liquid is transmitted to all other points. The brake systems of cars and some car jacks use this principle.

4 The Earth's atmosphere exerts a pressure at the Earth's surface of about 100 000 Pa.

Quick test 7

1 Define pressure.

2 A boy of mass 40 kg balances evenly on two stilts, each having an area of 8 cm^3 in contact with the ground. What is the pressure exerted on one stilt?

3 A car's tyres are inflated so that an area of 40 cm^2 of each is in contact with the ground. If the mass of the car is 1280 kg, and is evenly distributed between the four tyres, what is the pressure exerted on the ground by each one?

4 In which direction(s) do(es) the pressure act in a fluid?

5 A diver is 200 m below the surface of the sea. Calculate the pressure on his diving suit, given that the density of water is 1000 kg/m^3. Give units in your answer.

Chapter 8
Forces between molecules in solids

Before materials are used in the construction of machinery, bridges and buildings, tests are carried out to ensure that they are able to stand up to the stresses to which they are likely to be subjected. Brittle substances such as cast iron and masonry will support large forces of compression, but break easily if stretching forces are applied. When stretching forces are likely to be significant, materials such as steel have to be used. The behaviour of a material under the influence of applied forces depends on the forces holding the molecules of the material together.

8.1 Elasticity

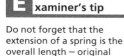

Examiner's tip

Do not forget that the extension of a spring is the overall length – original length.

Some knowledge of the forces between molecules of a solid can be gained by adding weights to a spiral spring and investigating how it stretches. A spiral spring is suspended vertically from a rigid support and a small pointer attached to its lower end (Fig. 8.1(a)).

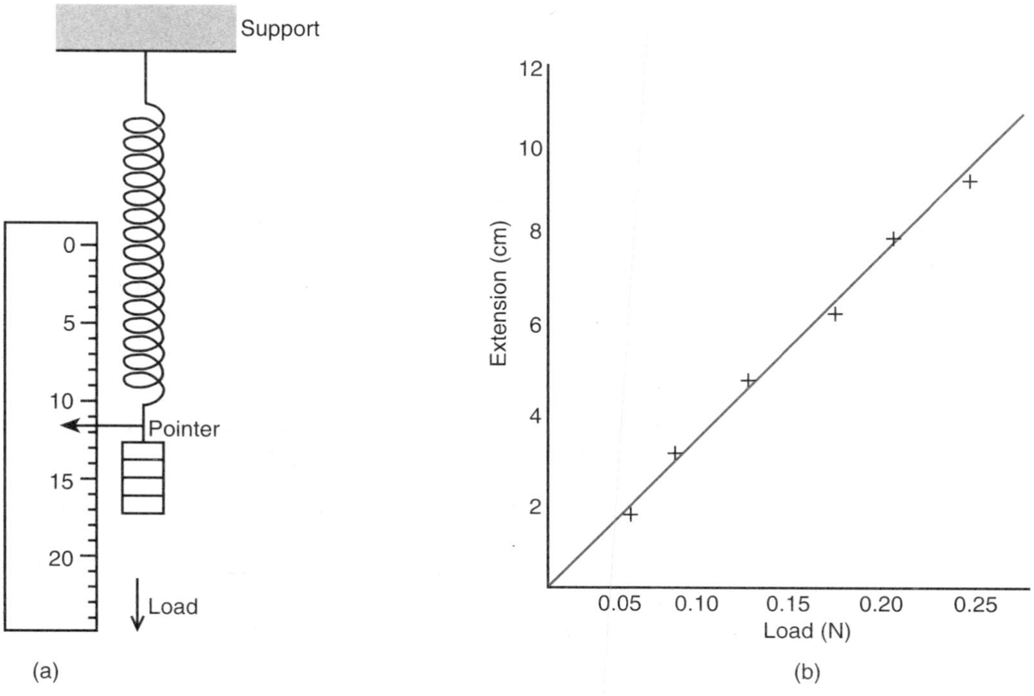

Fig. 8.1

The reading of the pointer against the scale is noted. Weights are then added in steps to the lower end of the spring and the reading of the pointer recorded after the addition of each weight. The weights are removed in similar steps and a second set of readings taken. For small loads the reading of the pointer should be the same for each set of results. The average extension for each load is then plotted against the load (Fig. 8.1(b)).

A straight-line graph passing through the origin shows that the extension is directly proportional to the load in the range of loads used; that is, the load/extension ratio is constant. This ratio is called **the spring or force constant.** It is the force needed to produce unit (1 cm or 1 m) extension and is normally quoted in units of N/m.

When a small weight is attached to the spring, the spring extends. When the weight is removed the spring returns to its original length. The property of regaining its original size or shape is called **elasticity** – thus putty is a very inelastic material whereas metals regain their original shape and are therefore elastic. In a metal the forces of attraction between the displaced molecules are sufficiently strong to restore the molecules to their original position.

If larger weights had been added to the spring a stage would have been reached when the spring would not have returned to its original shape on removing the weights. The spring is permanently stretched or deformed. Beyond a certain load the molecules do not return to their original positions when the load is removed. The extension at which this occurs is called the **elastic limit** of the spring. With greater loads the molecules are unable to keep their fixed positions in the metal.

The forces between the molecules of a metal can be further investigated by stretching a length of straight wire. A length of wire is suspended vertically from a fixed support and weights added to its lower end, in a similar way to the procedure for a spring. However, the extension of the wire within its elastic region is very small, and if this region is to be studied a more accurate method of measuring extension has to be used.

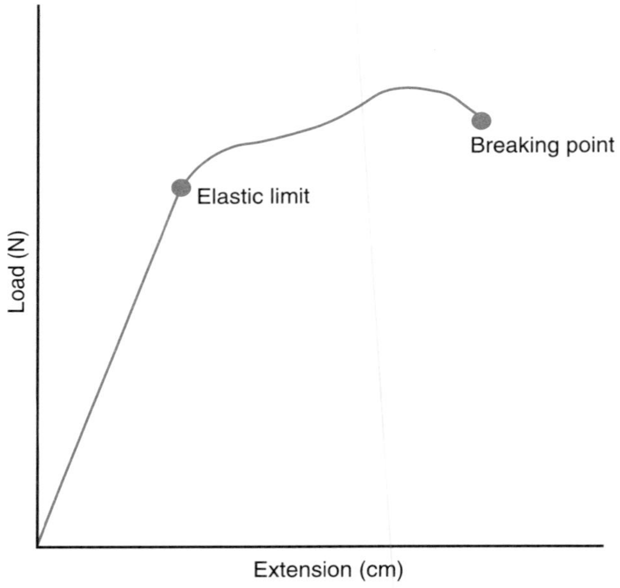

Fig. 8.2

The results for a wire (Fig. 8.2) are as for a spring, with a load/extension graph giving a straight line until the elastic limit is reached.

The results from these two experiments may be summarized in what is known as Hooke's law:

The deformation of a material is proportional to the force applied to it, provided the elastic limit is not exceeded.

While stretched the spring or wire has potential energy stored in it. The area under the load/extension graph is equal to this stored energy. If the elastic limit is not exceeded then this energy is released when the spring or wire returns to its original length. If the elastic limit is exceeded then the extra energy stored is used to permanently deform the spring or wire and becomes heat.

Summary

1 An object is said to behave elastically when equal increases in the force applied to it produce equal changes in length. That is, a graph of the force applied against the extension is a straight line through the origin. When this is so Hooke's law is said to be obeyed.

2 The **elastic limit** is the point beyond which the object no longer behaves elastically

3 When a spring or wire has been stretched, it has energy stored in it; temporarily if it is in the elastic region but permanently if the elastic limit has been exceeded.

Quick test 8

1 State Hooke's law.

2 State what you understand by the term **force or spring constant**.

3 State what you understand by the term **elastic limit**.

4 A spring has an unstretched length of 100 mm. When a force of 5 N is applied the new length of the spring is 150 mm. Assuming that the elastic limit is not exceeded, what is the length of the spring when a force of 7.5 N is applied?

5 Two springs are such that, when either is loaded with a mass of 200 g, it stretches 4 cm. The masses of the springs may be ignored.
The springs are suspended in parallel and a load of 100 g is attached. By what length does each spring stretch?

6 When a spring is stretched, energy is stored in it. What form does this energy take?

Chapter 9
Kinetic theory of matter

9.1 The states of matter

The molecules in a solid are each anchored to one position, about which they vibrate continuously, as if held in position by a framework of springs. When energy is supplied in the form of heat, thus raising the temperature, the molecules vibrate faster and through greater distances than before. Thus the extra energy is transformed into kinetic energy of the molecules.

If sufficient energy (heat) is supplied a solid will melt to form a liquid. The amplitude of vibration of the molecules becomes so large that they break away from the position to which they were anchored and move freely amongst each other. However, forces still act between the molecules holding them close to each other, and so although a liquid has no definite shape, it does have a definite volume. The volume of a liquid is much the same as the solid from which it forms, thus the average separations of the molecules are about the same in each case, as are the densities. The molecular separation in the liquid may be slightly greater than in the solid (e.g. wax) or slightly less (e.g. water).

Not all the molecules have exactly the same energy at a particular temperature. Some molecules in a liquid have more than average energy and if they are near the liquid surface they are able to escape; this is **evaporation**. If thermal energy (heat) is supplied to the liquid the average energy of each molecule increases; that is they move faster. Eventually all the molecules have sufficient energy to break away from each other and so a gas is formed, in which all molecules move independently. This change of state is known as boiling. *While boiling is taking place there is no change in the temperature of the liquid or gas.*

The molecules of a gas move continually, colliding with each other and with the walls of their containing vessel. The laws of mechanics apply to these collisions. Also they are elastic, that is, no kinetic energy is lost. When a molecule bounces back from the walls of the container its momentum is changed and so it must have experienced a force. The force the molecules exert on the walls accounts for the pressure. If a gas is heated its molecules move faster and exert a greater pressure on the walls. An example of this effect is that if the pressure of a car or bicyle tyre is measured on a hot day, it will be found to be greater than on a cold day, even though no gas has been allowed to enter or leave the tyre in the meantime.

In a gas the forces between the molecules are so small that the molecules can be considered to move independently of each other. A gas therefore fills all the available space and has no fixed volume or shape; it takes the volume and shape of the vessel containing it. When the pressure exerted by a gas is equal to atmospheric pressure its volume will be about 1000 times greater than the liquid from which it forms, and its density will therefore be about 1000 times less. This can be shown using the syringes illustrated in Fig. 9.1.

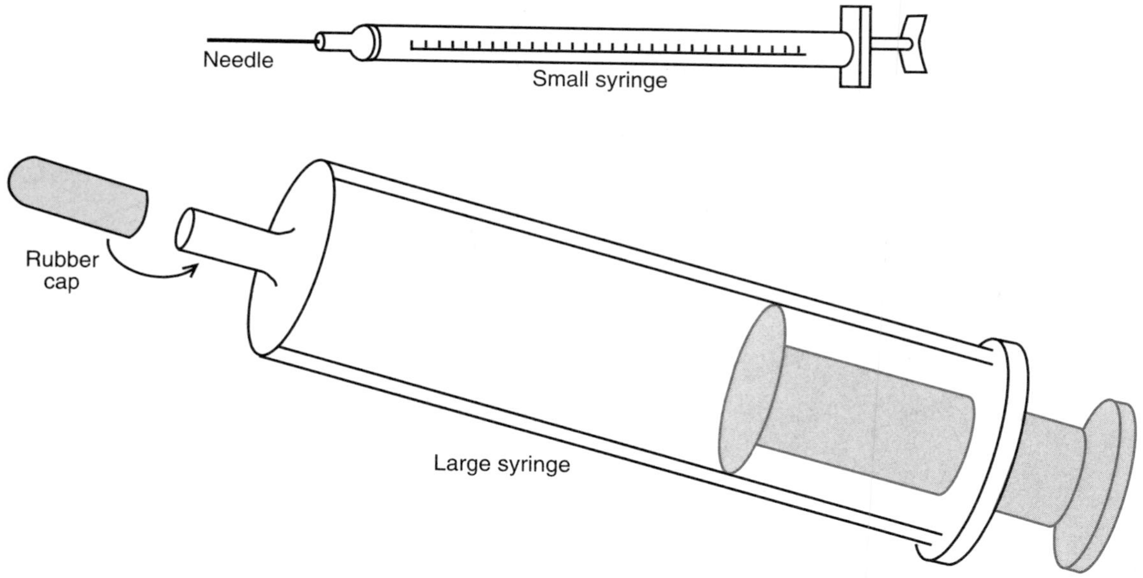

Fig. 9.1

A rubber cap is fitted over the end of the large syringe with its piston pushed down to zero volume. The small syringe with a hypodermic needle at its end is partially filled with water. 0.1 ml of water is then injected into the large syringe through the rubber cap via the hypodermic needle. When the needle is removed the cap seals. The large syringe is now inverted in a beaker of brine and the brine brought to the boil. The water in the syringe turns to steam and is seen to occupy a volume of about 100 ml; that is 1000 times larger than when it was water.

Evaporation takes place from the surface of a liquid at all temperatures, whereas boiling occurs only above a certain temperature and takes place throughout the liquid. However, the nearer the liquid is to its boiling temperature the faster the rate of evaporation.

Evaporation means that the faster molecules which happen to be near the surface escape from it. If the molecules which escape are free to move away from the space immediately above the liquid (or even encouraged to do so by a stream of air) evaporation will continue until the liquid has all evaporated. This is how puddles of water left on the road after rain eventually dry up. The higher the temperature of the liquid the quicker evaporation occurs.

As evaporation means that some of the more energetic molecules of the liquid are leaving it, the average energy of the molecules left behind falls; thus the liquid falls in temperature. For example, a bottle of milk may be kept cool by wrapping the bottle in a wet cloth. Some water evaporates from the cloth and the remaining water falls in temperature. In turn it extracts heat from the milk. This is more effective if the rate of evaporation can be speeded up by standing the wet bottle in a draught.

It is unwise for a human being to stand in a draught or breeze after taking vigorous exercise, however warm he feels. The perspiration on his body evaporates quickly under these conditions, thus cooling his body, and making it susceptible to a chill.

9.2 Brownian motion

The continual motion of molecules within a liquid or gas is call **Brownian motion**, after Robert Brown. In 1827 he used a microscope to examine pollen particles sprinkled on the surface of water and was surprised to notice that they were in a continuous state of haphazard movement. It appears that the motion of these relatively large particles is caused by the impact of moving water molecules. The same kind of movement can be seen in the case of smoke particles in air. The apparatus for this experiment is shown in Fig. 9.2.

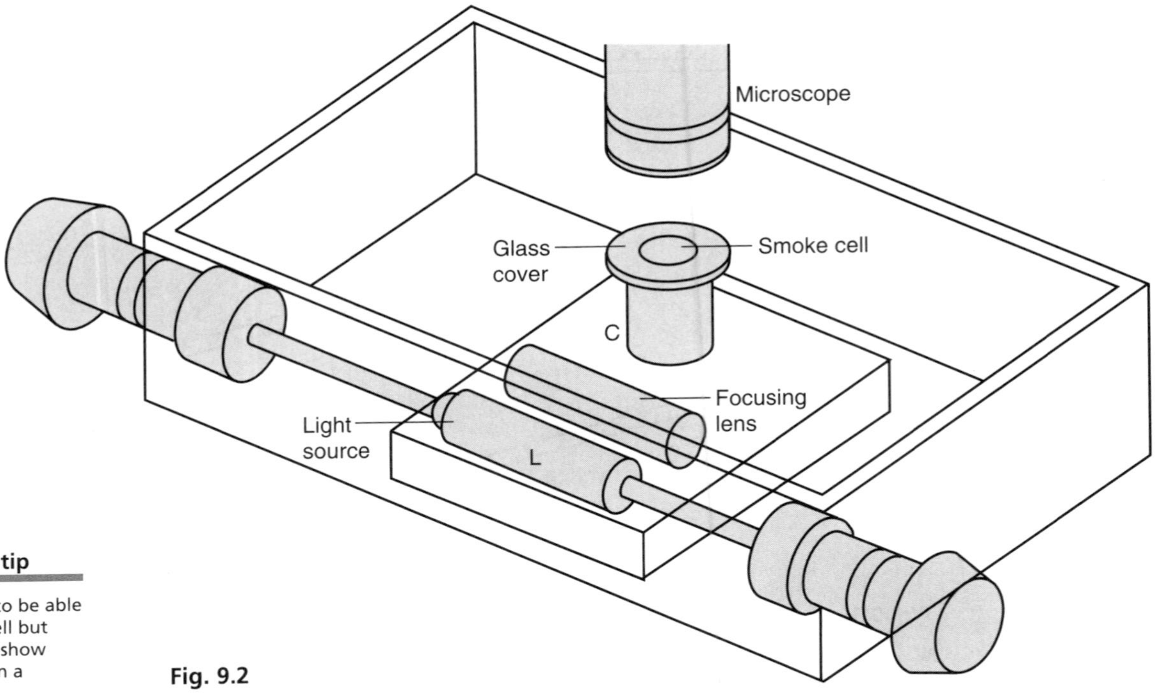

Fig. 9.2

Examiner's tip

You will not need to be able to draw a smoke cell but you might need to show Brownian motion in a diagram.

It consists of a small transparent cell *C*, with a cover, strongly illuminated from the side by a light *L*. A piece of cord or rag is set smouldering and some of the smoke which contains minute particles is collected by a syringe and injected into the cell. The cover is replaced and the microscope focused on the cell. The particles are seen to be moving in an irregular way, darting about suddenly, and always in motion.

The irregular motion of a particle is due to the movement of air molecules, which bombard it from all sides. The particle is relatively small and so the number of air molecules hitting it on one side are not balanced by an equal number hitting the opposite side at the same instant. The smoke particle thus moves in the direction of the resultant force. The irregular motion of the particles shows that air molecules move rapidly in all directions. At higher temperatures the molecules move even more rapidly and the motion of the particles is even more violent and irregular.

If the particles in a gas are very much bigger than the molecules of the gas they do not show this irregular movement. This is because the large number of molecules hitting one side is not relatively much greater than the number hitting the other at the same moment. The resultant force is thus relatively very small and the large particle is not so easily moved. For example, a table tennis ball suspended in air does not move for this reason.

Summary

1 Any material can exist in one of three states, as a solid, a liquid or a gas.

2 Energy is required to change a solid to a liquid and a liquid to a gas. *While* the change of state is taking place there is *no change in temperature.*

3 The volume of any material is about the same when it is a liquid as when it is a solid.

4 When a material changes to a gas its volume increases about one thousand-fold.

5 Evaporation takes place only from the surface of a liquid whereas boiling takes place from the whole body of the liquid.

6 The continual random motion of molecules within a liquid or gas is called **Brownian motion**.

Quick test 9

1 A solid has both a fixed volume and a fixed shape. Say whether you think a gas has either a fixed volume and/or a fixed shape. Justify your answer.

2 State what you think is responsible for giving a solid its fixed shape.

3 A fixed mass of water is boiled at atmospheric pressure. By what factor, approximately, is the volume of steam greater than the volume of water?

4 What is the difference between **evaporation** and **boiling**?

5 Describe **Brownian motion** and explain how you might observe it.

Chapter 10
The behaviour of gases

The volume of a gas can be changed not only by altering its temperature, but also by changing the pressure exerted on it. Thus a gas has three quantities: **volume**, **temperature** and **pressure** all of which may change. In order to make a full study of the behaviour of a fixed mass of gas three separate experiments are therefore carried out to investigate:

1. the relation between volume and pressure at constant temperature (**Boyle's law**);
2. the relation between volume and temperature at constant pressure (**Charles' law**);
3. the relation between pressure and temperature at constant volume (**pressure law**).

10.1 Boyle's law

The volume of a fixed mass of gas is inversely proportional to the pressure, provided the temperature remains constant; that is, the pressure multiplied by the volume is constant.

$$pV = \text{constant}$$

One version of the apparatus used to show this law is illustrated in Fig. 10.1. It consists of a volume of air trapped in a vertical tube by some oil with a low vapour pressure. Pressure is applied to the oil in the reservoir by a pump. The Bourdon gauge measures the pressure of the air above the oil in the reservoir. This is a little greater than the pressure of the air trapped in the tube, due to the vertical oil column, but the error is so small that for practical purposes it may be ignored.

Air is first pumped into the reservoir until the Bourdon gauge reaches its maximum reading. The tap is closed and readings taken of the length h of the trapped air column and also the pressure reading of the Bourdon gauge p. The tap is then opened to allow a little air to escape, closed again, and a further set of readings recorded. This procedure is repeated until the Bourdon gauge registers atmospheric pressure once more. It is possible, using a suction pump, to obtain readings below atmospheric pressure. If h is now plotted against $1/p$ a graph is obtained similar to that in Fig. 10.2.

As the volume V is proportional to the length of the column of trapped air h, the fact that the graph is a straight line through the origin shows that:

$$V \div 1/p = \text{a constant}$$

or $$pV = \text{a constant}$$

or $$p_1V_1 = p_2V_2 \text{ etc.} \qquad (10.1)$$

Examiner's tip

Do not forget that the **units** of pressure and volume must be the same on both sides of the equation.

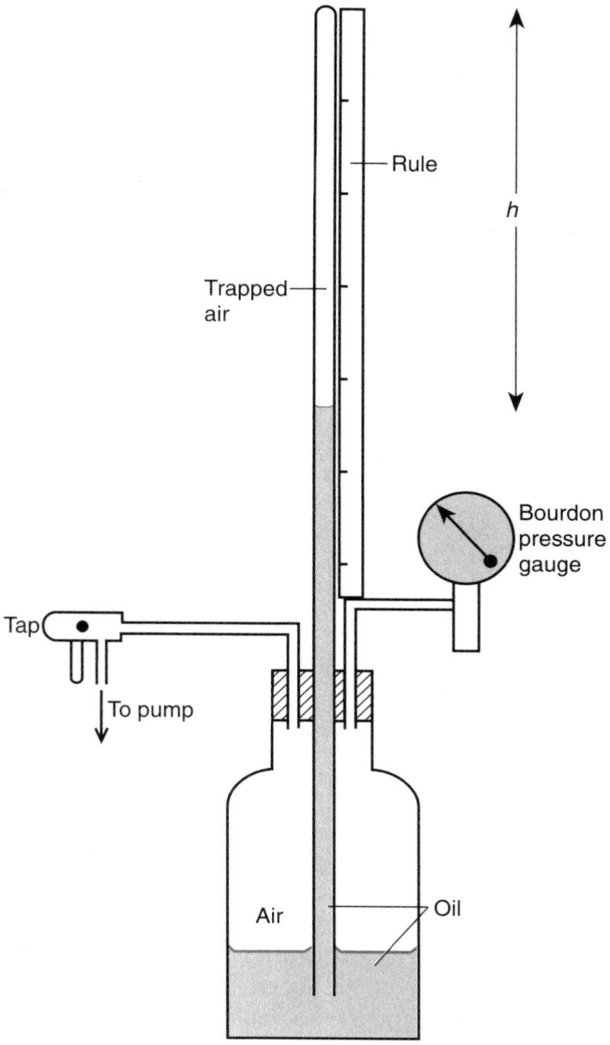

Fig. 10.1

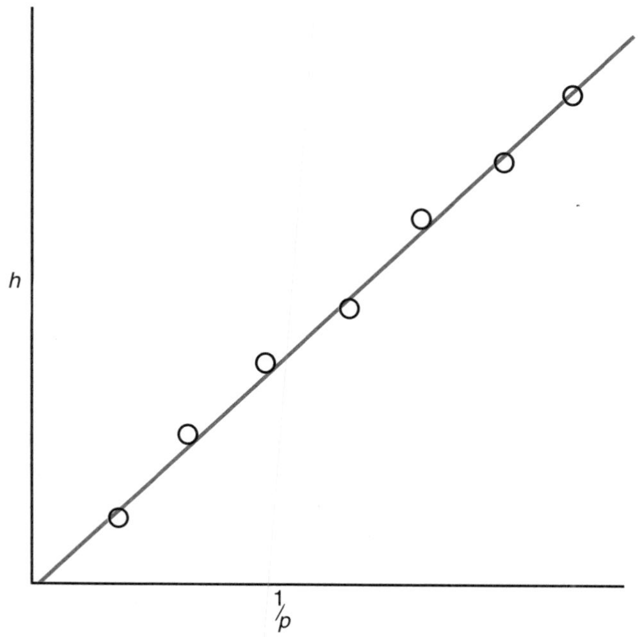

Fig. 10.2

10.2 Charles' law

The volume of a fixed mass of gas is directly proportional to its absolute temperature provided the pressure remains constant; that is, the volume divided by the absolute temperature is constant.

$$\frac{V}{T} = \text{constant}$$

A simple apparatus for verifying this law is shown in Fig. 10.3. It consists of a capillary tube sealed at its lower end. Some air has been trapped in the tube by a short thread of mercury *M*. A centimetre scale is attached to the tube so that the length of the trapped air column can be easily noted. The capillary tube and scale are placed in a beaker of water alongside a thermometer *T*.

The temperature of the water and the length of the air column are first noted. The water is then heated through about 10 °C, time is allowed for the heat to reach the air, and the temperature and length of the air column are recorded. This process is repeated several times. The volume *V* of trapped air is proportional to the length of the column as the tube is of uniform bore. The trapped air is kept at constant pressure by the mercury index moving up the tube as the temperature increases.

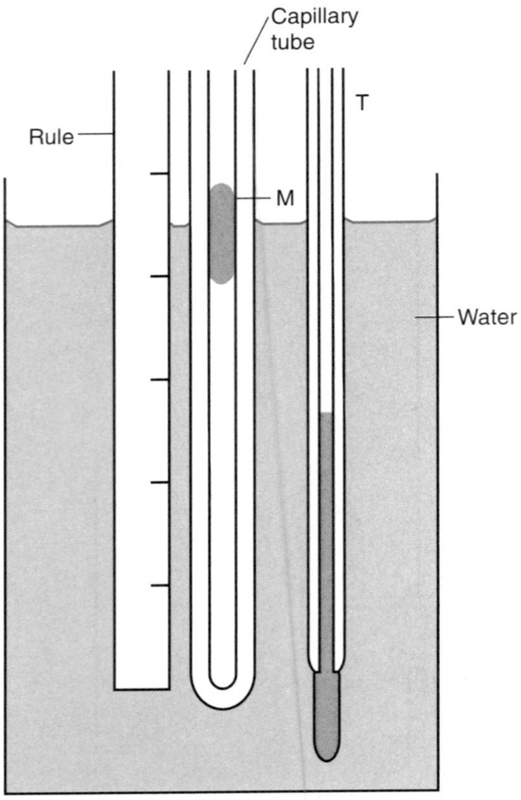

Fig. 10.3

From the results obtained a graph of length against temperature is plotted (Fig. 10.4). The graph is a straight line showing that air expands uniformly with temperature as measured on the mercury thermometer.

If the graph is produced backwards it cuts the temperature axis at a point which gives the temperature (−273 °C) at which the volume of the gas would contract to zero, assuming the gas continues to contract uniformly below 0 °C. As we cannot imagine it possible for a gas to have a volume of less than zero, it is reasonable to assume that −273 °C is the lowest temperature it is possible to obtain, and thus represents the absolute zero of temperature. This assumption cannot be directly tested by experiment as gases liquefy before they reach this temperature, and so the gas laws no longer apply. However, experiments have shown that while temperatures close to −273 °C have been reached, it has not been possible to go below this value.

The value −273 °C has thus been taken as the zero of a new scale of temperature called the **Absolute** or **Kelvin** scale. Temperatures on this scale are represented by *T*, and are expressed in units of K. Temperatures on the Celsius scale are converted to the Kelvin scale by adding 273. Thus 0 °C = 273 K.

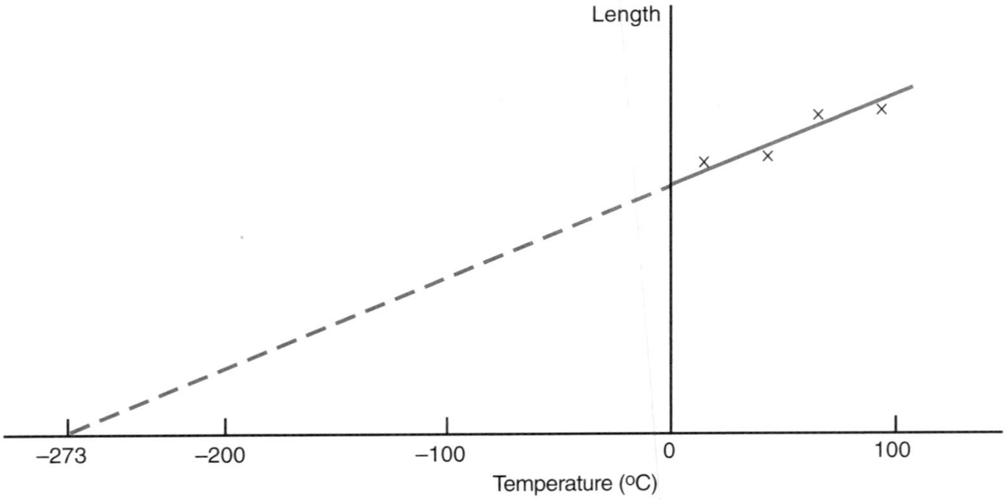

Fig. 10.4 Variation of volume with temperature at constant pressure

The graph in Fig. 10.4 is a straight line through the origin of our new temperature scale. Thus the volume of the gas is proportional to its temperature measured on the Kelvin scale and we may write:

Examiner's tip

Do not forget that temperatures must be in Kelvin.

$$V \propto T$$

$$\text{or} \quad \frac{V}{T} = \text{a constant} \qquad (10.2)$$

$$\text{or} \quad \frac{V_1}{T_1} = \frac{V_2}{T_2} \text{ etc.}$$

10.3 Pressure law

The pressure of a fixed mass of gas is directly proportional to its absolute temperature provided its volume remains constant; that is, the pressure divided by the absolute temperature is constant.

$$\frac{p}{T} = \text{constant}$$

The apparatus for demonstrating this law is shown in Fig. 10.5. It consists of a flask connected by rubber tubing to a Bourdon gauge. The flask is surrounded by water in a beaker. A thermometer T is also used.

The apparatus, particularly the rubber tubing, is first inspected for leaks. The temperature of the water and the reading on the Bourdon gauge are noted. The water is then heated while being stirred. After the temperature of the water has risen by about 10 °C, heating is stopped, time is allowed for the heat to reach the air in the flask, and then the temperature and the pressure are again noted. This procedure is repeated several times until the water is near boiling.

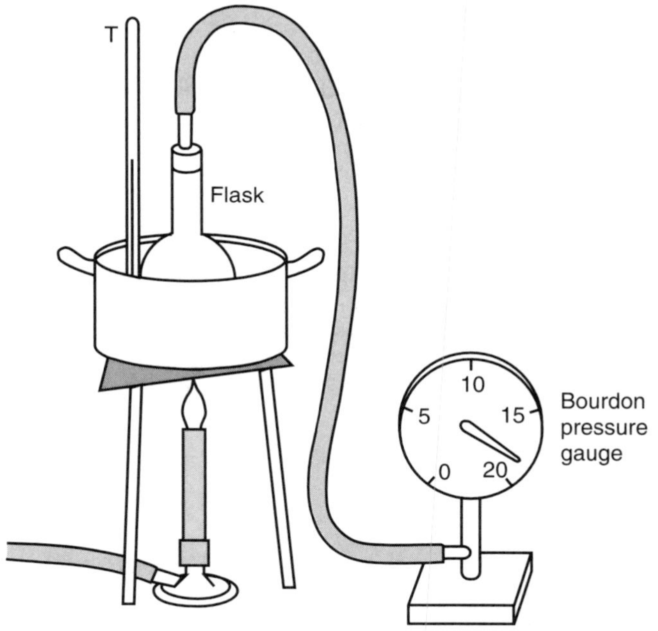

Fig. 10.5

From the results a graph of pressure against temperature is plotted (Fig. 10.6). It is a straight line passing through −273 °C or 0 K. Thus the pressure of the gas is proportional to its temperature measured on the Kelvin scale and we may write:

$$p \propto T$$

$$\text{or} \quad \frac{p}{T} = \text{a constant} \qquad (10.3)$$

$$\text{or} \quad \frac{p_1}{T_1} = \frac{p_2}{T_2} \text{ etc.}$$

This apparatus can be used to measure temperature (constant volume gas thermometer).

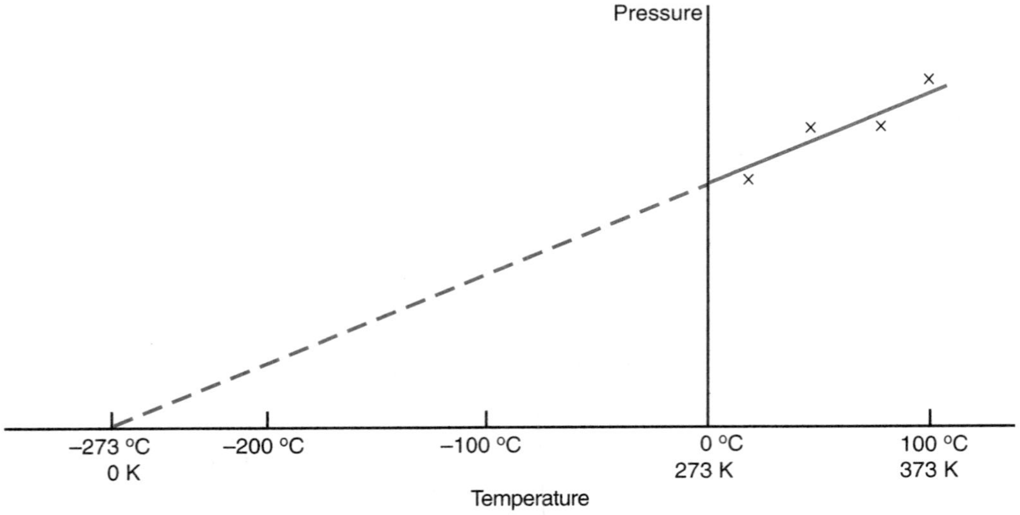

Fig. 10.6 Variation of pressure with temperature at constant volume

10.4 The universal gas law

The equations (10.1), (10.2) and (10.3) can be combined in a more general equation which we may write:

$$\frac{pV}{T} = \text{a constant} \tag{10.4}$$

or

$$\frac{p_1 V_1}{T_1} = \frac{p_2 V_2}{T_2} \text{ etc.} \tag{10.5}$$

If we always consider one mole (one gram molecular weight) of a gas, the constant is the same for all gases and we may write equation (10.4) as follows:

$$\frac{\boldsymbol{pV}}{\boldsymbol{T}} = \boldsymbol{R}$$

where R is the universal gas constant.

Suppose a fixed mass of gas, occupying 1 litre at 27 °C, is heated to 227 °C and at the same time the pressure on the gas is doubled. We may find its final volume by using equation (10.5), but first we must convert the temperatures to the Kelvin scale.

$$27\ °\text{C} = 300\ \text{K} \quad \text{and} \quad 227\ °\text{C} = 500\ \text{K} \quad \text{and} \quad p_2 = 2p_1$$

$$\frac{p_1 V_1}{T_1} = \frac{p_2 V_2}{T_2}$$

thus

$$\frac{p_1 \times 1}{300} = \frac{2p_1 \times V_2}{500}$$

hence

$$V_2 = \frac{500}{300 \times 2} = \frac{5}{6} \text{ litre}$$

10.5 Models of a gas

The following models give an idea of how we think molecules of a gas behave. The first model consists of several marbles placed on the base of a tray or baking tin. The tray is moved horizontally by hand in short, sharp random jerks. The marbles are seen to move, making random collisions with each other and the sides of the tray. To obtain a clear impression it is best to watch one marble carefully.

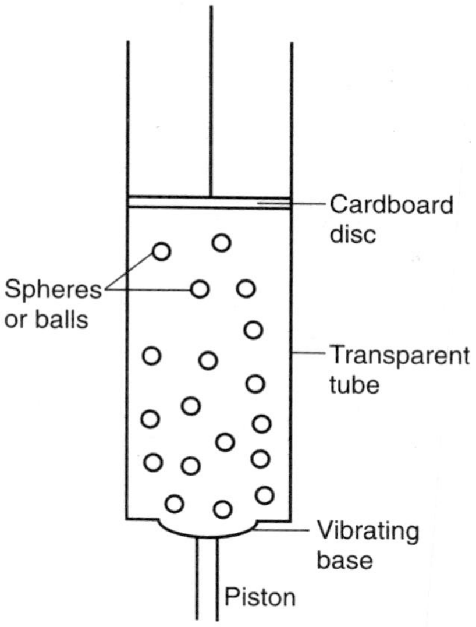

Fig. 10.7 Three-dimensional model of a gas

Although this model is useful, it is two-dimensional, whereas molecules move in three dimensions. Figure 10.7 shows a better model. Some small polystyrene spheres or phosphor bronze ball bearings are contained in a vertical transparent tube. The base of the tube is connected to a piston which is driven by an electric motor. The oscillating piston causes the base to vibrate; the frequency of vibration is changed by altering the speed of the motor. An alternative arrangement is to use a loudspeaker as the base of the tube and to connect the loudspeaker to a signal generator the frequency of which can be altered.

When the base vibrates, the spheres on it are thrown into random motion in the cylinder. They collide with each other and with the walls of the container on which they thus exert a pressure. They also exert a pressure on the cardboard disc which sits on top of them. If the amplitude of vibration of the base is increased, the average energy of the spheres is increased. The spheres thus move faster and keep the disc at a higher level. This illustrates the expansion of a gas when it is heated at constant pressure. Instead of allowing the disc to rise when the spheres are made to move faster, masses can be added to the top of the disc to keep it at the same height. The masses increase the external pressure that the disc exerts on the spheres. This illustrates the increase in the pressure that a gas exerts when it is heated at constant volume.

Summary

1 For a fixed mass of gas the following equation is true:

$$\frac{pV}{T} = \textbf{a constant}$$

where p is the pressure of the gas, V the volume that it occupies and T its temperature on the Kelvin scale (°C + 273).

2 If one mole of gas is used the equation becomes

$$\frac{pV}{T} = R$$

where R is the universal gas constant.

3 If one of the quantities p, V or T is kept constant three simpler equations may be used. They are

$$pV = \textbf{a constant}, \text{ when } T \text{ is kept constant}$$

$$\frac{p}{T} = \textbf{a constant}, \text{ when } V \text{ is kept constant}$$

$$\frac{V}{T} = \textbf{a constant}, \text{ when } p \text{ is kept constant}$$

Quick test 10

1 State Boyle's law.

2 The pressure of a fixed mass of gas at constant temperature is halved. What happens to the volume of the gas?

3 A fixed mass of gas occupying a volume of 1000 cm^3 has its temperature increased from 77 °C to 252 °C at constant pressure. What is its new volume?

4 A fixed mass of gas at a pressure of 100 000 Pa has its temperature raised from 27 °C to 127 °C at constant volume. What is its new pressure?

5 A fixed mass of gas has its pressure halved and its temperature, on the Kelvin scale, doubled. By what factor does volume change?

Chapter 11
Specific heat capacity

Heat is a form of energy and like any other form of energy it is measured in joules.

If we take equal masses of water and oil and warm them for the same time in separate containers using similar immersion heaters, the temperature of the water will rise much less than the temperature of the oil. We say these substances have different specific heat capacities.

The specific heat capacity of a substance is the quantity of heat required to raise the temperature of one kilogram of it by 1 K. It has units of joules per kilogram per kelvin (J/kg K).

It follows that if m kilograms of a substance, of specific heat capacity c, are to be raised in temperature by θ K, then the heat required will be $mc\theta$ joules.

Examiner's tip

As θ is a temperature change, you can measure it in Kelvin or °C.

$$\text{Heat required} = mc\theta \text{ joules}$$

It happens that for water 4200 joules of heat are required to raise the temperature of one kilogram by 1 K. The specific heat capacity of water is thus 4200 J/kg K. This value is high compared with most other substances. A great deal of energy is required to raise the temperature of water a certain amount compared with the same mass of another substance. Likewise water cools more slowly because it contains more energy than the same mass of other substances at the same temperature. Water is therefore used to fill radiators and hot water bottles.

11.1 To measure the specific heat capacity of a solid

This is best measured by the steady heating of a block of the solid by a heater immersed in it, as shown in Fig. 11.1.

A 12 V immersion heater, H, with a power of 24 or 36 W, is sunk into a hole specially drilled in the solid for this purpose. It is convenient, but not essential, if the block has a mass of 1 kg. A second, smaller hole in the block contains a thermometer, T. To ensure good thermal contact between the heater and the block and the thermometer and block, a few drops of thin oil are placed in each hole. The block can be surrounded by an insulating jacket to reduce heat losses.

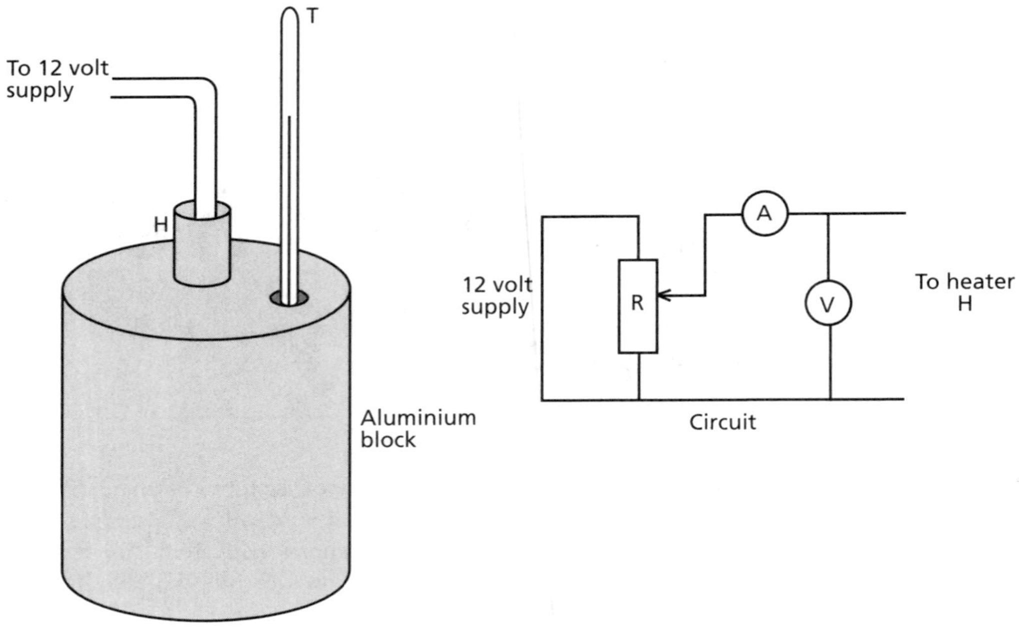

Fig. 11.1

The apparatus is connected up and switched on for a known time (between 10 and 30 minutes depending on the material of the block). During this time the voltage and current are kept as constant as possible, by adjusting the variable resistor, R, and their values noted. At the beginning and end of the experiment the temperature of the block is noted. The specific heat capacity c of the material of the block is worked out using the equation:

$$\text{energy supplied electrically} = \text{heat gained by the block}$$
$$VIt = mc\,(\theta_2 - \theta_1)$$

where θ_1 and θ_2 are the initial and final temperatures of the block.

11.2 To measure the specific heat capacity of a liquid

The electrical heating method already described for a solid is also suitable for a liquid. The liquid (1 kg for convenience) is contained in a plastic cup (or aluminium saucepan). The heater is immersed in the liquid, care being taken not to short the connections. The procedure is the same as described for a solid. Strictly speaking, in working out the specific heat capacity of the liquid, account should be taken of the heat used in raising the temperature of the plastic cup. However, both the mass and specific heat capacity of the cup are much less than the values for the liquid, so no great error is involved in ignoring the heat absorbed by the cup. Calculation of the result is then the same as for a solid.

Summary

1 **The specific heat capacity of a substance is the quantity of heat required to raise the temperature of one kilogram of it by 1 K**. It has units of joules per kilogram per kelvin (J/kg K).

2 The heat required to change mass m of a substance by a temperature of θ kelvin is given by

$$\textbf{heat required} = mc\theta \textbf{ joules}$$

where c is the specific heat capacity of the substance.

3 The specific heat capacity of a solid or liquid is usually measured electrically, the electrical energy supplied being equal to VIt joules.

Quick test 11

1 Explain what is meant by the **specific heat capacity** of a substance.

2 An electric heater supplies 30 J of energy every second. It is immersed in 0.05 kg of oil. The temperature of the oil rises from 20 °C to 50 °C in 100 s. What is the value of the specific heat capacity of the oil?

3 Explain why it is that a cup of tea takes quite a long time to cool.

Chapter 12
Heat transfer

Energy flows from warmer to cooler surroundings in one of three ways: **conduction**, **radiation** or **convection**.

12.1 Conduction

If a metal spoon is left in a teacup for a short length of time the handle becomes warm. Heat travels along the spoon by means of conduction. Metals contain electrons which are very loosely attached to atoms, and are easily removed from them. When a metal is heated these 'free electrons' gain kinetic energy and move independently of the atoms. They drift towards the cooler parts of the metal thus spreading the energy to those regions.

In substances where no free electrons are present the energy is transferred from one atom to another by collision. This is a much slower process and such substances are called poor conductors of heat.

Most metals are good conductors of both heat and electricity, free electrons being responsible for both. Substances such as wool, cotton, cork and wood are bad conductors. A number of materials lie between these extremes. The best saucepans are made of copper as heat is rapidly conducted through this metal. Many materials are poor conductors of heat because they trap tiny pockets of air between their fibres, and air, like all gases, is a poor conductor of heat. Textiles and glass fibre are examples. Glass fibre is frequently used as lagging for attics and hot water tanks.

12.2 Radiation

Both conduction and convection are ways of transferring heat from one place to another which require the presence of a material. Radiation does not need a material medium; it is the means by which heat travels from the Sun through the empty space beyond the Earth's atmosphere. Radiation consists of electromagnetic waves which pass through a vacuum. On striking a body these waves are partly reflected and partly absorbed, and can cause a rise in temperature.

The rate at which a body radiates depends on its temperature and the nature of its surface. For a given temperature, a body radiates most energy when its surface is dull black and least when its surface is highly polished. A comparison of the radiating powers of different surfaces may be made using a hollow metal cube, each side of which has a different surface. One is dull black, one highly polished, another may be shiny black and the fourth painted white. The cube is filled with hot water and an infrared detector placed at the same distance from each face in turn (Fig. 12.1). In each case the thermometer reading is noted.

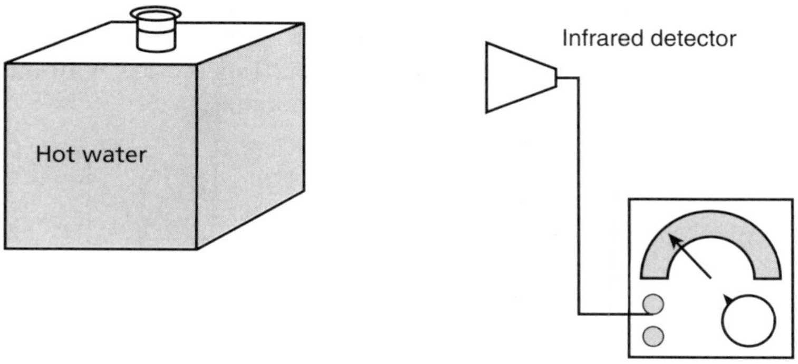

Fig. 12.1 Radiation – Leslie's cube

The results show that the dull black surface gives the highest reading and the highly polished one the lowest. This shows that the dull black surface is the best radiator and the highly polished one the worst.

The absorbing powers of different surfaces may be compared using a small electric fire (Fig. 12.2). The heater is placed about 10 to 15 cm behind a heat insulating screen, faced with a polished metal surface towards the heater. The screen has a hole in it 2 or 3 cm in diameter. If a piece of aluminium foil is fixed to the back of one's hand by damping it, it is found that the hand may be held over the hole in the screen without discomfort. If the foil is now painted over with lamp black (or matt black paint) and the hand again placed over the hole, the hand has to be removed after a few seconds or it becomes burnt. This shows that a dull black surface is a good absorber of heat as well as a good radiator, whereas a highly polished surface is poor in both respects. Solar panels use this property, see Unit 3.11.

Radiation from the Sun is mostly in the form of visible light and infrared rays. These pass through glass and hence may reach the ground and plants inside a greenhouse, which absorb them. These objects also radiate, but due to their relatively low temperature, the infrared rays they emit are of longer wavelength and cannot penetrate the glass. The energy is thus trapped inside the greenhouse.

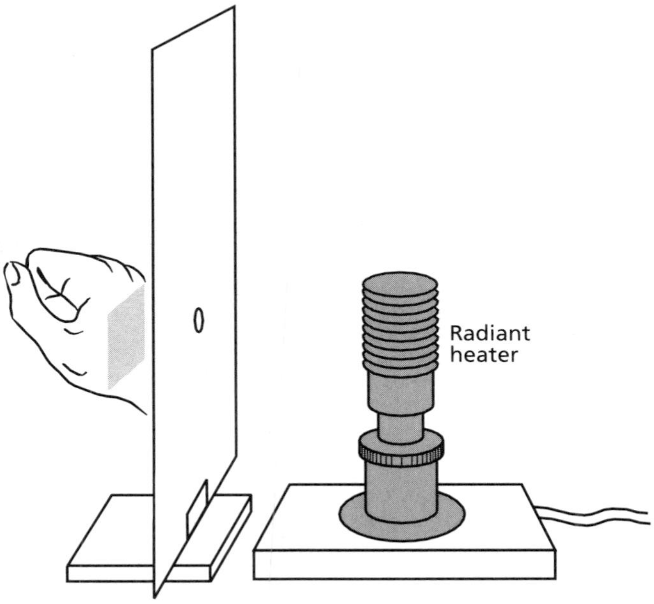

Fig. 12.2 Radiation

12.3 Convection

When a vessel containing a liquid is heated at the bottom, the liquid in that region becomes warm, less dense, and as a result rises. Its place is taken by cooler, more dense liquid moving downwards. In **convection** the heat is carried from one place to another by the movement of the molecules of the liquid. The existence of convection currents may be shown by dropping a large crystal of potassium permanganate to the bottom of a beaker of water. The beaker is gently heated under the crystal, which is usually placed near the centre of the base. An upward current of coloured water will rise from the place where the heat is applied. This current spreads out at the surface and then moves down the sides of the beaker (Fig. 12.3). A domestic hot water system relies on convection currents for its functioning.

Convection currents exist in gases as well as liquids. Warm air, for example, is less dense than cold air and rises. Cooler air then moves in to replace it. It is this process which is responsible for sea breezes towards the end of a warm summer's day. The relatively dark land absorbs more heat than the sea. Its specific heat capacity is less than that of water. As a result of both of these facts, towards the end of a summer's day, it reaches a higher temperature than the sea. The land warms the air over it which rises and is replaced by the cooler air from over the sea. Late on a clear summer's night the reverse is likely.

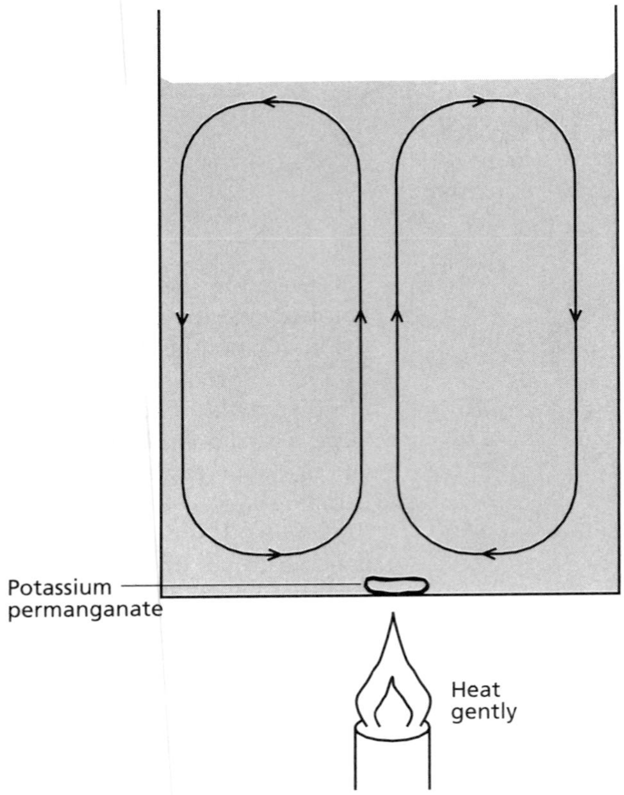

Fig. 12.3 Convection

12.4 Preventing heat transfer

Fat and air are good insulators. Seals have a thick layer of fat surrounding their body and can survive all winter in very cold Arctic waters where we would perish in a few minutes. Birds have feathers; other animals have thick fur. Both reduce heat transfer by trapping a layer of air next to the body, that is they prevent convection currents in the air next to the body. In cold weather we wear layers of clothing made from materials such as wool. These materials trap air in a similar way to birds' feathers.

A home may have draught excluders, loft insulation, cavity-wall insulation, double glazing or several of these. Draught excluders stuck around doors and windows prevent the loss of warm air to the outside. Loft insulation consists of mineral wool or glass fibre which traps the air between the joists, thus preventing loss of heat due to convection currents. In a similar way cavity-wall insulation (often foam) prevents air from circulating between the two layers of bricks. In double glazing the layer of air between the two glass sheets acts as an insulator. The layer must be thin to prevent convection currents.

Summary

1 Heat is transferred from one place to another by conduction, convection or radiation.

2 **Conduction** takes place in solids. In good conductors such as metals 'free electrons' gain kinetic energy and move independently of the atoms. They move to the cooler parts of the solid thus spreading the energy to those regions. In substances where no 'free electrons' are present the energy moves from one atom to another by collision. This is a much slower process and such substances are called poor conductors of heat.

3 **Radiation** takes place by the transmission of electromagnetic waves from a hot object to any other object. Radiation can take place through a vacuum as in the case of heat from the Sun reaching the Earth.

4 When liquids or gases are heated their density decreases and the warm liquid or gas rises. Cooler liquid or gas falls to take its place. **Convection** currents are set up and heat is transmitted from one place to another.

5 Loss of heat can be reduced by preventing convection currents occurring.

Quick test 12

1 Explain what it is about the structure of metals which makes them good conductors of heat (and electricity) whereas other solids are less good conductors.

2 How does heat travel through a vacuum?

3 Describe how energy is transferred from one place to another by convection.

4 Explain how onshore sea breezes occur on a warm afternoon in summer.

5 How does double glazing improve the heat insulation of houses?

6 Name and explain two ways of reducing the heat lost from a house, other than double glazing.

Chapter 13
Introduction to waves

13.1 Progressive waves

The idea of **progressive waves** is best illustrated using a spiral spring or 'slinky' stretched on a bench (Fig. 13.1). If one end of the spring is shaken at right angles to its length (Fig. 13.1(a)) a wave is seen to travel along the spring. As the wave is moving it is said to be progressive. In this example the motion causing the wave is at right angles to the direction of travel of the wave and the wave is termed **transverse**. In Fig. 13.1(b) one end of the spring is shaken in the direction of the spring's length and a concertina effect travels the length of the spring. In this case the motion causing the wave is in the same direction as the wave travels and the wave is called **longitudinal**.

Fig. 13.1 Waves along a spring: (a) transverse; (b) longitudinal

Examples of transverse waves are television, radio, heat, light, ultraviolet, X-rays, γ-rays (all electromagnetic waves) and water waves. In electromagnetic waves the electric and magnetic disturbances are at right angles to the direction the wave travels. At any moment a transverse wave has the shape of a sine wave and can be drawn as such (Fig. 13.2).

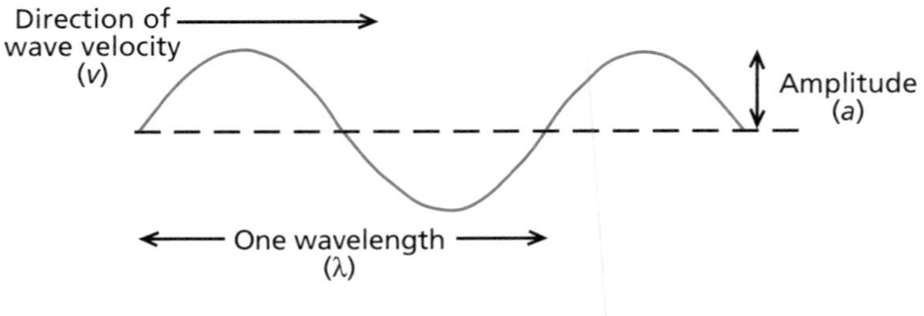

Fig. 13.2 Sine curve representing wave motion

Sound, on the other hand, is a longitudinal wave motion. The molecules of the material through which the sound travels vibrate to and fro along the direction of motion of the wave. At a given time each molecule is at a different point in its motion. A longitudinal wave may be represented by a sine curve, but it must be remembered that although the y direction still represents the size of the displacement, the direction of the displacement is in fact parallel to the direction of travel of the wave.

In Fig. 13.2 the **amplitude of the wave** is denoted by a. The amplitude represents the maximum displacement of the wave from the zero position. The distance between corresponding points on two successive waves is known as the **wavelength** λ. The number of waves produced every second by the source is called the **frequency** f. The length of wave motion produced every second by the source is the number of waves produced every second (f) multiplied by the length of each wave (λ). This product is clearly the speed v of the wave motion. Thus

$$v = f\lambda$$

It is usual to measure the speed in metres per second, the frequency in hertz and the wavelength in metres.

13.2 The ripple tank

A good understanding of the properties of all types of waves can be obtained from studying the behaviour of water waves in a ripple tank. The construction of a ripple tank is shown in Fig. 13.3.

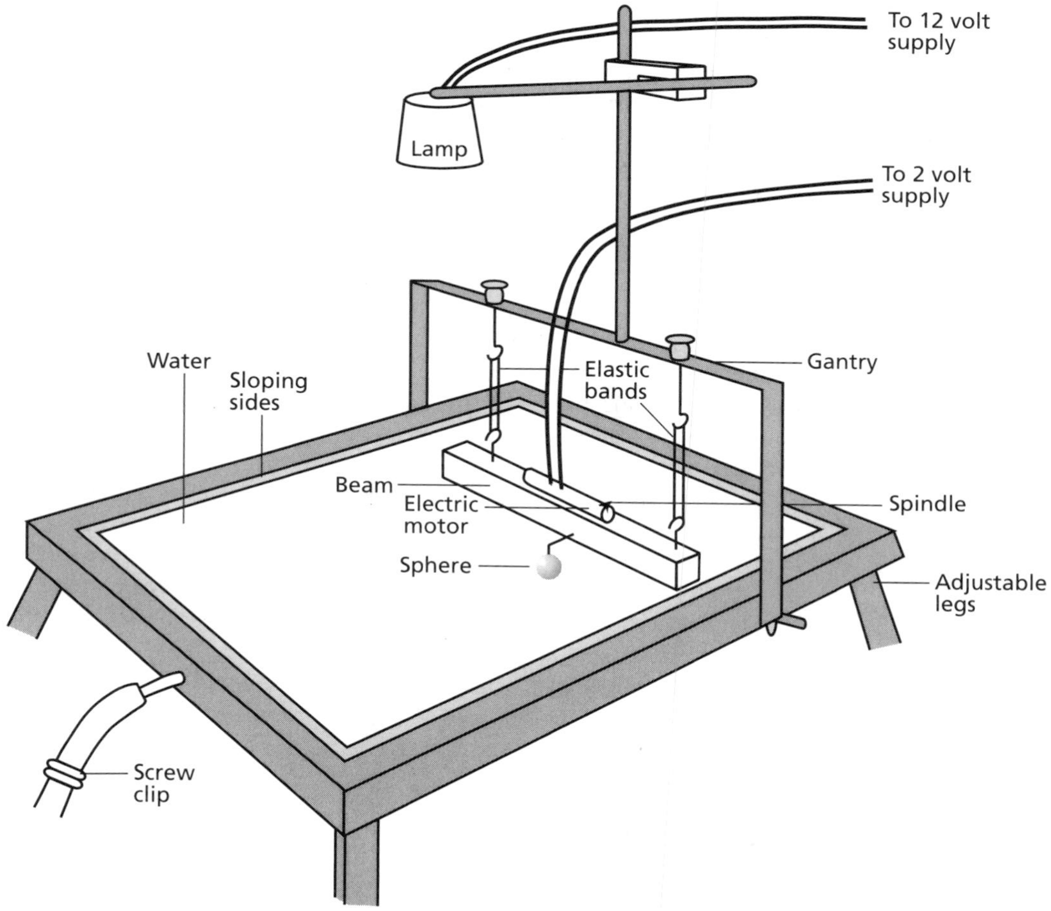

Fig. 13.3 A ripple tank

The apparatus consists of a shallow tray with a glass bottom and sloping sides to reduce reflection. The tray is mounted on four legs, each of which can be adjusted in length by a screw foot. In this way the tray can be levelled. A gantry stands above one end of the tank. On this gantry is a post on which a lamp is fixed. A beam, with a motor mounted on its top, is hung from the gantry. A number of spheres, each of which can be lowered to project below the beam, are fixed to it.

The behaviour of the waves is best seen by using the lamp to cast a shadow of the water surface on a sheet of paper below the tank. Wave peaks and troughs are clearly seen on the paper. In diagrams lines are drawn to represent the peaks or troughs. These lines may be considered to represent the surface over which energy from the source spreads out, and are called **wavefronts**.

Two simple types of wave formation are worth studying; straight and circular waves. A small number of straight waves may conveniently be made by rolling a short length of dowel rod to and fro on the bottom of the tank. A few circular waves may be produced by touching the water surface with a pencil the required number of times.

For many experiments it is necessary to produce a continuous series of waves of one type.
This is done by connecting the motor to a suitable power unit (often 2 V d.c.) whereupon the spindle, which is unevenly weighted, sets the beam bouncing up and down.

The speed of the motor determines the frequency of the waves.
If straight waves are required the lower edge of the beam should be a few millimetres below the water surface; if circular waves are wanted then the beam should be raised clear of the surface but one or more spheres turned down so that they are partly submerged by the same amount.

Fig. 13.4 Hand stroboscope

When the motor is producing a continuous series of waves it is often very difficult, if not impossible, for the eye to follow them across the paper below the tank. If this is so, it is helpful to use a hand stroboscope to 'freeze' the picture of the waves. A typical stroboscope is shown in Fig. 13.4. The handle is held in one hand while the disc is turned using one finger of the other hand. The rotating disc is placed between the eye and the wave pattern on the paper. The speed of rotation of the disc is increased until the waves appear stationary.

The slits in the disc allow glimpses of the waves at equal intervals of time. At one particular speed of rotation each wave moves forward to the position of the wave in front of it, in between successive glimpses. The wave pattern thus appears stationary. If the stroboscope is rotated slightly more slowly the wave pattern appears to be moving slowly forward. The opposite is the case if the disc is rotated slightly too fast.

13.3 Reflection

To see reflection clearly only a small number of waves are required. Therefore it is best if the ripple tank motor is not used, the waves being produced in the way already described. Figure 13.5 shows the results of the incidence of both straight and circular waves on straight and circular reflecting barriers *R*.

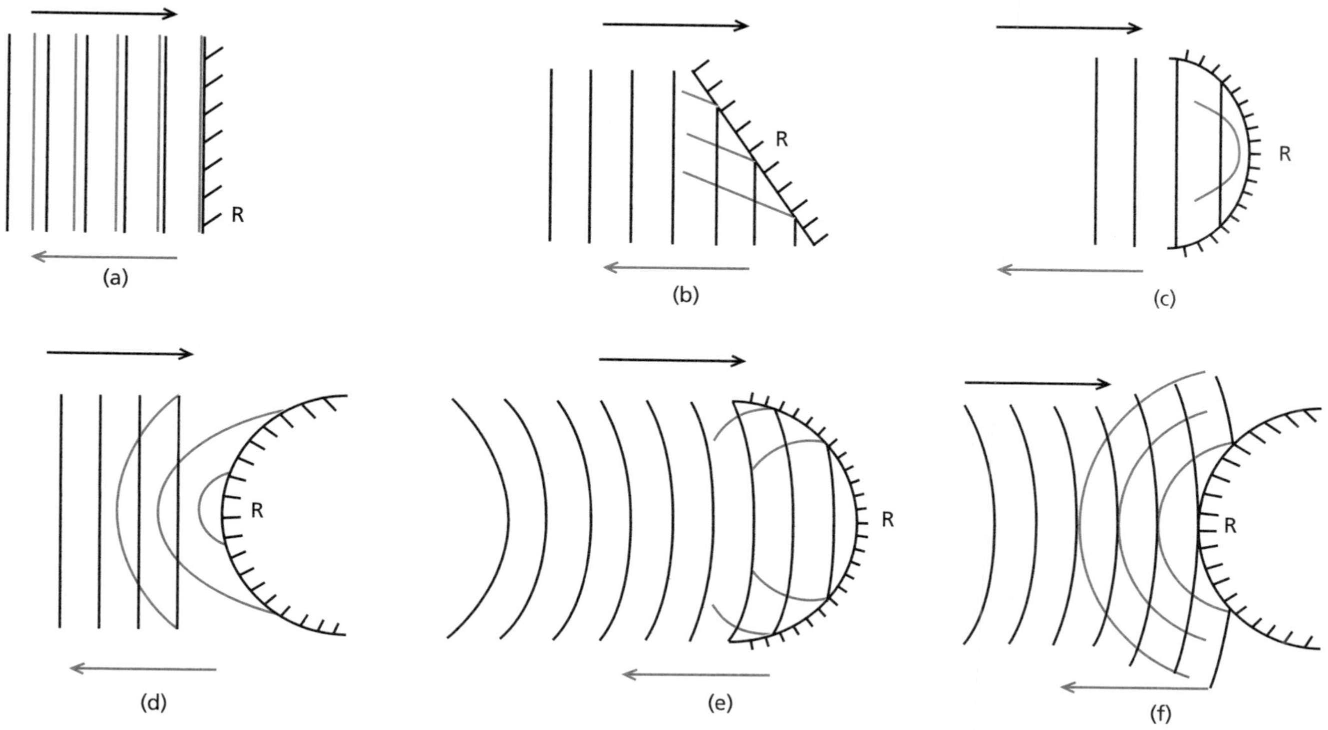

Fig. 13.5 Reflection of waves

In each case the waves bounce off the barrier without changing their speed. This is called **reflection**. Their behaviour after reflection can be worked out by considering which part of the incoming waves reaches the particular barrier first. This part of the wave will be reflected first. For example, in Fig. 13.5(d), the centre of each incoming straight wave obviously strikes the reflecting barrier first. The centre of each returning wave will therefore be in front, giving the curved shape shown.

In Fig. 13.5(c) and (e) the waves, after reflection, are approximately circular and converge to a point. This point is the image formed by waves from the point source (a distant source in Fig. 13.5(c)) after reflection at the barrier. In Fig. 13.5(d) the reflected waves appear to come from a point behind the barrier. This point represents a virtual image of the source.

13.4 Refraction

If water waves come to a region where their speed changes abruptly, then their direction of travel may change abruptly. This is called **refraction**. The best way of achieving this change in speed is to alter the depth of water by placing a sheet of glass in the tray of the ripple tank, since it is found that if the water is shallower the speed is reduced. This can be seen as waves approach a sloping beach. The body of the waves slows, but the crest is less affected and falls forward, causing the waves to break.

The sheet of glass should be placed in the tray so that it is covered by water to a depth of only one or two millimetres. A little experimentation will give the best depth. Straight waves, produced by either the beam or dowel rod, reach the leading edge of the glass plate at an angle (Fig. 13.6). As soon as part of the wave comes over the shallow region it slows down. It is clear that the end of the wave which has been in the shallow region longer will fall behind the other end. Thus the direction of the wavefront changes as shown.

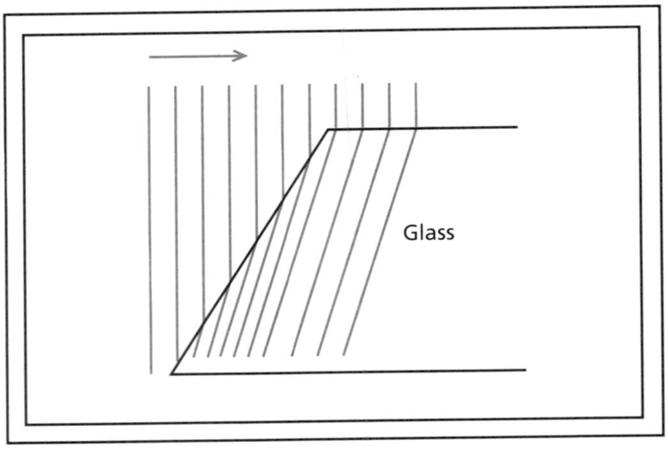

Fig. 13.6 Refraction of waves at a plane boundary

13.5 Diffraction

If straight water waves are passed through a narrow gap in a barrier or past a small object some bending of the waves round the edges of the barrier or the object is noticed. Thus some change in the direction of travel of the waves occurs round these edges. This effect is called **diffraction**.

For diffraction to be obvious the size of the gap or object has to be about the same as the wavelength of the waves. In Fig. 13.7(a) the gap between the barriers is much greater than the wavelength and little bending occurs. In Fig. 13.7(b) the gap size and the wavelength are about the same and the bending is considerable. In fact the waves become circular after passing through the gap and look the same as if the gap were replaced by a point source of waves. In Fig. 13.7(c) where the object is about the same width as the wavelength the bending is again very noticeable.

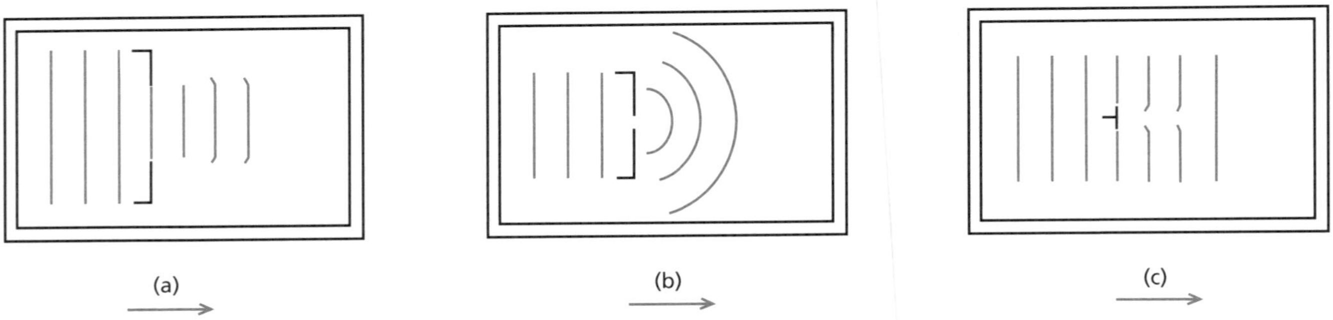

Fig. 13.7 Diffraction of waves: (a) wide gap; (b) narrow gap; (c) small object

A clear understanding of the behaviour of water waves discussed in this chapter will make it easier to understand the properties of light and sound waves discussed in later chapters, as they behave in a similar way.

Summary

1 There are two types of waves:
(a) **Longitudinal** waves in which the motion causing the wave is in the same direction as the wave travels.
(b) **Transverse** waves in which the motion causing the wave is at right angles to the direction in which the wave travels.

2 All types of wave motion, other than sound, are transverse. Sound is a longitudinal wave motion.

3 The equation connecting the velocity v, the frequency f and the wavelength λ of a wave motion is

$$v = f\lambda$$

It is usual to measure the velocity in metres per second (m/s), the frequency in hertz (Hz) and the wavelength in metres (m).

4 **Reflection** is the change in direction of a wave when it hits a solid boundary. It does not change speed.

5 **Refraction** is the change in direction of travel of a wave motion caused by its change in speed.

6 **Diffraction** is the spreading out which occurs when waves pass round a small object or through a narrow gap.

Examiner's tip

Frequencies are often given in kHz (1000 Hz). Check the question before doing any calculations.

Quick test 13

1 State the difference between **transverse** and **longitudinal** waves.

2 Which (if any) of the following types of wave are longitudinal: radio, sound, infrared, light and gamma rays?

3 In a ripple tank, waves travel a distance of 45 cm in 3 s. If the distance apart of the crests is 3 cm, what is the frequency of the vibrator causing the waves?

4 State what happens when a wave, on the surface of a ripple tank, goes into very shallow water at an angle. What is the name of this effect? Explain what causes it.

5 Describe what happens when water waves pass through a gap in a barrier which is about the same width as their wavelength. What is this effect called?

Chapter 14

The passage and reflection of light

In some experiments it is more convenient to consider the behaviour of **rays** rather than wavefronts. Rays are lines drawn at right angles to wavefronts and thus represent the direction in which the wave is travelling. A ray box is a device for producing rays; one version is shown in Fig. 14.1.

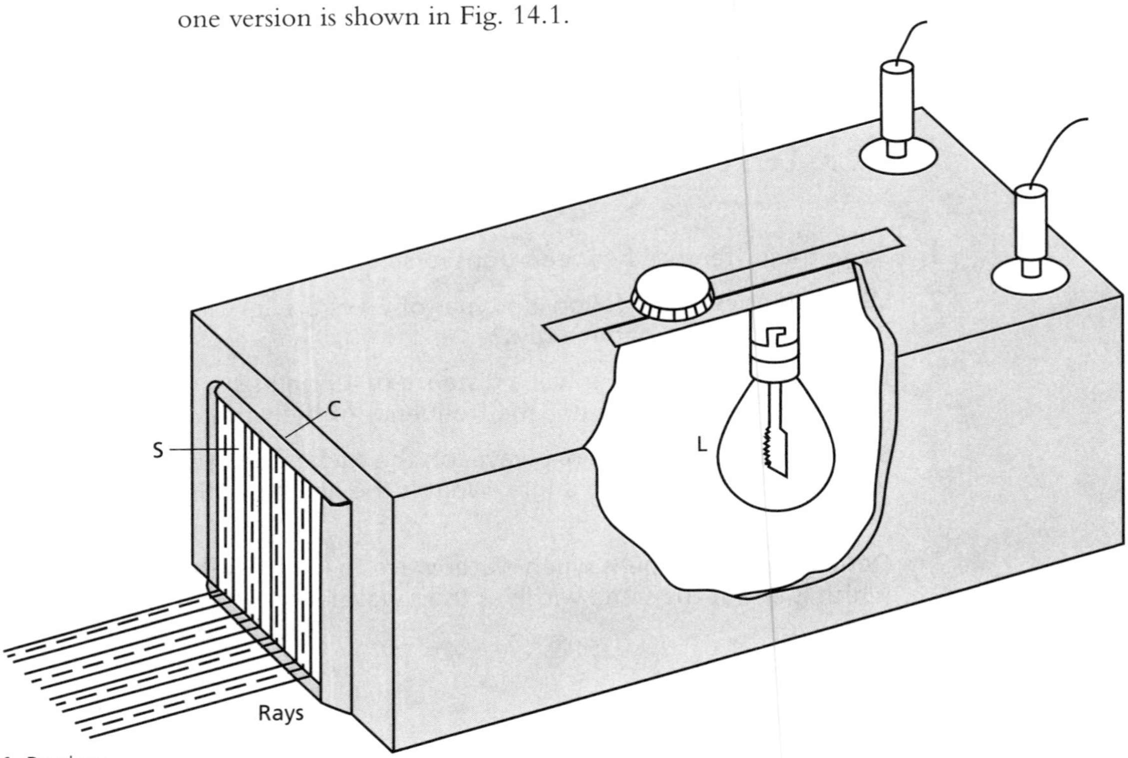

Fig. 14.1 Ray box

A small filament lamp L is enclosed in a box with a cylindrical convex lens C and a 'comb' S containing parallel slits in front of it. A diverging, converging or parallel beam of rays (Fig. 14.2) may be obtained by moving the lamp L.

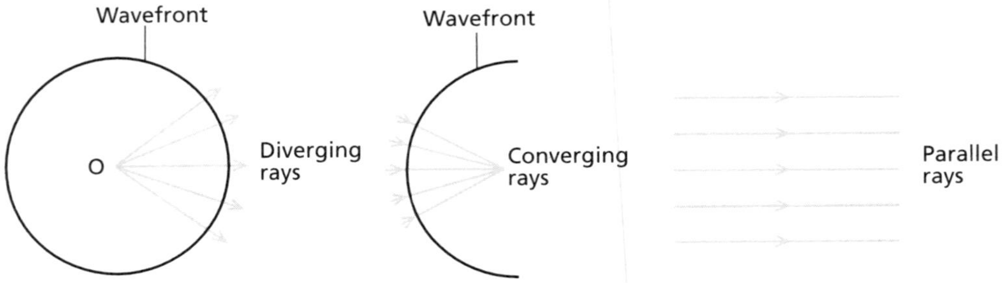

Fig. 14.2

14.1 Rectilinear propagation

If a ray box is placed on a sheet of white paper and switched on, a ray is obtained through each slit of the comb. This ray is actually a very narrow beam of light with straight sharp edges. It can be said that light travels in straight lines (**rectilinear propagation**) in this case. The existence of shadows and eclipses of the Sun and Moon is further evidence that light travels in straight lines.

When an obstacle is placed in the path of light coming from a point source the shadow formed on a screen is uniformly dark and has sharp edges (Fig. 14.3). As no light reaches the region of shadow (umbra) it is concluded that light travels in straight lines.

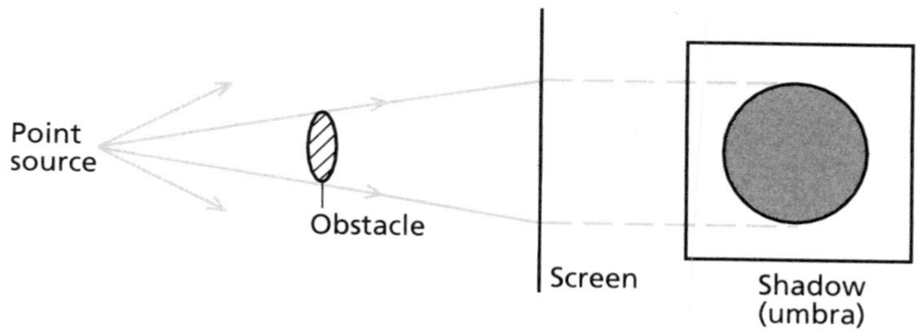

Fig. 14.3

If an extended light source is used the shadow is edged with a border of partial shadow (penumbra). The area of partial shadow receives light from some points on the source, but other points on the source are obscured from it by the obstacle (Fig. 14.4).

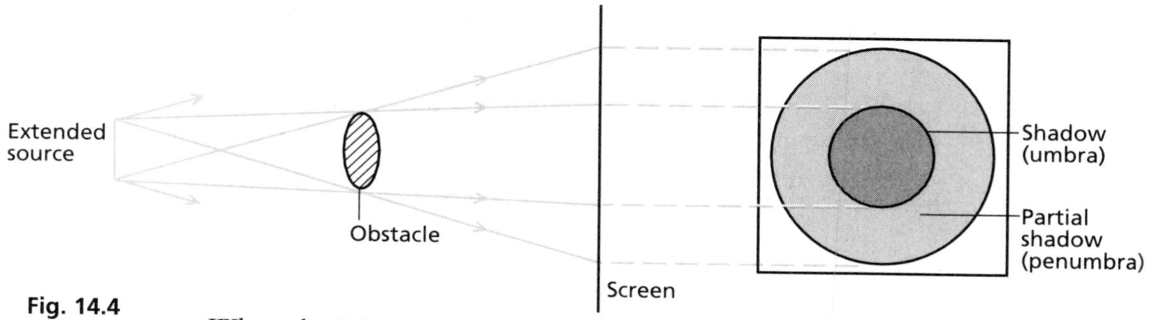

Fig. 14.4

When the Moon passes between the Sun and the Earth it casts a shadow or partial shadow on parts of the Earth's surface (Fig. 14.5). This effect is known as an eclipse or partial eclipse of the Sun. Area *c* is total shadow, *b* and *d* are partial shadow, and *a* and *e* receive light from the whole of the Sun's surface. On some occasions the Moon is a little further from the Earth than shown in the diagram and there is no area of complete shadow.

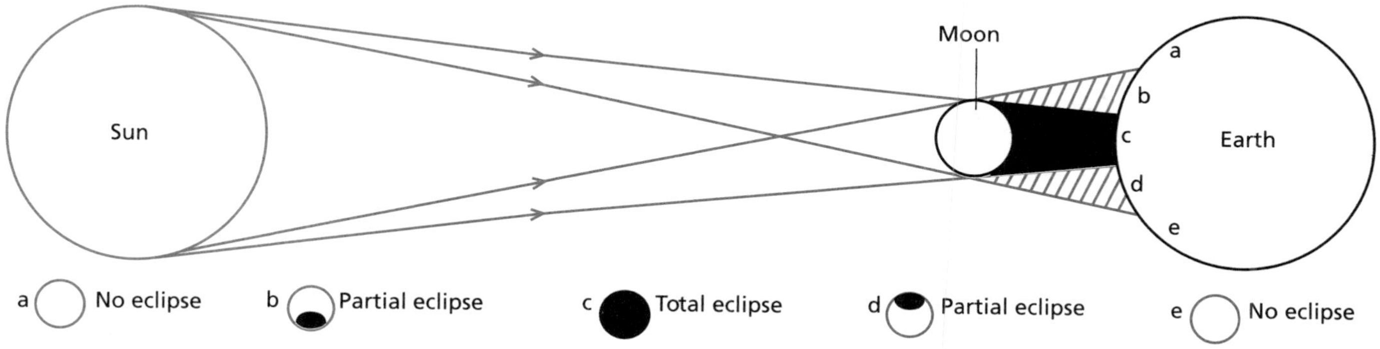

Fig. 14.5 Eclipse of the Sun

The pin-hole camera relies on the fact that light travels in straight lines to produce a clear image. It is a very simple version of a camera, invented well before lenses were used to produce images (Fig. 14.6(a)).

A pin-hole camera may be made by removing the back of a small cardboard or metal box, and replacing it with a piece of semi-transparent paper (the screen). A pin-hole is punched in the side of the box opposite the screen. When the hole is held towards a bright lamp, such as a carbon filament lamp, in a darkened room, an inverted image of the lamp filament can be seen on the screen. A narrow beam of light from point A on the source enters the camera through the pin-hole and strikes the screen at A'. Likewise light from B arrives at B'. Narrow beams of light from all the different points on the object will fall on the screen between A' and B'. Each point on the object is thus responsible for a point of light on the screen and a complete **inverted** image is seen. This image is formed on a screen and is said to be **real**. An image which cannot be shown on a screen, but only seen by the eye, is called **virtual**.

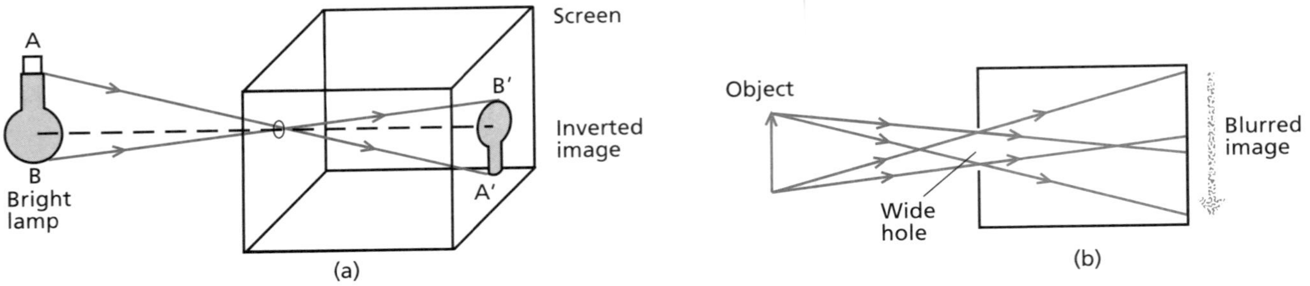

Fig. 14.6 Pin-hole camera

If the pin-hole camera is moved closer to the lamp the image becomes bigger. The small hole means that little light enters the camera. A larger hole would improve this, but would lead to blurring of the image (Fig. 14.6(b)), unless a lens was used. Thus the exposure time needed to produce a picture on a film using a pin-hole camera is long.

14.2 Reflection at a plane surface

Reflection of light may be examined by using a plane mirror supported vertically on a sheet of white paper. A line XN, the normal, is drawn at right angles to the mirror surface so that N is near the centre of the mirror (Fig. 14.7). Further lines are drawn from N so that they are inclined at angles such as 20°, 30°, etc., to XN. A ray box is now placed so that a single ray follows one of the drawn lines. The position of the reflected ray is marked with dots. The ray box is moved to each of the lines in turn and the procedure repeated. In each case the angle of incidence i of the ray is noted and the corresponding angle of reflection r measured. Within the limits of experimental accuracy the two are found to be equal.

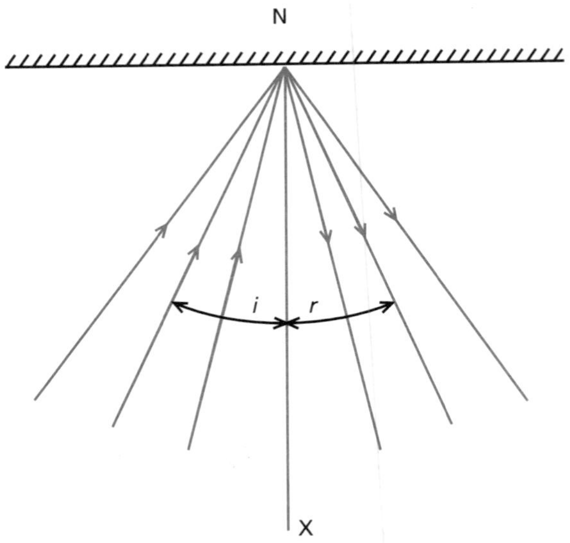

Fig. 14.7 Reflection at a plane mirror

The laws of reflection at plane surfaces are summarized as follows:

1. **The incident ray, the reflected ray and the normal all lie in the same plane.**
2. **The angle of incidence equals the angle of reflection.**

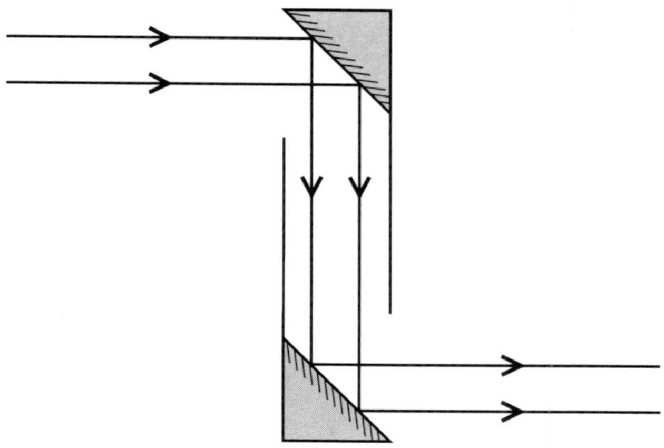

Fig. 14.8 A periscope

A periscope (Fig. 14.8) is a good example of the application of the reflection of light by a plane mirror. The rays of light enter the upper mirror, are reflected by a total of 90° and travel to the lower mirror where a similar reflection takes place. Periscopes are used in submarines to view the surface of the sea without the submarine needing to surface. They can also be used so a car driver can see over the top of the caravan he is towing and to enable short people, such as children, to see over a crowd.

If a beam of divergent rays is reflected from a plane mirror, the rays will appear as in Fig. 14.9(a). A beam of convergent rays would give Fig. 14.9(b).

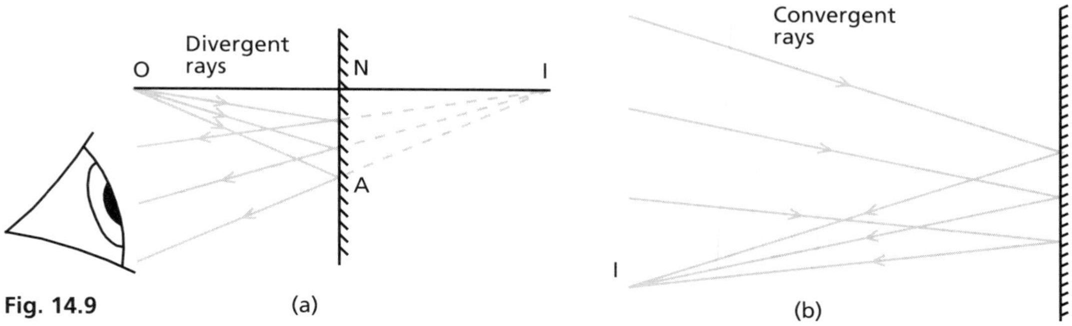

Fig. 14.9

In Fig. 14.9(a) the image I is the point from which rays entering the eye appear to have come. These rays have been reflected according to the laws just stated and consideration of the triangles ONA and INA will show that they are similar. Thus the distance IN is the same as the distance ON; that is the image is as far behind the surface of the mirror as the object is in front of it. As the rays do not actually come from I the image is virtual. In Fig. 14.9(b) the reflected rays cross at the point I to form a real image there.

If a person looks at the image of an object in a mirror he notices that it appears the wrong way round; it is said to be **laterally inverted**. Figure 14.10 shows how this comes about. If L and R represent the left and right sides of the object viewed directly, it will be seen that L', the image of L, appears on the right side of the image in the mirror.

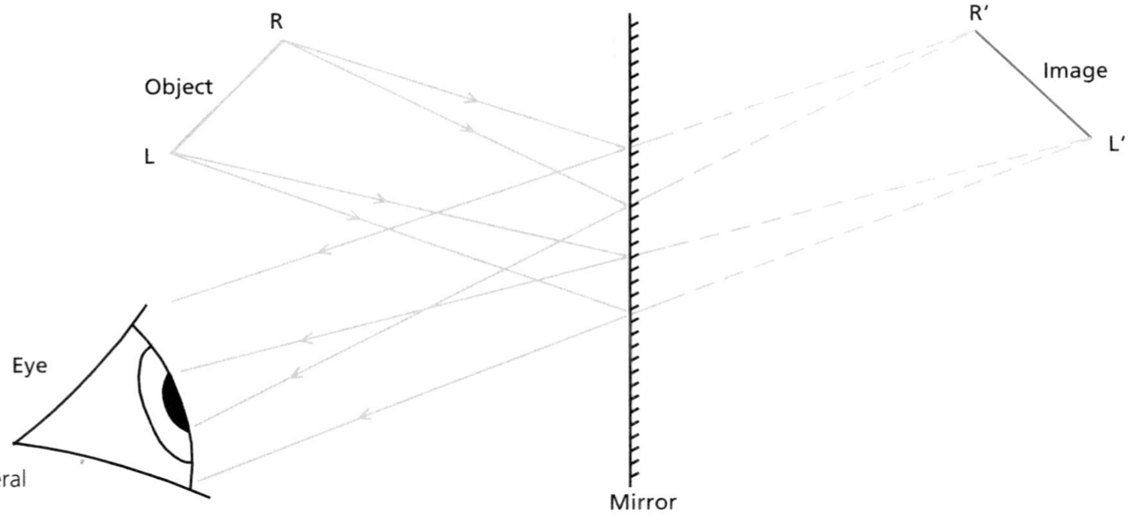

Fig. 14.10 Lateral inversion

Summary

1 Light normally travels in straight lines. This results in the formation of shadows and eclipses when an object is in a beam of light.

2 When a ray of light is reflected at a surface such as a mirror the angle of reflection equals the angle of incidence.

Quick test 14

1 What evidence do we have for stating that light normally travels in straight lines?

2 Explain how an eclipse of the Moon happens.

3 Explain, with the aid of a diagram if you wish, how it is that a pinhole camera produces an inverted image.

4 What happens to the size and brightness of the image in a pinhole camera if the camera is brought closer to the object?

5 State the two laws of reflection.

6 When you look into a dressing table mirror you see an image of yourself. Name the type of image you see and state its position.

Chapter 15
Refraction of light

The laws of refraction are:

1. **The incident and refracted rays are on opposite sides of the normal at the point of incidence and all three are in the same plane.**
2. **The ratio of the sine of the angle of incidence to the sine of the angle of refraction is a constant.**

15.1 Refraction at a plane boundary

The refraction of rays of light can be studied using a ray box. We will consider what occurs when a single ray of light strikes a plane air to glass boundary (Fig. 15.1).

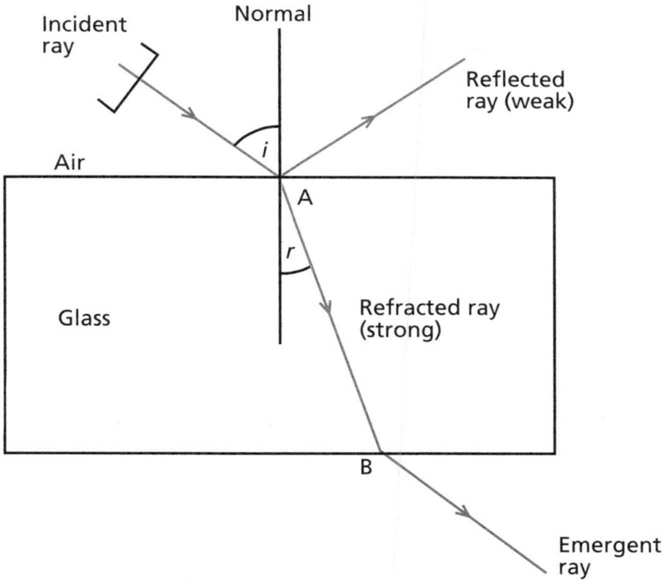

Fig. 15.1 Refraction at a plane boundary

The glass block stands on a sheet of white paper. A line at right angles to the boundary to be used is constructed near the middle of the face (a normal). It is arranged that the single ray strikes the glass block at A at various angles of incidence, i, in turn. The position of this ray and the emerging ray in each case are marked on the paper with dots. The angle of refraction r, within the block, is constructed by joining the points AB for each ray. The angle r is measured and, in each case, found to be less than the corresponding value of i; that is the ray always bends towards the normal.

Another example of refraction at a plane surface takes place in a prism (Fig. 15.2).

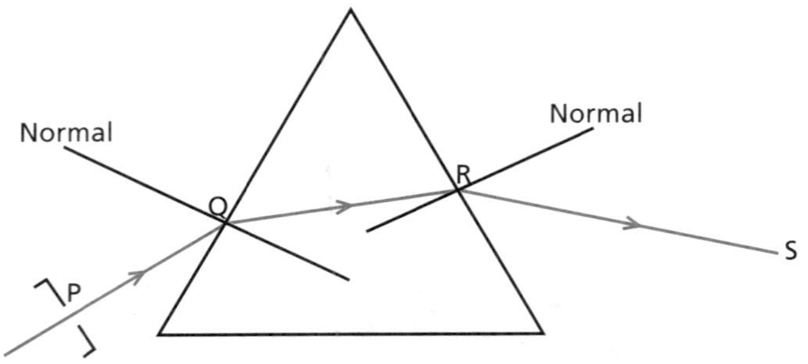

Fig. 15.2 Refraction by a prism

When light enters the glass prism at *Q*, its velocity is reduced and refraction takes place towards the normal. The reverse takes place at *R* as the light leaves the prism. In the case of a rectangular glass block, the refracting faces are parallel, and the emerging ray is parallel to the incident ray. For a prism the refracting faces are not parallel and this results in the emerging ray not being parallel to the incident ray. The angle between these two rays is called **the angle of deviation**. If the incident light is not all of the same wavelength, but a mixture, different wavelengths will undergo slightly different deviations at each face. Thus, for example, blue light will be deviated through a greater angle than red light.

A spectrum is obtained if a parallel beam of white light falls on a prism in the direction *PQ* (Fig. 15.2) and a screen is placed on the far side of the prism. The separate colours are visible in order from red to violet, red being the least deviated. However, the spectrum is not very good: a pure spectrum is obtained if a converging lens is added on the far side of the prism such that the screen passes through the focal point of the lens. This lens then focuses the parallel rays of the different colours which leave the prism; each colour to one place on the screen.

15.2 Internal reflection and critical angle

When light passes from one medium to a more optically dense medium (i.e. the speed of the light is reduced) refraction occurs for all angles of incidence, together with a very small amount of reflection. But refraction does not always occur at the surface of a less optically dense medium, for example when light is passing from glass or water to air.

Consider a ray passing from glass or water to air with a small angle of incidence (Fig. 15.3(a)). Here we get both a refracted and a reflected ray, the latter being relatively weak. If the angle of incidence is gradually increased the reflected ray becomes stronger and the refracted ray weaker, until for a certain **critical angle of incidence** c, the angle of refraction is 90°. This special case is shown in Fig. 15.3(b). The value of the critical angle for a glass to air boundary is about 42° and for water to air about 48°.

Since it is impossible to have an angle of refraction greater than 90°, it follows that all the light is internally reflected for angles of incidence greater than the critical angle. There is no refracted ray and this condition is known as **total internal reflection** (Fig. 15.3(c)).

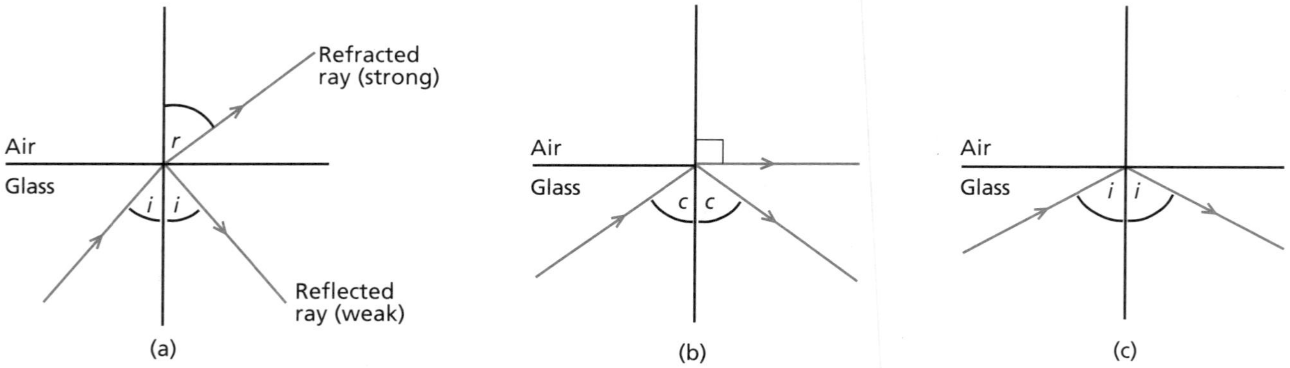

Fig. 15.3 (a) Refraction; (b) critical angle; (c) total internal reflection

This effect is used in the transmission of information in fibre optics (Fig. 15.4). Glass is drawn out into thin fibres. A narrow beam of light which enters one end of a fibre will spread out a little. Light which strikes the inside of the glass to air boundary will always do so at an angle much greater than the critical angle and almost all of it will be internally reflected. This will even be the case if the fibre is bent, as its length is so much greater than its width. Therefore, almost no energy is lost as the light passes along the fibre and the vast majority of it reaches the far end. Unlike electrical pulses, pulses of light carrying information can be transmitted great distances without any need to amplify the signal.

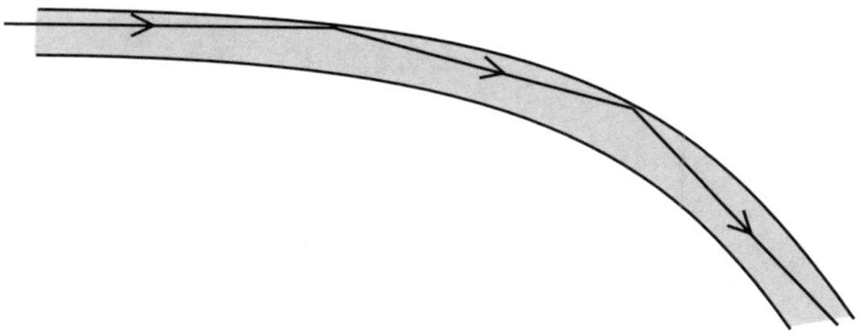

Fig. 15.4

15.3 Lenses

Refraction of light at a spherical surface follows the same rules as refraction at a plane surface (see the beginning of this chapter).

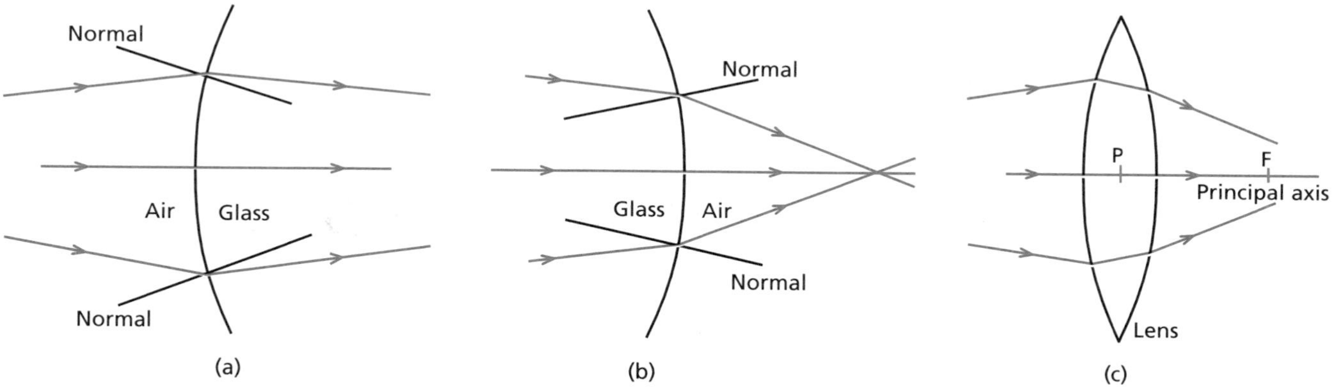

Fig. 15.5 Refraction at lens surfaces

Consider Fig. 15.5(a) showing three rays passing from air to glass. The three rays are all refracted according to the rules stated. However, in this case, refraction results in the rays being brought together or focused. If the rays leave the glass through a second boundary, curved the other way, before they have come together, further focusing occurs (Fig. 15.5(b)), as they bend away from the normal. The combined effect of the two surfaces is to provide us with a converging lens as shown in Fig. 15.5(c).

The point F is the point through which rays incident parallel to the principal axis pass after refraction by the lens. It is called the **focal point** or **principal focus** of the lens. The distance PF is known as the **focal length** f.

The behaviour of a diverging lens is shown in Fig. 15.6. The point, F, is the point from which rays incident parallel to the principal axis appear to come after refraction by the lens. It is called the **focal point** of the lens. The distance PF is known as the **focal length**, f. Because the rays do not actually pass through the focal point F it is virtual and the focal length f is therefore negative.

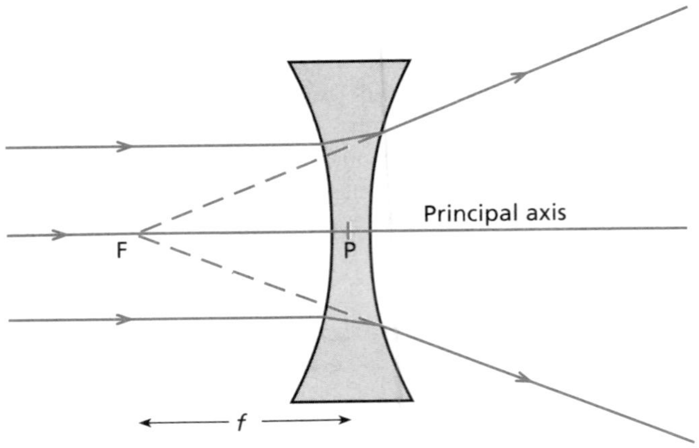

Fig. 15.6 Diverging lens

How much higher (or wider) the image is than the object is called the magnification, which is defined by

$$\text{Magnification} = \frac{\text{height of image}}{\text{height of object}}$$

also

$$\text{magnification} = \frac{\text{distance of image from lens}}{\text{distance of object from lens}}$$

For both converging and diverging lenses it can be shown that:

$$\frac{1}{u} + \frac{1}{v} = \frac{1}{f}$$

where u = object distance from lens
v = image distance from lens
f = focal length of lens

Virtual distances carry a negative sign, including the focal length of diverging lenses.

15.4 Simple microscope (magnifying glass)

Figure 15.7 shows the use of a lens as a magnifying glass. Suppose that, without the lens, *I* is the closest to the eye that the object could normally be placed for clear focusing. Using the lens the object may now be placed at *O* and still be seen clearly as, to the eye, the object appears to be at *I*. The lens has thus enabled the object to be placed closer to the eye than would be the case without it, and the object appears larger because it appears to be closer.

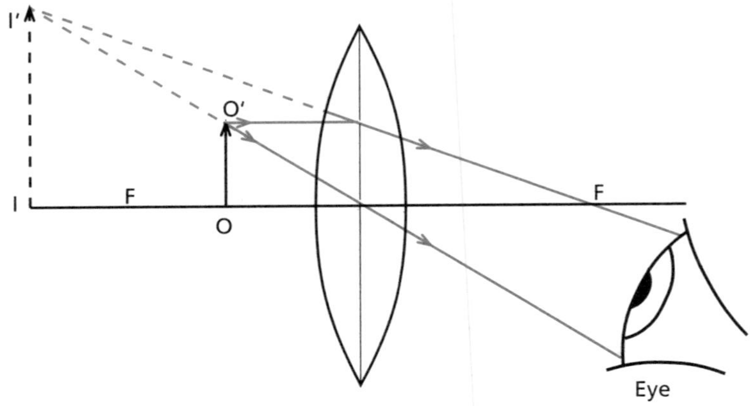

Fig. 15.7

15.5 The camera

The camera consists of a lens and light-sensitive film mounted in a light-tight box.
The distance of the lens from the film may be adjusted using the focusing ring.
This is marked in metres to show the distance at which an object will give a clear image. The amount of light entering the camera is controlled by a diaphragm of variable aperture (hole size) and the speed of the shutter. These, used together, allow the correct amount of light to reach the film and give the right exposure. The main features are shown in Fig. 15.8.

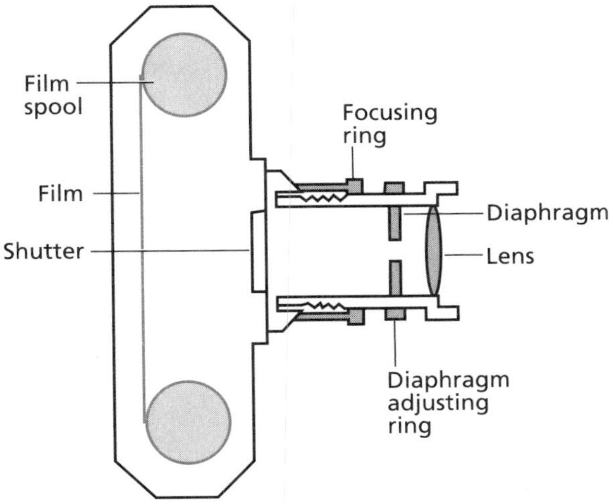

Fig. 15.8 Camera

15.6 The eye

A simplified diagram of the human eye is shown in Fig. 15.9. In many ways the eye is similar to the camera. An image is formed by the lens on the sensitive retina at the back of the eye.

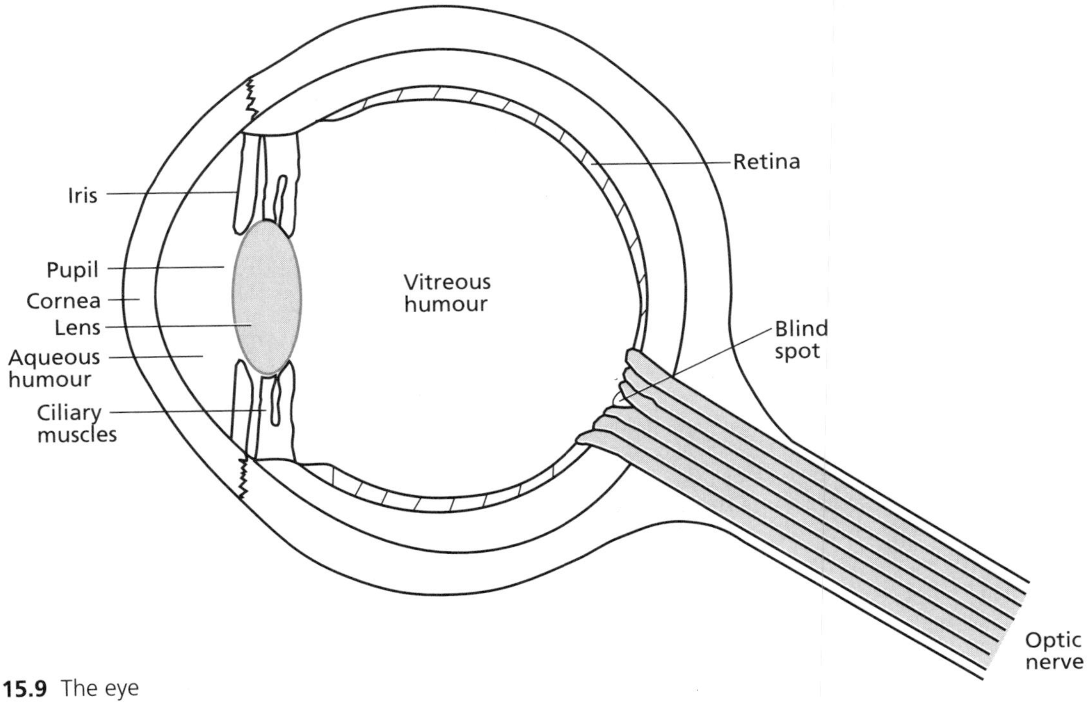

Fig. 15.9 The eye

The iris automatically adjusts the size of the circular opening in its centre, known as the pupil, according to the brightness of the light falling on it. Focusing of the image on the retina is achieved partly by refraction at the curved surface as light enters the eye, and partly by the action of the lens. The ciliary muscles vary the thickness of the lens and hence its focal length. When the muscles are relaxed the lens is thin. Unlike the camera, the position of the lens does not alter.

If the ciliary muscles weaken, the eye lens cannot be made sufficiently fat to clearly focus close objects. However, distant objects can be clearly focused. The eye is said to suffer from **long sight**. The same defect occurs if the eyeball is too short, and it may be corrected by using spectacles containing a converging lens (Fig. 15.10(a)). In the case of **short sight** the muscles do not relax sufficiently and consequently distant objects are focused in front of the retina. Short sight also occurs if the eyeball is too long. The defect can be corrected with a diverging lens (Fig. 15.10(b)).

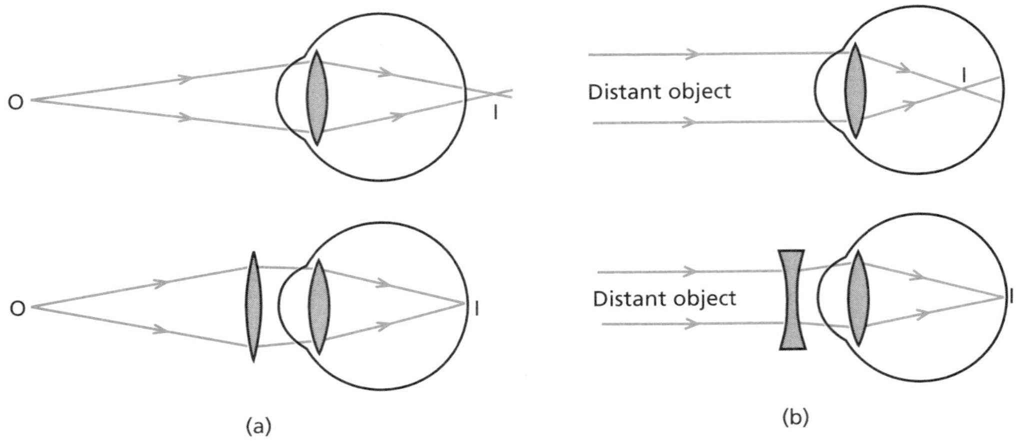

Fig. 15.10 Eye defects and their correction: (a) long sight; (b) short sight

In the case of long sight bifocal spectacles are frequently worn. Each eyepiece is in two halves, the upper half often being a plane sheet of glass through which to look at distant objects and the lower half being a converging lens through which to view close objects, such as a book or newspaper. Such an arrangement removes the necessity to be continually removing and replacing spectacles.

Summary

1 When light enters a different material its speed changes. This results in a change in its direction of motion (**refraction**) unless it crosses the boundary between the two materials at 90°. For example, when a ray of light enters glass from air it bends towards the normal. On leaving it bends away from the normal.

2 The **focal point *F*** of a lens is the point through which rays incident parallel to the principal axis pass after refraction by the lens. The distance between ***F*** and the centre of the lens is known as **the focal length** f.

3 A converging lens bends rays of light inwards (towards the principal axis). Its focal length is positive. A diverging lens bends them away. Its focal length is negative.

4 For any lens

$$\frac{1}{u} + \frac{1}{v} = \frac{1}{f}$$

where u is the distance the object is away from the lens and v the distance the image is away from the lens. Real distances are treated as positive, virtual distances as negative.

5 Long sight occurs if the eye lens cannot be made sufficiently fat to clearly focus close objects or the eyeball is too short.

6 Short sight occurs if the eye lens cannot be made sufficiently thin to clearly focus distant objects or the eyeball is too long.

Quick test 15

1 Explain, using wave ideas, why a beam of light usually changes direction on entering glass from air.

2 What is meant by **critical angle**?

3 Explain how light is able to travel along a glass fibre without energy being 'lost' to the outside.

4 What is meant by the **focal length** of a lens?

5 Explain the difference between a **real** and a **virtual image**.

6 Explain how the lens in an eye focuses light coming from objects at different distances.

7 State two differences in the way lenses work between a camera and an eye.

8 What is meant by **short sight**? How may it be corrected?

Chapter 16
Electromagnetic waves

16.1 Diffraction

The **diffraction** or spreading out which occurs when waves pass through a narrow gap or round a small object has already been mentioned in Chapter 13 in terms of water waves. It was then stated that the size of the gap or object had to be about the same as the wavelength of the waves, if significant bending was to occur. Light has a wavelength (about 5×10^{-7} m) very much less than the wavelength of water waves. The dimensions of the gap or object must be very small therefore if diffraction of light is to be observed. In practice a slit which is sufficiently narrow for the purpose can be made by drawing a sharp razor blade across the surface of a blackened microscope slide.

If the slide is held close to the eye and a light filament viewed through the slit, the filament looks much broader than it does with the naked eye, thus showing that light has been diffracted round the edges of the slit. The effect is most obvious if the filament and slit are parallel to each other. A similar effect can be obtained by partially closing your eyes, until there is a narrow slit between the eyelids, and then looking at a light.

Radio waves suffer diffraction if they pass through a narrow gap between two metal plates or pass round a narrow metal object. Again, significant diffraction occurs only if the gap or object has a width about equal too or less than the wavelength of the radio waves. In the case of vhf, this means about a few centimetres; in the case of medium wave, a few hundred metres.

16.2 The electromagnetic spectrum

Light waves are just one small part of a family of waves called the **electromagnetic spectrum**. This family includes radio and television waves, infrared rays, light, ultraviolet light, X-rays and γ-rays. All members travel with a velocity of 3×10^8 m/s in space. Their difference lies in their frequency and wavelength. Radio waves lie at the long wavelength–low frequency end of the spectrum and γ-rays at the short wavelength–high frequency end. Because of their differing frequencies and wavelengths, different regions of the spectrum exhibit different properties. Some of these properties are summarized in Table 16.1.

Radio waves form the basis of all long distance 'wireless' communication. The behaviour of these waves is determined largely by the presence round the Earth of the ionosphere. This region of ionized gas, at heights between 80 and 400 km above the

Earth's surface, acts as a mirror for radio waves of many frequencies. Waves of long wavelength and low frequency are reflected by this layer and such waves are thus very useful for communications round the Earth's surface. Waves of short wavelength and high frequency (>30 MHz) are able to penetrate the ionosphere and are used for all communications with artificial satellites. Radio waves can pass comparatively easily through brickwork and concrete.

Table 16.1

Wavelength (λ(m))	Type	Production	Reflection	Refraction	Diffraction and interference
$>10^{-4}$	Radio	Electrons oscillating in wires	Ionosphere	Atmosphere	Two stations
$7 \times 10^{-7} \rightarrow 10^{-4}$	Infrared	Hot objects	Metal sheet		
$4 \times 10^{-7} \rightarrow 7 \times 10^{-7}$	Visible	Very hot objects	Metal sheet	Glass	Grating
$10^{-8} \rightarrow 4 \times 10^{-7}$	Ultraviolet	Arcs and gas discharges			
$10^{-12} \rightarrow 10^{-8}$	X-rays	Electrons hitting metal targets			Crystals
$<10^{-10}$	γ-rays	Radioactive nuclei			

Any object heated nearly to red heat is a convenient source of infrared radiation. The radiation is readily absorbed (and also emitted) by objects with rough black surfaces, but strongly reflected by light polished ones. This radiation may therefore readily be detected by painting the bulb of a thermometer black and allowing the radiation to fall on the bulb. The thermometer reading rises. Also it can be detected by thermal imaging cameras which are used in warfare to detect the presence of the enemy at night (by detecting the heat given off by humans or vehicles) and to 'find' those buried under rubble after an earthquake or humans obscured by smoke.

Radiation with wavelengths just shorter than that of the violet end of the visible spectrum is termed ultraviolet radiation. It is emitted by any white hot body, such as the filament of an electric light bulb. However, in this case the radiation is absorbed by the glass envelope of the bulb. A discharge tube containing mercury vapour (with a quartz envelope) is a more intense source of ultraviolet radiation. A great deal of ultraviolet radiation is emitted by the Sun, but the majority of this is absorbed by the Earth's atmosphere and only a small fraction reaches the surface of the Earth. It is this which causes browning of the skin and can cause skin cancer. One of the best known properties of ultraviolet radiation is its ability to cause substances to **fluoresce**. This is the term given to the emission of visible light by substances when ultraviolet radiation is shone on them. Examples are real diamonds, uranyl salts and paraffin oil.

The X-ray region of the electromagnetic spectrum is defined more by the method of generation of the radiation than by its precise wavelength. The method used is to cause electrons to hit a metal target. X-rays are used in medicine. Their ability to penetrate matter depends on the atomic number (see Unit 27.1) of the nuclei of the material through which they pass. X-rays are comparatively easily absorbed by bone which contains calcium ($Z = 20$), whereas they pass much more readily through organic material which contains hydrogen ($Z = 1$) and carbon ($Z = 6$). In addition, X-rays affect a photographic plate in a similar manner to visible light. An X-ray photograph may therefore be taken of the human leg, for example, and a bone fracture detected. X-rays are dangerous in too intense quantities. They eject electrons from the region on which they fall and can cause damage to living cells. In controlled quantities they can be used to kill off diseased tissue. X-rays like other forms of electromagnetic radiation show diffraction effects. The atomic spacing in crystals is comparable with the wavelength of X-rays, and thus X-rays are appreciably diffracted by atoms in crystals. The development of the science of X-ray crystallography has led to a much more detailed understanding of the structure of materials.

γ-rays are distinguished from X-rays in that they are emitted by the nuclei of natural or artificial radioactive materials. They are generally more penetrating, more dangerous and more difficult to screen than X-rays. They are mentioned in more detail in the unit on radioactivity (Unit 27.3).

Summary

1 **Diffraction** is the spreading out which occurs when electromagnetic waves pass through a narrow gap or round a small object. The width of the gap or object should be equal to or smaller than the wavelength of the radiation if spreading out is to be significant.

2 The electromagnetic spectrum is a family of waves all of which travel with a velocity of 3×10^8 m/s in space. The family includes radio and television waves (longest wavelength and lowest frequency), infrared rays, light, ultraviolet light and X-rays and γ-rays (shortest wavelength and highest frequency).

Quick test 16

1 State the condition under which diffraction of light through a narrow slit is significant.

2 Arrange the following in order of **decreasing** wavelength; ultraviolet rays, infrared rays, yellow light, radio waves, gamma rays.

3 Which type of radiation is best described by the following statement? 'The wavelength is slightly longer than that of visible light and it may be used for heating.'

4 The frequency of Radio 4 is 198 kHz. Calculate its wavelength.

5 Distinguish between X-rays and γ-rays.

Chapter 17
Sound

Sound waves differ from waves of the electromagnetic spectrum in that they are mechanical waves requiring a medium through which to pass. This may be demonstrated by placing an electric bell inside a glass jar from which the air can be removed (Fig. 17.1).

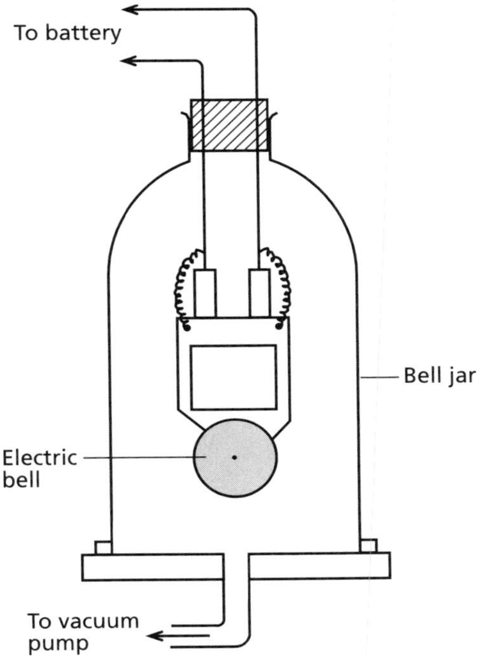

Fig. 17.1 Passage of sound

When all the air has been pumped from the jar the ringing can no longer be heard, although the hammer can still be seen striking the gong. The faint vibration which is still audible comes from the passage of sound through the connecting wires. Sound travels through air at a speed of about 340 m/s.

Sound waves travel through solids and liquids as well as gases. If one person places his ear near a long metal fence while a second person gives the fence a tap some distance away two sounds will be heard. The first is due to transmission through the fence; the second comes through the air. Sound travels about 15 times faster through a solid than through air. Fishermen are using transistor 'bleepers' which, when lowered into the water, attract fish up to one mile away. The speed of sound in water is about 1400 m/s.

Sound waves are **longitudinal** rather than transverse; that is the wave particles oscillate in the same direction as the wave travels and not at right angles to it. Owing to their longitudinal nature sound waves consist of a series of **compressions** and **rarefactions**.

Figure 17.2 shows how a vibrating tuning fork sends out a sound wave. The prongs are set vibrating by striking the fork. When the right-hand prong moves to the right it pushes the layers of air in that direction to the right. These layers are thus pushed closer together; that is, they are compressed. This disturbance is transmitted from one layer of particles to the next with the result that a compression pulse or high pressure region moves away from the fork. Similarly, when the prong moves to the left, a low pressure region or rarefaction occurs to its right. Compressions and rarefactions move alternately through the air. The particle at the centre of a compression is moving through its rest position in the same direction as the wave, whilst a particle at the centre of a rarefaction is moving through its rest position in the opposite direction to the wave. At regular intervals in the material through which the sound is travelling, there will be particles undergoing exactly the same movement at the same moment. Such particles are said to be **in phase**.

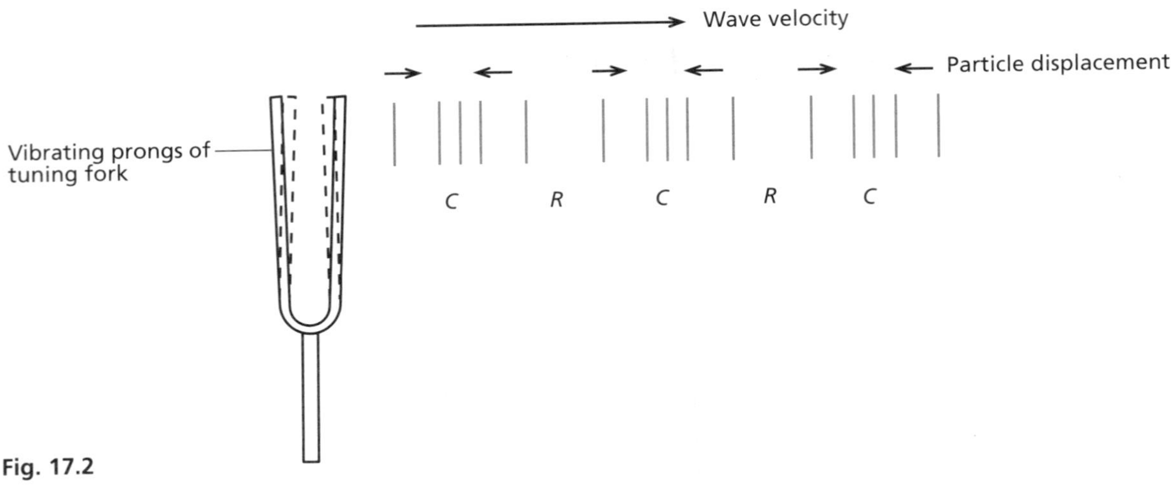

Fig. 17.2

As in the case of transverse waves, the distance between two successive particles in the same phase is called the **wavelength** λ.

The **amplitude** a of a wave is the maximum displacement of a particle from its rest position.

The **frequency** f is the number of complete oscillations made in one second. The unit is the hertz (Hz).

The **velocity** v is the distance moved by the wavefront in one second.

As in the case of transverse waves, the velocity, frequency and wavelength are related by the equation:

$$v = f\lambda$$

which is proved in the unit on progressive waves (see Unit 13.1).

17.1 Echoes

Echoes are produced by the **reflection** of sound from a hard surface such as a wall or cliff. Sound obeys the same laws of reflection as light. Thus if a person claps their hands, when standing some distance from a high wall, he will hear a reflection some time later. In order that the reflection may be heard separately from the original clap it must arrive at least 1/10 s later. As the speed of sound in air is 340 m/s, this means that the wall must be at least 17 m away.

Echoes may be used to measure the speed of sound in air reasonably accurately. One person should make the sound and another carry out the timing. The first person claps their hands and listens for the echo from a wall. For accurate results the time interval will need to be about half a second; thus they need to be about 100 m from the wall. Having obtained an estimate of the time interval, the person continues to clap their hands and adjust the rate of striking until each clap coincides in time with the arrival of the echo of the previous clap. When the correct rate of striking has been achieved the second person times 30 or more intervals between claps with a stopwatch. The speed of sound is then calculated by dividing the distance to the wall and back by the interval between two successive claps. The experiment should be repeated several times and an average value calculated.

17.2 Refraction

When sound travels from one material into another it is refracted in a similar way to light (Unit 15.1). Sound travels more quickly in a liquid or a solid than it does in a gas, such as air. Therefore, on passing from air into water, for example, at any angle other than 90° to the normal, it bends away from the normal rather than towards it. The angle through which it bends depends on its relative speed in the two materials.

17.3 Pitch

The **pitch** of a note depends on its frequency relative to other notes. This can be demonstrated by connecting a signal generator to a loudspeaker. If the frequencies 120, 150, 180 and 240 Hz (that is a ratio of 4:5:6:8) are produced in quick succession, the familiar sequence doh, me, soh, doh will be recognized. However, the same familiar sequence is noted when the frequencies 240, 300, 360 and 480 Hz are produced one after the other. The musical relation between notes thus depends on the ratio of their frequencies rather than their actual frequencies. An octave is always in the ratio 1:2.

Ultrasonic waves have a frequency higher than the upper limit of the hearing range for humans. When such waves meet a boundary between two different materials, they are partly reflected. The time taken for the reflections of ultrasonic pulses to reach the detector (usually next to the source) is a measure of how far away the boundary is. This effect is used in industry to detect flaws in metal castings and in medicine to examine embryos in the uterus. The information is usually processed to produce a visual display.

17.4 Diffraction

The **diffraction** or spreading out which occurs when waves pass through a narrow gap or round a narrow object has already been mentioned in Chapter 13 in terms of water waves. The size of the gap or object must be about the same size or smaller than the wavelength of the waves, if significant spreading is to occur. Sound has a wavelength between 0.5 m and 2.0 m. Thus 'large' gaps, such as doorways and those between buildings cause significant diffraction and sound can be heard round corners.

17.5 Intensity and loudness

The most important factor affecting the **intensity** of a sound of given frequency is its **amplitude**. The intensity depends on the square of the amplitude and thus, if the amplitude is doubled the intensity increases by a factor of four. Intensity is a measure of energy.

The **loudness** of a sound will obviously depend on its intensity. However, it also depends on the sensitivity of the human ear to sounds of different frequency. Loud sounds cause a greater pressure change on an eardrum than soft sounds. In normal conversation an eardrum will experience a pressure change of about one newton per metre squared (1 N/m^2 or 1 pascal), which is very small compared with atmospheric pressure (100 000 pascal).

Loud noises can cause pressure changes of about 100 pascal. These sounds are painful and can damage the eardrum. Laws now limit the noise level from industrial machinery, aeroplanes and discos. Double glazing and insulating panels made of material which traps many small pockets of air help to reduce noise levels. People who work with noisy machinery are required to wear ear-protectors.

17.6 Resonance

Resonance occurs when a vibrator is forced to vibrate at its own natural frequency. A car or washing machine may vibrate quite violently at a particular speed. When this occurs, the frequency of a rotating part is equal to the natural frequency of the body of the car or washing machine. When resonance occurs the maximum amount of energy is transferred from the forcing vibrator (motor, wheel or drum) to the driven vibrator (the body of the car or washing machine) and the amplitude of the vibrations of the driven vibrator greatly increases.

The effect of resonance is used in string instruments such as the violin, cello and double bass, where the case resonates at the frequencies produced by the strings and the sound is amplified. The same effect happens in pipes (e.g. flute and organ), where the fundamental note produced in a particular pipe by the reed causes the air in the pipe to resonate and amplify the sound.

In some cases the amplitude of the oscillation builds up sufficiently to cause self-destruction, e.g. the suspension bridge over the Tacoma Narrows.

Summary

1. Sound is a longitudinal wave motion.
2. The equation $v = f\lambda$ applies (see Unit 13.1).
3. Sound is reflected according to the same rules as light. Reflected sound is often called an **echo**.
4. The **pitch** of sound depends on its frequency.
5. The **intensity** of sound is a measure of energy and depends on the square of the amplitude of the sound wave.
6. **Resonance** occurs when a vibrator is forced to vibrate at its own natural frequency. Energy is transferred from the driver to the driven, whose amplitude of vibration builds up.

Quick test 17

1. State two ways in which sound waves differ from electromagnetic waves.
2. A loudspeaker gives out a note of frequency 100 Hz. If the speed of sound is 330 m/s, what is the wavelength of the sound?
3. When a bat squeaks, the sound has a frequency of 30 000 Hz. The wavelength of the sound is 0.01 m. Calculate the speed of sound.
4. Which property of sound is responsible for **echoes**?
5. Write down what you understand by **ultrasound**.
6. What do you understand by the term **resonance**?

Chapter 18
Magnets

Certain materials have the property to attract iron; this property is known as **magnetism**. One such material is an iron ore called lodestone or magnetite; others are iron, steel, cobalt and nickel. Alni, alcomax and ticonal are alloys of nickel and cobalt which are used for making powerful permanent magnets. Mumetal is an alloy which has been developed for the electromagnet and transformer, in which temporary magnets are used.

When a bar magnet is placed on a cork floating on water, so that it can swing in a horizontal plane, it comes to rest with its axis approximately in the north–south direction. The vertical plane in which the magnet lies is called the **magnetic meridian**. The end which points towards the north is called the north-seeking pole, or the N pole for short, and the other end the south-seeking or S pole.

If the N pole of a second bar magnet is brought near the N pole of the magnet on the floating cork, repulsion occurs and the cork and magnet tend to swing round. Repulsion occurs between two S poles in a similar way. However, a N and a S pole attract one another. These results may be summed up by saying:

Like poles repel, unlike poles attract

18.1 Making magnets

Magnetization by an electrical method is an efficient way of making magnets. A cylindrical coil is wound with about 500 turns of insulated copper wire and connected to a direct current supply (see Fig. 18.1). A coil of this kind is called a **solenoid**. A steel bar is placed inside the coil and the current switched on. The current creates a strong magnetic field within the coil and the steel immediately becomes a magnet, retaining its magnetism when the current is switched off.

A magnet may be demagnetized by placing it in the same coil but this time passing an alternating current through the coil. The magnet is slowly removed from the coil with the current still switched on.

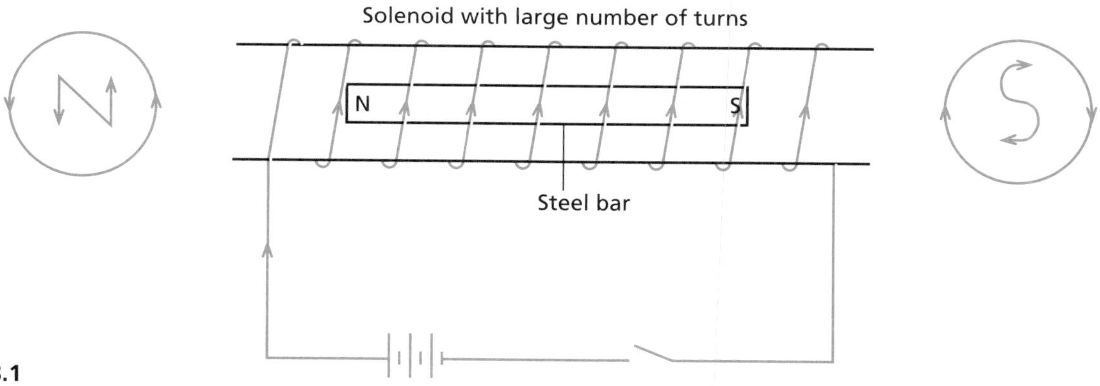

Fig. 18.1

18.2 Magnetic fields

In the space around a magnet a force is exerted on a piece of iron. This region is called a **magnetic field**. A magnetic field may be plotted by using a plotting compass to follow the lines of force. Figure 18.2 shows how this is done.

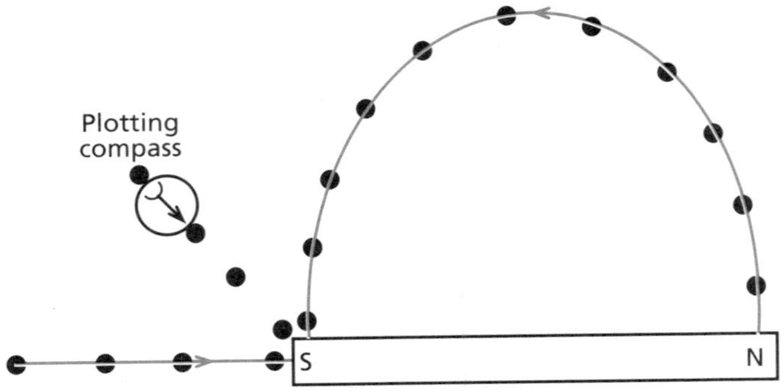

Fig. 18.2

A bar magnet is placed on a sheet of white paper. Starting near one end of the magnet, the positions of the ends of the compass needle are marked by pencil dots. The compass is then moved until the near end of the needle is exactly over the dot furthest from the magnet and a third dot made under the other end of the needle. This process is repeated many times until the compass reaches the other end of the magnet. Further lines of force may then be plotted in a similar way. Conventionally the lines of force are labelled with an arrow indicating the direction in which a north pole would move; i.e. from N to S. The strength of the magnetic field in a particular region is indicated by the closeness of the lines of force.

A plotting compass is sensitive and can be used to plot relatively weak fields. It is unsuitable for fields in which the direction of the lines of force changes rapidly in a short distance, for example in the region of two magnets placed close together. These fields are best investigated using iron filings, although these do not indicate in which of the two possible directions the magnetic field is acting.

The magnets whose field is to be studied are placed beneath a sheet of stiff white paper. A thin layer of iron filings is then sprinkled from a caster. If the paper is tapped gently the filings form a pattern indicating the lines of force. Each filing becomes magnetized by induction and, when the paper is tapped, the filings jump and are able to turn in the direction of the magnetic force.

Figure 18.3 illustrates the magnetic field close to various arrangements of magnets. Figure 18.3(a) shows the magnetic field due to the Earth alone, while (b) shows the field due to a bar magnet alone. Figures 18.3(c) and (d) illustrate the fields resulting when a bar magnet is placed in the Earth's field. Figures 18.3(e) and (f) show the magnetic field resulting when two bar magnets are placed close together end to end. The points marked *X* are regions where the total field is zero. Such regions are called **neutral points**. The shape of the magnetic field round a bar magnet – Fig. 18.3(b) – is similar to that in the region of a solenoid through which an electric current is passing.

Summary

Examiner's tip

Make sure you do not confuse magnetic poles and charges.

1. Some materials such as iron, steel, cobalt and nickel have the property to attract iron and are said to be magnetic.
2. A magnet has two poles, N and S. Unlike poles attract, whereas like poles repel.
3. In the space around a magnet a force is exerted on a piece of iron. This region is called a **magnetic field**.
4. A magnetic field is represented by lines with arrows on them. The arrows show the direction in which a N pole would move; i.e. N to S. Lines drawn close together represent a strong field.

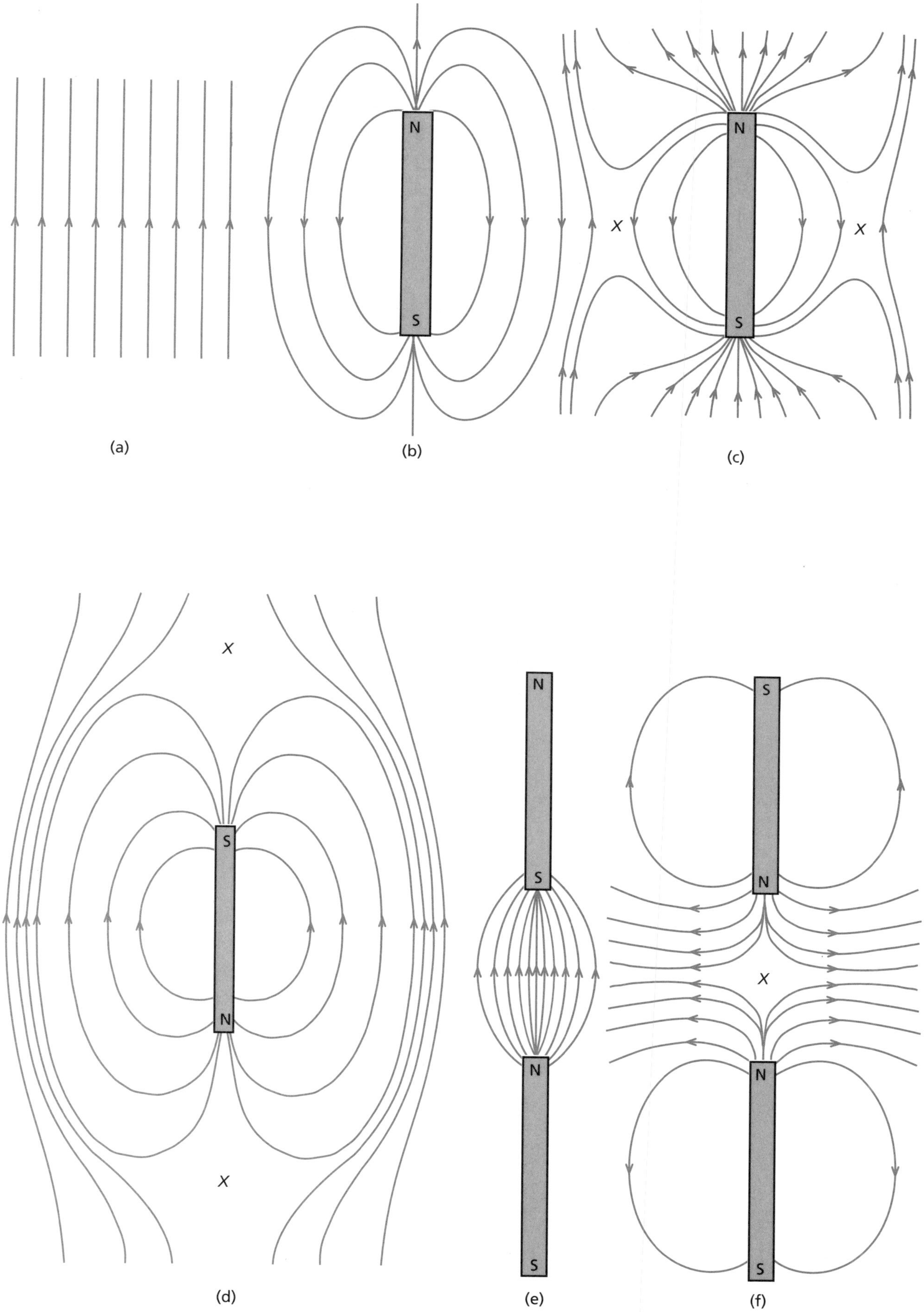

Fig. 18.3

Quick test 18

1 Explain how it is that a N pole points towards the north magnetic pole of the Earth.

2 Explain what is meant by a **magnetic field**.

3 Describe how you would plot the magnetic field round a bar magnet. Draw its shape.

Chapter 19
Electrostatics

If a rubber balloon is rubbed with a duster it will attract dust particles. Perspex, cellulose acetate and the vinyl compounds which were used for LPs (gramophone records) show the same attraction. This is because the materials have become charged with static electricity. Charging by friction is sometimes associated with a crackling sound. This is often heard when dry hair is combed or a terylene or nylon shirt is removed from the body. The crackling is caused by small electric sparks which may be seen if the room is in darkness.

If a rod is charged by rubbing and then touched on a small pith ball, the ball becomes charged. If two pith balls are suspended close to each other on nylon threads and charged from the same rod, they repel. However, if the balls are charged from two rods made of different materials they may attract each other. This behaviour indicates the presence of two types of static charge, referred to as **positive** and **negative** charge. It is found that **like charges repel and unlike charges attract**.

In experiments on static electricity the standard method for obtaining positive charge is to rub glass or cellulose acetate with silk. Negative charge is obtained on an ebonite rod by rubbing it with a duster.

Glass, cellulose acetate, ebonite and polythene are examples of materials which are electrical insulators. That is, the charges produced on their surfaces do not move along or through the material, but remain at the spot where they are produced. If a piece of one of these materials is placed in an electric circuit, no current flows as the charge cannot pass through the piece of material.

Metals are examples of electrical conductors. Conductors can be charged by rubbing, for example by flicking a duster across the cap of a gold-leaf electroscope. However, if a metal rod is held in the hand and rubbed, the charge formed flows through the metal and is lost to earth via the hand. If a piece of metal forms part of an electric circuit, the charge will pass through it and a current flows round the circuit. Some other materials conduct an electric charge but much less readily than metals. Only a very small current will pass round electric circuits containing such materials.

19.1 Uses and hazards of static electricity

Many power stations still burn coal to produce electrical energy. When coal is burnt a lot of soot is produced and it is important to remove this before it gets into the atmosphere. This can be done using an electrostatic precipitator (Fig. 19.1). Inside the precipitator there are some wires which carry a large negative charge. As the soot passes close to these wires, the soot particles become negatively charged and are then repelled away from the wires and attracted to some positively charged plates nearby. The soot particles stick to the plates and are removed later. In some power stations a precipitator removes as much as 40 tonnes of soot per hour.

Photocopying machines use the same principle. A photocopier contains a plate, whose surface is positively charged when in the dark but uncharged when in light. An image of the document to be copied is projected on to the plate. The dark parts of the plate become charged. Now the plate is covered with a dark powder (toner) the particles of which have been negatively charged. Thus the toner sticks to the dark parts of the plate leaving a dark image. Next, a piece of paper, which has been positively charged, is pressed on to the plate and the toner is attracted to it. Lastly, the paper is heated so that the toner melts and sticks to it, thus forming a permanent copy of the document.

On board a tanker great care has to be taken to avoid making sparks which might easily ignite any oil fumes. For example, the crew wear 'anti-static' clothing and shoes which do not produce or store static electricity. Sparks are most likely to ignite the oil when it is being unloaded. To avoid this the oil is covered with a 'blanket' of nitrogen, a gas that does not burn, so that a spark will not cause an explosion.

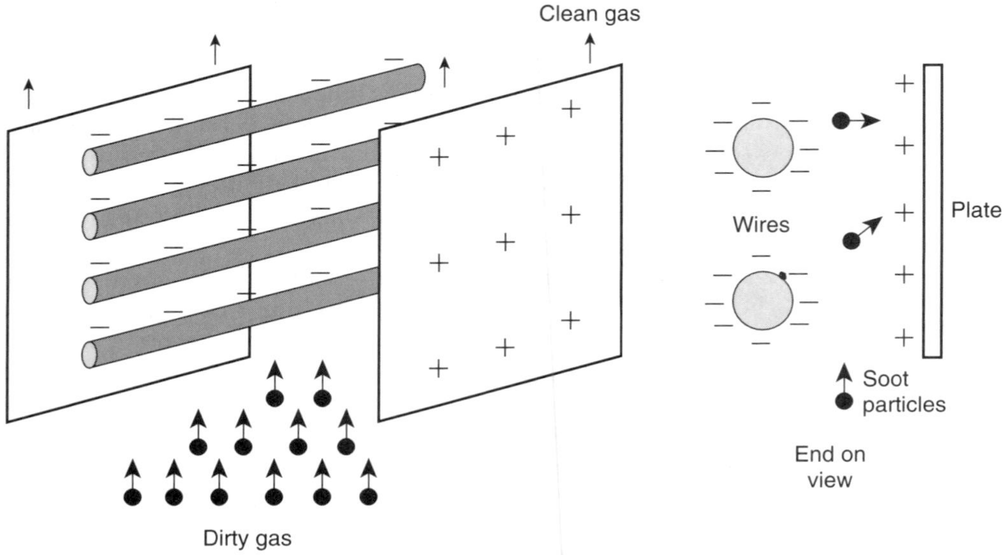

Fig. 19.1

19.2 Capacitance

If two equal quantities of charge are given to conductors of different sizes they will acquire different potentials (voltages). The capacitance of a conductor to store charge is defined as the ratio of its charge to its potential.

$$\textbf{capacitance} = \frac{\textbf{charge}}{\textbf{potential}},\ C = \frac{Q}{V}$$

Electric charge is measured in coulombs, potential in volts and capacitance in farads.

The unit of capacitance, the **farad (F)**, is defined as **the capacitance of a conductor such that a charge of 1 coulomb changes its potential by 1 volt**.

A conductor with a large capacitance has the ability to store more charge at a given potential than one with a small capacitance.

19.3 Capacitors

A capacitor is a device for storing charge. The simplest example of a capacitor is the parallel plate capacitor. It consists of two flat metal plates or thin films placed a small distance apart. The space between the plates or films is often filled by a sheet of insulating material, such as polythene. The three factors which determine the size of the capacitance of a parallel plate capacitor are the area of the plates, their separation, and the nature of the insulating material placed between them. Increasing the area of the plates increases the capacity of the system as more charge can be stored without increasing the charge density and hence the potential difference of the plates. Increasing the separation of the plates, with a fixed charge, requires work to be done against their force of attraction and hence increases the potential of the capacitor. It is then storing the same charge at a higher potential. From the definition of capacitance in the last unit it will be seen that it now has a lower value of capacitance. Placing an insulating material, such as polythene, between the plates lowers the potential between them, without altering the value of the charge. It can be seen from the same definition that this leads to an increase in the value of the capacitance.

Capacitors are important components of electrical circuits. Figure 19.2 shows two common types.

Examiner's tip

The circuit symbol for a capacitor is 

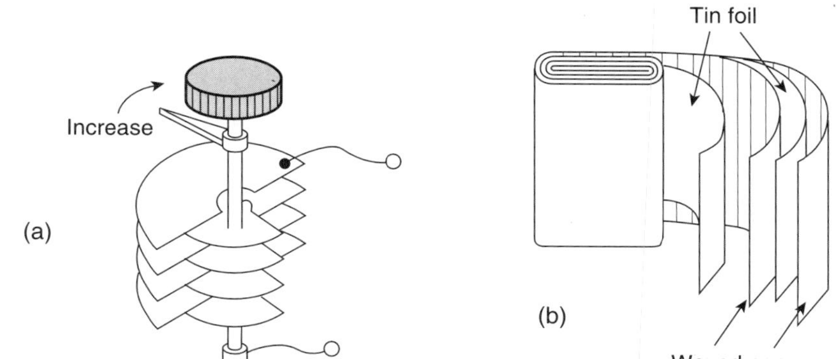

Fig. 19.2 Capacitors

A variable capacitor (Fig. 19.2 (a)) is used for tuning radios. One set of plates is fixed and the other is rotated by a knob to alter the area of the plates which overlap. Fig. 19.2 (b) shows the construction of a paper capacitor. This type is cheap but only useful at low frequencies. It contains two long strips of tin foil separated by waxed paper. The whole is rolled up and sealed in a metal container. For large values of capacitance electrolytic capacitors are normally used.

Summary

1 **Like electrical charges repel, unlike charges attract.**

2 An ebonite rod rubbed with a duster, or a rubbed polythene strip, acquires a negative charge; a glass rod rubbed with a duster or a rubbed cellulose acetate strip acquires a positive charge.

3 Metals, the human body and the Earth are examples of conductors; glass, ebonite and plastics are normally insulators.

4 Static electricity can be put to good use as, for example in a photocopier or an electrostatic precipitator in a factory chimney. However, it can be dangerous, as in the case of oil tankers.

5 The capacitance **C** of a capacitor in farads = $\boldsymbol{Q/V}$, where Q is the charge in coulombs and V is the potential difference in volts.

6 The capacitance of a capacitor increases: (i) the greater the common area of the plates; (ii) the smaller the distance between the plates; (iii) the higher the constant of the medium (e.g. polythene) between the plates.

Quick test 19

1. Name two materials which are electrical insulators. In what ways do their properties differ from those of electrical conductors?
2. Name and explain one use of electrostatics.
3. Name and explain one place where static electricity is a hazard.
4. Describe what a capacitor is designed to do.
5. List two ways in which the capacitance of a capacitor can be increased.

Chapter 20
Electric current

All atoms possess small negatively charged particles called electrons. In the case of metals some of these electrons are very weakly attached to their atoms and can easily be detached and made to flow through the metal. Metals are therefore good conductors of electricity.

In a battery one plate is at a positive potential and the other plate is at a negative potential, this potential difference being a property of the chemicals of which the battery is made. If the battery terminals are joined by a length of wire, the potential difference which exists between the ends of the wire will result in the weakly bound electrons already mentioned flowing through the wire. This constitutes an electric current.

Charge is conducted through liquids, such as the diluted sulphuric acid in a battery or copper sulphate solution, by the movement of the ions in solution. The positive ions are attracted to the negative plate (cathode) and the negative ions to the positive plate (anode).

Before the nature of an electric current was fully understood, the direction chosen to indicate current was, unfortunately, from the positive plate to the negative, that is, opposite to the flow of electrons. This is known as the *conventional* current and is the one normally used.

When the rate of flow of a charge past a point is 6×10^{18} electrons per second, the current is 1 **ampere (A)**.

As an electric current is a flow of an electric charge, the quantity of electric charge which passes any point in a circuit will depend on the strength of the current and the time for which it flows. The unit of electric charge is the **coulomb**. **A coulomb is the quantity of electric charge conveyed in one second by a steady current of one ampere.**

Thus

$$\textbf{charge } (Q) = \textbf{current } (I) \times \textbf{time } (t)$$

$$Q = It$$

20.1 Potential difference

In order to achieve current flow in a circuit a potential difference V must exist. The unit of potential difference is the **volt (V)**. **Two points are at a potential difference of one volt if one joule of work is done per coulomb of electric charge passing between the points.**

20.2 Resistance

As the potential difference between the ends of a conductor is increased the current passing through it increases. **If the temperature of the conductor does not alter,**

the current which flows is proportional to the potential difference applied (Ohm's law). Figure 20.1(a) shows this effect.

The gradient of this graph has a constant value, obtained by dividing the potential difference at any point by the current. The value of this constant gradient is known as the **resistance *R*** of the conductor. The unit of resistance is the **ohm (Ω)**.

Examiner's tip

You should be able to rearrange this to give $I = V/R$.

$$\frac{V}{I} = \textbf{constant} \quad (R) \quad \textbf{(Ohm's law)}$$

hence $$V = IR$$

A good conductor is one with a low resistance, a poor one has a high resistance.

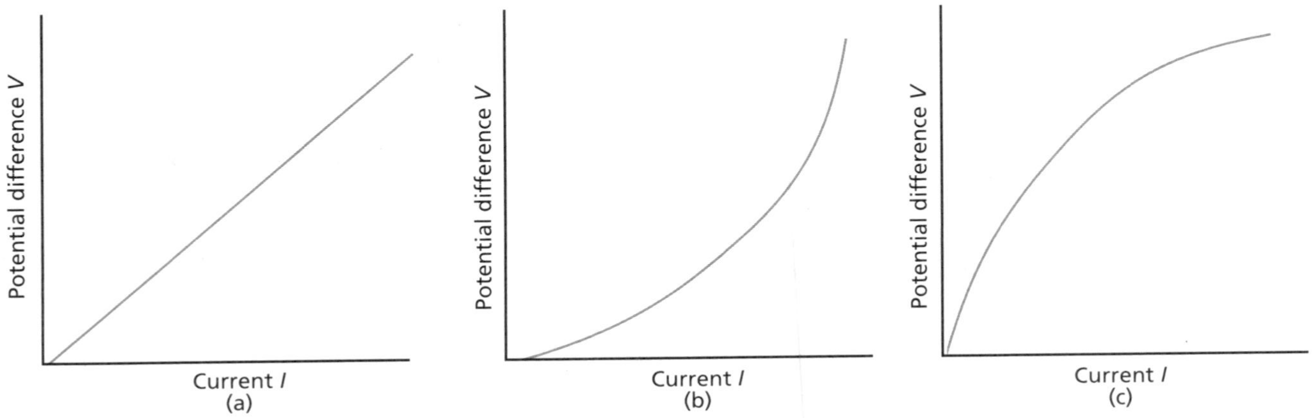

Fig. 20.1

In some conductors the current is not proportional to the potential difference between its ends. In a light bulb V/I is found to increase with temperature, that is R is not constant but increases as the temperature of the filament of the bulb increases. Figure 20.1(b) shows the relationship between potential difference and current in such cases.

Figure 20.1(c) shows results that might be obtained from a thermistor for which the resistance decreases with increasing temperature.

20.3 Ammeters and voltmeters

An **ammeter** is used to measure the electric current through a conductor and must be in series with the conductor. It has a resistance; however, this should be as small as possible so that it only reduces the current to be measured by a very small amount.

A **voltmeter** measures potential difference between two points in a circuit. It must be in parallel with the part of the circuit concerned. In order that it should take as little current as possible out of the main circuit it must have as large a resistance as possible.

Figure 20.2 shows an ammeter (A) and a voltmeter (V) correctly connected to determine the value of the resistance *R*.

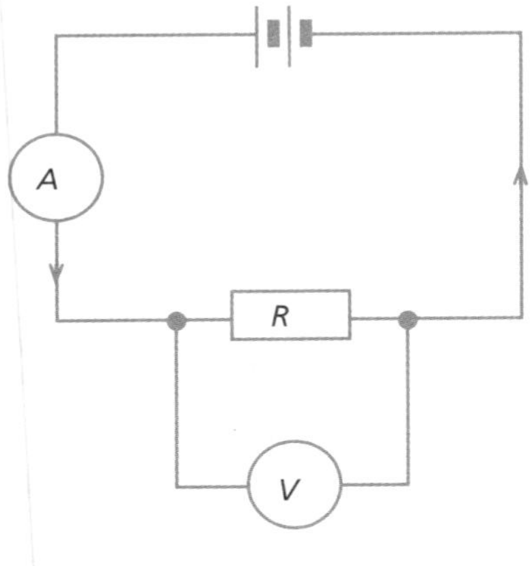

Fig. 20.2

20.4 Resistors

There are a wide variety of resistors. Filaments in lamps consist of a thin coiled length of tungsten wire, which glows white hot. The resistance of the filament is between about 500 and 1000 ohms depending on the power of the lamp. Hair dryers, irons, electric fires, electric kettles and hotplates have filaments made from nickel alloys such as nichrome. All these appliances have resistors of fixed value.

Sometimes it is essential to be able to vary the resistance in a circuit or in an electrical appliance. Variable resistors are used to vary the voltage output of power supplies, the brightness of lamps and televisions.
The circuit symbol for a variable resistor is shown in Fig. 20.3.

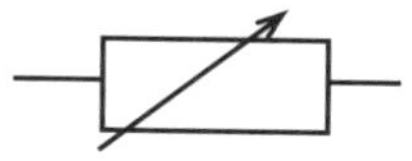

Fig. 20.3

20.5 Resistors in series

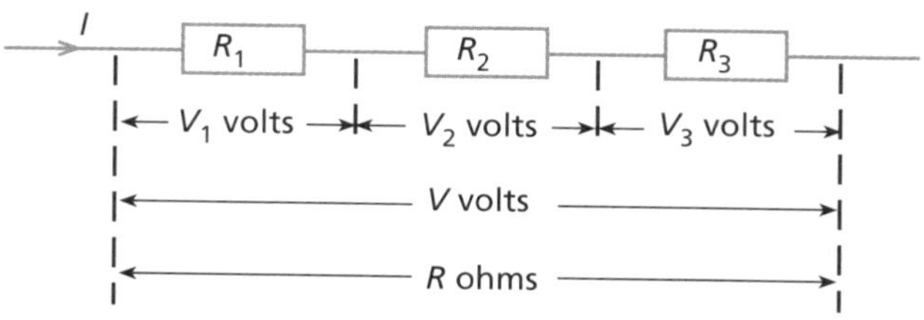

Fig. 20.4 Resistors in series

A number of **resistors** R_1, R_2, R_3, are said to be connected **in series** if they are connected as shown in Fig. 20.4. The current I must be the same throughout the circuit as it has only one route to follow.

If R is the combined resistance of R_1, R_2, and R_3 and V is the total potential difference across them, then

$$V = IR$$

but V is the sum of the potential differences across R_1 R_2, and R_3. Thus

$$V = V_1 + V_2 + V_3$$

and $$V = IR_1 + IR_2 + IR_3$$

therefore $$IR = IR_1 + IR_2 + IR_3$$

and hence $$\mathbf{R} = \mathbf{R}_1 + \mathbf{R}_2 + \mathbf{R}_3$$

The same argument may be applied to any number of resistors in series.

In Fig. 20.2 the electromotive force E of the battery must not only provide the potential difference to drive the current through the resistors, but also through itself V_b. The battery is said to have its own resistance r, known as its **internal resistance**. The total resistance of the circuit must include r, and is equal to the sum of r, R_1 R_2 and R_3 (Fig. 20.4). Now

$$V = V_1 + V_2 + V_3$$

and $$E = V_1 + V_2 + V_3 + V_b$$

hence $$E - V = V_b$$

V_b is usually referred to as the *lost volts* in the circuit.

20.6 The potential divider

If connections are made across any one of the resistors R_1, R_2 or R_3 in Fig. 20.4 , then the individual potential difference V_1, V_2 or V_3 can be obtained and used. Such a device is called a **potential divider**. If one variable resistor is used in a circuit, and the potential difference between the centre connection and one end measured, any potential difference between 0 and V can be obtained by turning the knob.

20.7 Resistors in parallel

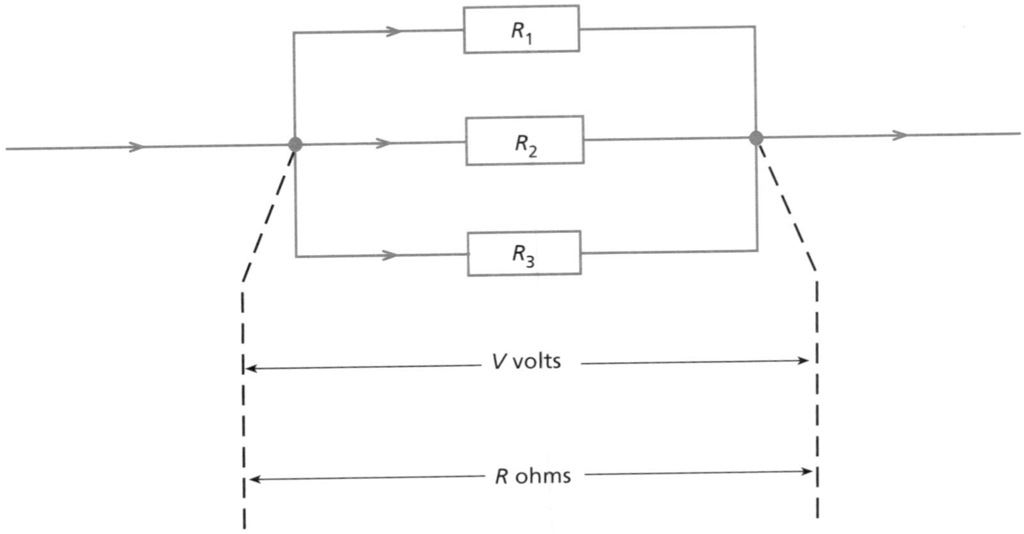

Fig. 20.5 Resistors in parallel

Resistors are said to be **in parallel** when they are placed side by side in a circuit (Fig. 20.5). The sum of the currents flowing in the parallel branches equals the total current in the main circuit. The total resistance R of the three resistors R_1, R_2 and R_3 is given by

$$\frac{1}{R} = \frac{1}{R_1} + \frac{1}{R_2} + \frac{1}{R_3}$$

The same argument may be applied to any number of resistors in parallel. As an example consider a 2-ohm resistor and a 4-ohm resistor in parallel with each other.

$$\frac{1}{R} = \frac{1}{2} + \frac{1}{4} = \frac{3}{4}$$

Thus $$R = \tfrac{4}{3} = 1\tfrac{1}{3}\,\Omega$$

The combined resistance of any number of resistors in parallel is always less than the value of any one of them. This is clear when one realizes that placing one resistor in parallel with another provides an alternative route for the current and thus eases its passage round the circuit.

Summary

1 **Charge (Q) = current (I) × time (t).**

2 In order to achieve current flow a potential difference must exist. The unit of potential difference is the volt (V). Two points are at a potential difference of one volt if one joule (J) of work is done per coulomb of electricity passing between the points.

Examiner's tip

Make sure you know all your circuit symbols.

3 The resistance of a conductor is defined by the equation

$$\textbf{Resistance } (R) = \frac{\textbf{potential difference } (V)}{\textbf{current } (I)} \quad \text{(Ohm's law)}$$

Current is measured in amperes (A) and resistance in ohms (Ω).

4 A good conductor has a low resistance and a poor conductor has a high resistance.

5 In a simple series circuit the current has the same value at all points round the circuit.

6 The total resistance R of a number of resistors R_1, R_2, R_3, in series is given by

$$R = R_1 + R_2 + R_3 \text{ etc.}$$

7 In a parallel circuit the total current entering a junction must equal the total current leaving it.

8 The total resistance R of a number of resistors R_1, R_2, R_3 all in parallel with each other is given by

$$\frac{1}{R} = \frac{1}{R_1} + \frac{1}{R_2} + \frac{1}{R_3} \text{ etc.}$$

Quick test 20

1 A charge of 10 coulombs passes round a circuit in 4 s. Calculate the average current.

2 A potential difference of 12 V drives a current of 2 A through a resistor. What is the value of the resistor?

3 A current of 1.5 A flows through a resistor of 4 Ω. What is the potential difference between the ends of the resistor?

4 State and explain whether you think that an ammeter should have a high or a low resistance.

5 Calculate the value of a 1 Ω, a 2 Ω and a 3 Ω resistor (a) all in series, (b) all in parallel.

6 Similar cells, ammeters and resistors are used in the circuit shown below. The cells and ammeters have negligible resistance. When one cell is connected in series with one ammeter and one resistor the ammeter reading is 0.1 A. What are the values of the currents through the ammeters A_1 and A_2?

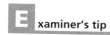

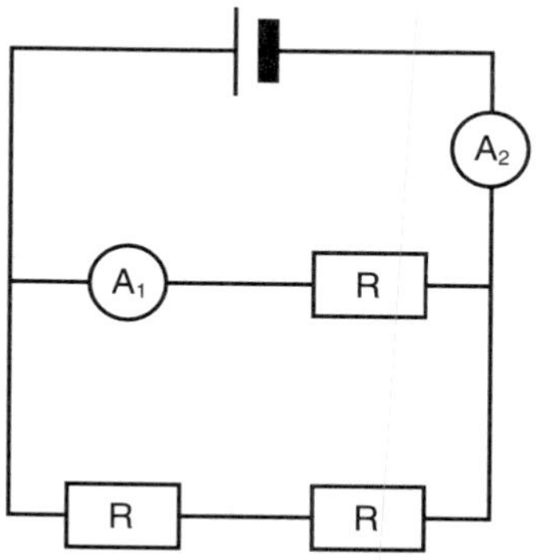

Chapter 21
Electrical energy, power and cost

21.1 Energy

When a potential difference is applied to the ends of a conductor some of the electrons inside it are set in motion by electric forces. Work is therefore done and the electrons acquire energy. The moving electrons form an electric current, and the energy of this current appears in various forms according to the type of circuit of which the conductor forms a part. For example, in an electric fire the energy of the current is mainly made available as heat, in an electric light as heat and light, and in an electric motor as mechanical energy of rotation. Energy in these various forms is produced at the expense of the source of electricity.

From the definition of the volt it can be seen that if a potential difference of one volt is applied to the ends of a conductor and one coulomb of electricity passes through it, then the work done, or energy transformed, is 1 joule. Hence if the potential difference applied is V volts and the quantity of electricity that passes is Q coulombs then the work done is QV joules.

However Charge (Q) = current (I) × time (t)

or $Q = It$

therefore work done = $QV = VIt$ joules

Two other expressions for the work done may be obtained by using Ohm's law. As

$$V = IR$$

$$\textbf{Work done} = \boldsymbol{VIt = I^2Rt = \frac{V^2t}{R}}$$

21.2 Power

The definition of power, given in Unit 4.5, is the rate of doing work or transferring energy.

$$\text{Power} = \frac{\text{work done}}{\text{time taken}}$$

If the work done is measured in joules, the unit of power is the **watt (W)**. Using the equations for energy given in the last unit, power may be obtained by dividing by time.

$$\textbf{Power} = VI = I^2R = \frac{V^2}{R} \textbf{ watts}$$

The first expression in words is:

$$\text{Power} = \text{potential difference} \times \text{current}$$

Example:

Find (a) the current taken by, and (b) the resistance of, the filament of a lamp rated at 240 V, 40 W.

$$\text{Power} = \text{potential difference} \times \text{current}$$

therefore
$$\text{current} = \frac{\text{power}}{\text{potential difference}}$$

$$= \frac{40}{240} = \frac{1}{6} = 0.16 \text{ A}$$

but
$$\text{potential difference} = \text{current} \times \text{resistance}$$

thus
$$\text{resistance} = \frac{\text{potential difference}}{\text{current}}$$

$$= \frac{240}{1/6} = 1440\ \Omega$$

In the case of an ordinary lamp only a small proportion (about 20%) of the electrical energy transformed becomes light; the remainder (about 80%) becomes heat. The lamp is thus about 20% efficient. Because it works in a different way a fluorescent tube is about 80% efficient. In other words the same intensity of light can be obtained for about one quarter of the cost.

Table 21.1 shows the power ratings of some typical appliances used in the home.

Table 21.1 Power ratings of domestic appliances

Appliance	Power	
	W	kW
Stereo	40	0.04
Television	70	0.07
Lamp	100	0.1
Fridge	150	0.15
Computer	250	0.25
Iron	750	0.75
Toaster	1500	1.50
Fan heater	2000	2.00
Kettle	2500	2.50
Immersion heater	3000	3.00
Electric shower	7000	7.00
Cooker	8000	8.00

21.3 Cost

If an electricity meter is inspected it will be found to have the abbreviation 1 kWh on it. This stands for kilowatt-hour, the commercial unit of electrical energy. It is the energy supplied in one hour by a rate of working of 1000 W.

$$\begin{aligned}1 \text{ kilowatt-hour} &= 1000 \text{ watt-hours}\\ &= 1000 \text{ joules/second for 1 hour}\\ &= 1000 \times 60 \times 60 \text{ joules}\\ &= 3\ 600\ 000 \text{ joules or } 3.6 \text{ MJ}\end{aligned}$$

Example:

Find the cost of running a 2 kW fire for 3 hours if the cost of electrical energy is 8.0 pence per kilowatt-hour (unit).

$$\begin{aligned}\text{Total energy consumed} &= \text{power} \times \text{time}\\ &= 2 \times 3 \text{ kWh}\\ &= 6 \text{ kWh}\\ \text{Cost} &= 6 \times 8.0 = 48 \text{ pence}\end{aligned}$$

Figure 21.1 shows a labelled copy of a typical electricity bill.

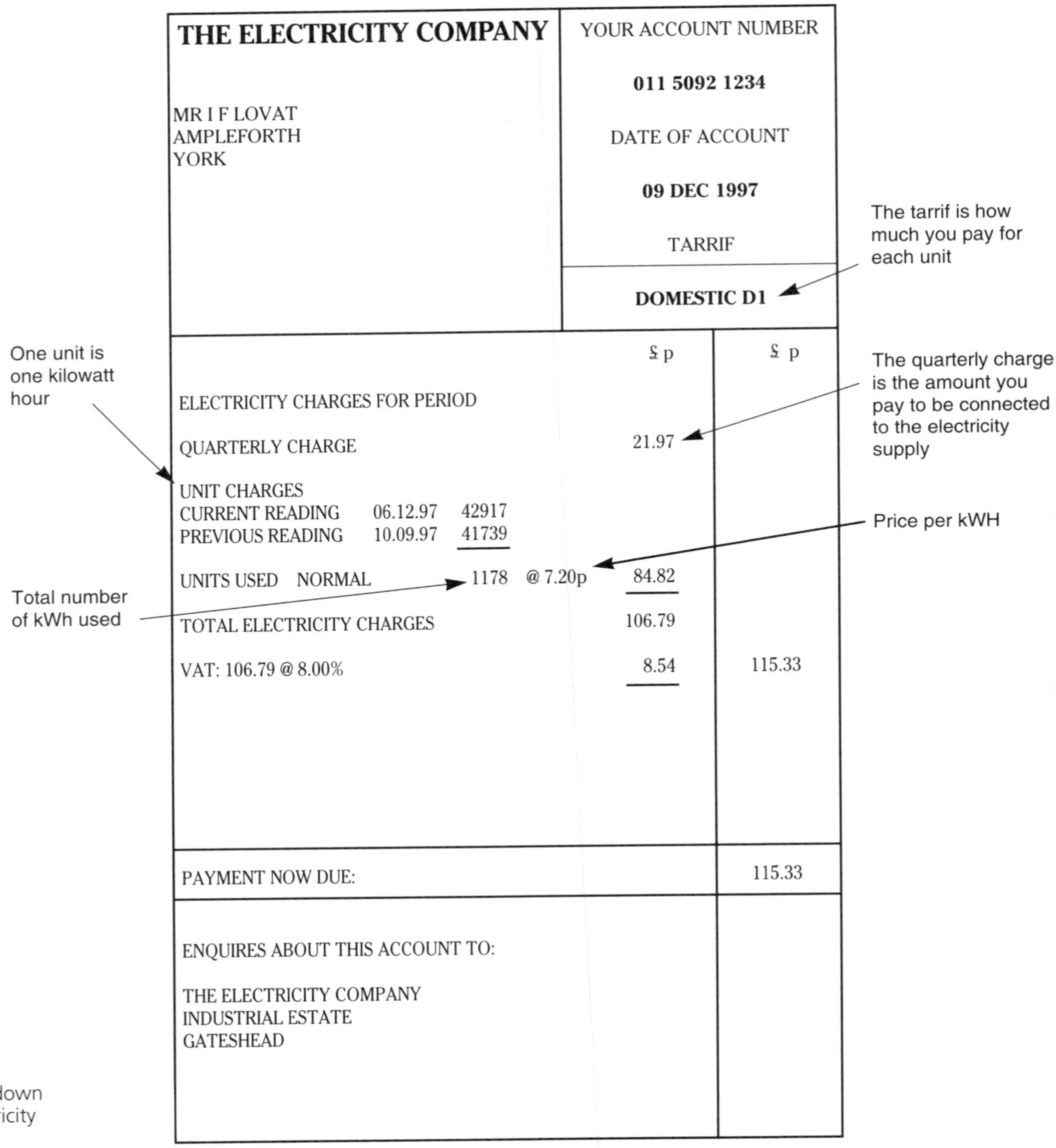

THE ELECTRICITY COMPANY

YOUR ACCOUNT NUMBER
011 5092 1234

MR I F LOVAT
AMPLEFORTH
YORK

DATE OF ACCOUNT
09 DEC 1997

TARRIF
DOMESTIC D1

		£ p	£ p
ELECTRICITY CHARGES FOR PERIOD			
QUARTERLY CHARGE		21.97	
UNIT CHARGES			
CURRENT READING 06.12.97 42917			
PREVIOUS READING 10.09.97 41739			
UNITS USED NORMAL	1178 @ 7.20p	84.82	
TOTAL ELECTRICITY CHARGES		106.79	
VAT: 106.79 @ 8.00%		8.54	115.33
PAYMENT NOW DUE:			115.33

ENQUIRES ABOUT THIS ACCOUNT TO:

THE ELECTRICITY COMPANY
INDUSTRIAL ESTATE
GATESHEAD

Fig. 21.1 Breakdown of a typical electricity bill

Summary

1 The work done or energy transformed by the flow of an electric current is given by

$$\textbf{work done} = VIt = I^2Rt = \frac{V^2t}{R}$$

2 Power is the rate of doing work or transforming energy.

$$\textbf{power} = \frac{\textbf{work done}}{\textbf{time taken}} = VI = I^2R = \frac{V^2}{R}$$

3 Electrical energy is charged by the kilowatt-hour (kWh) – 1 unit.

1 kWh = 3.6 MJ

Quick test 21

1 Calculate the energy transformed when a current of 0.4 A flows through a 240 V electric lamp for 6 hours.

2 4500 joules of energy are transformed in 6 s by a 240 V electric iron. What is the current flowing in the iron?

3 An electric lamp converts 200 joules in 5 s. What is the power of the lamp?

4 Arrange the following items in order of **increasing** power: iron, 2 kW fire, electric lamp.

5 A 24 W, 12 V headlamp is lit by connecting it to a 12 V battery of negligible resistance. What is the current through the headlamp?

6 An electric fire is rated 250 V, 1000 W. If electricity costs 7 p per unit, what is the cost of running the fire for 5 hours?

Chapter 22
Electricity in the home

22.1 Wiring a plug

Figure 22.1 shows a correctly wired plug. The following points are important.

- The wires must be connected to the correct terminals; earth is green/yellow, live is brown and neutral is blue.
- The insulation on each wire must not be stripped back too far.
- The outside thick insulation must be firmly held under the cord grip.
- The screws must be done up tightly so that the metal ends of the wires do not spread out from under them.
- The right value fuse must be used.

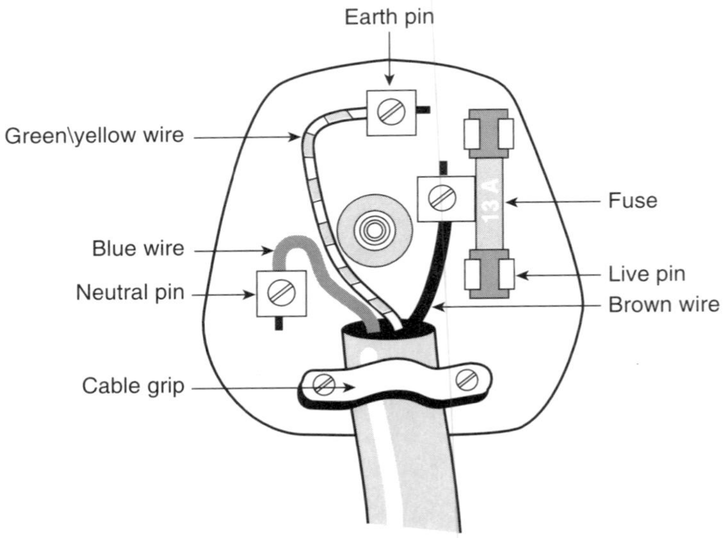

Fig. 22.1

22.2 Circuit breakers

These are used in consumer units instead of fuses. There are two types. The first contains an electromagnet which, when the current exceeds the rated value of the circuit breaker, becomes sufficiently strong to separate a pair of contacts and breaks the circuit. The second type, the Residual Current Circuit Breaker (RCCB), compares the currents in the live and neutral wires and, if they differ by even a small amount (indicating a leakage to earth), it throws open a switch which can be reset when the fault has been corrected.

22.3 Fuses

For safety reasons all domestic electrical appliances are fused. That is, in at least one place on each circuit, a fuse is fitted, which will 'blow' if a fault develops in the circuit and too great a current passes through it. This arrangement protects the wiring against the possibility of overheating and setting fire to the house.

The main house fuses for the different circuits generally consist of short lengths of tinned copper wire fitted into porcelain carriers. These fuses are usually situated under the stairs or in a cupboard which also contains the electricity meter and Electricity Board fuse.

In addition, items which are separately plugged into power sockets – for example, fires – contain a fuse in the plug. This type of fuse consists of a small glass cartridge with a thin wire through its centre. Such a fuse is rated at 2, 5, 10 or 13 A to suit the appliance to which it is connected. For example, the value of the fuse which should be used in the plug of a 240 V, 2 kW fire is calculated as follows.

$$\text{Power} = \text{voltage} \times \text{current}$$

thus

$$2000 = 240 \times \text{current}$$

and the

$$\text{current} = \frac{2000}{240}\text{ A} = 8.33\text{ A}$$

A 10 A fuse would thus be suitable.

If a fault develops in the appliance, the fuse in its plug will normally 'blow' rather than the larger one in the main fuse box. This avoids other appliances being put out of action at the same time.

The thickness of wire used in any fuse is such that it will overheat and melt if the current passing through it exceeds its specified rating by much. Once the wire has melted the circuit is broken.

When a fuse has 'blown' it is essential that the cause of the fuse blowing is found before the fuse is repaired or replaced and the appliance used again. Sometimes a fuse 'blows' because the fuse wire is very old and has become weakened by oxidation, or it can blow due to a fault in the circuit, such as a short circuit in the flex where the insulation has worn and frayed. Whatever the fault it must be found and put right before a new fuse is fitted.

Two other types of fuse are worth mentioning. An **anti-surge** fuse is designed not to melt if there is a surge of current for a very short time but it is designed to melt if a large current flows for a longer time. A current surge often happens when a circuit is first switched on. A **quick blow** fuse does just what its name implies; it melts very quickly if a large current flows.

22.4 Earthing

Besides the live (brown) and neutral (blue) wires, all power circuits are provided with a third wire (green and yellow stripes) which has been earthed by a good electrical joint to the cold water supply. When an appliance is connected to the circuit the earth wire provides a low resistance route between the casing of the appliance and the earth. This is a safeguard to prevent anyone receiving a shock by touching the casing should this become 'live'. Such a danger would arise if the insulation on the live flex had become worn and allowed the live wire to come into contact with the casing of the appliance. If this happened in a properly earthed appliance, a large current would instantaneously flow to earth and the fuse would blow, thereby cutting off the supply.

Loose connections in plugs are another potential source of danger to the person. Proper earthing again removes the danger.

Parts of many modern appliances, such as the bases of electric lamps, are made from plastic. In such cases there is no need for an earth wire since plastic does not conduct electricity. This method of protection is called double insulation and is denoted by the sign ▣.

22.5 House electrical installation

The cable bringing the mains electricity supply into a house contains two wires, one of which is 'live', and the other 'neutral'. The neutral wire is earthed at the local transformer substation, so it is at earth potential. At some convenient place inside the house the mains cable enters a sealed box, where the live wire is connected to the Electricity Board's fuse. On the far side of this box the power cable enters the meter and from there it goes to the main fuse box. The fuse box contains a separate fuse for each of the lighting circuits, ring circuit(s) and cooker circuit (Fig. 22.2).

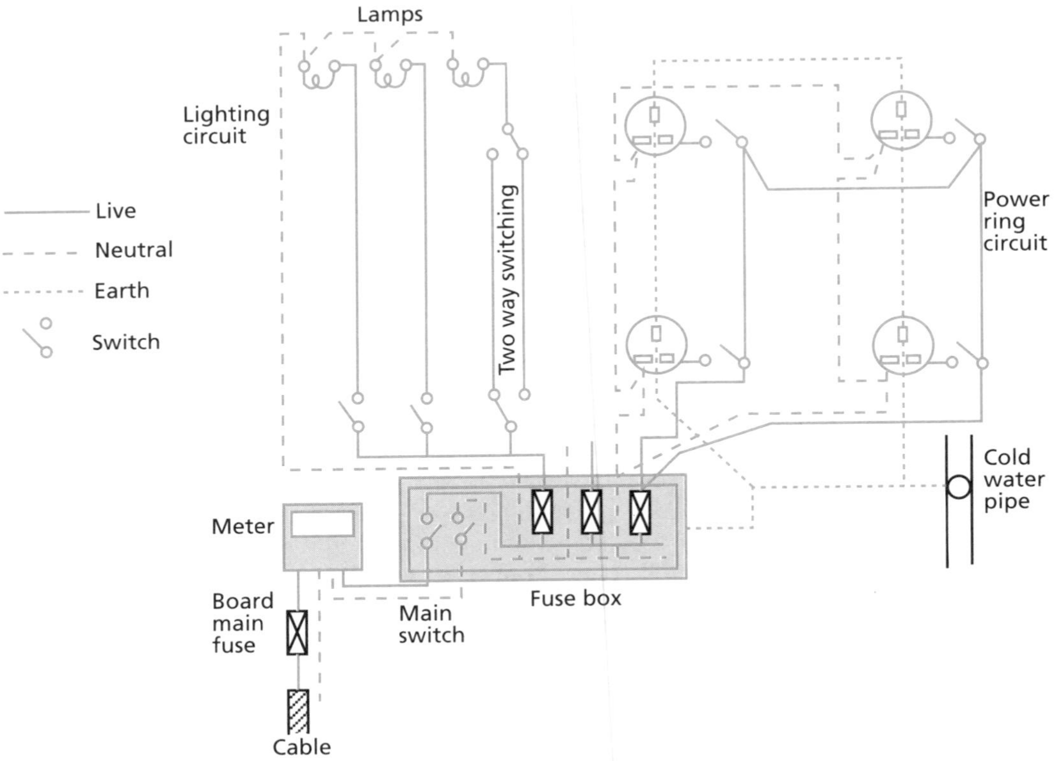

Fig. 22.2 House electrical installations

In modern installations the power sockets are tapped off a ring circuit. This cable passes through the various rooms in the house and has both its ends connected to the mains supply. Thus there are two paths by which the current may get to a particular socket, which effectively doubles the capacity of the cable.

It can be seen from Fig. 22.2 that all light and power switches and fuses are placed in the live side of the supply. If they were in the neutral side all light and power sockets would remain live when the switches were in the off position.

Summary

1 Correct wiring of plugs is essential. Five important points are listed in the first unit of this chapter. Do you know them? Do you follow them?

2 The fuse is the weakest point in a circuit. The fuse wire melts and breaks the circuit if more current flows than the circuit is designed to take. The fuse protects the appliance and the circuit from damage.

3 The earth wire provides a low resistance route between the casing of an appliance and earth. It prevents anyone receiving a shock by touching the casing should the casing become 'live'.

Quick test 22

1 Describe how a Residual Current Circuit Breaker works.

2 Fuses are available which melt when the current through them exceeds 2,5,10,15 or 30 A. Which one of these would be the most suitable for a circuit in which an electric fire rated at 2.5 kW is to be connected, if the supply voltage is 240 V?

3 What is the purpose of a fuse? How does it work?

4 An electric cooker is not plugged into a socket but has its own separate power cable. Why is this?

5 Why is the outer casing of an electric iron generally connected to earth?

Chapter 23
Electromagnetism

Whenever an electric current flows in a conductor a magnetic effect is present in the region of the conductor. This can most easily be demonstrated by passing a current down a vertical conductor, such as a retort stand (Fig. 23.1).

At some convenient height the conductor passes through a hole in a horizontal platform. A number of small compasses are placed on the platform.
When the current is switched on the compass needles swing from pointing to magnetic north and re-align themselves in a circular path around the wire.
The influence of the current in the region of the wire is called a **magnetic field**.

This result can be remembered using the following rule. Imagine the wire to be grasped in the right hand with the thumb pointing along the wire in the direction of the current. The direction of the fingers will give the direction of the lines of force. This rule is purely an aid to memory; it does not explain how the lines occur.

A knowledge of the magnetic field around a straight conductor can be used to predict the pattern round other simple geometrical arrangements of current-carrying wires – for example, a flat coil and a solenoid.

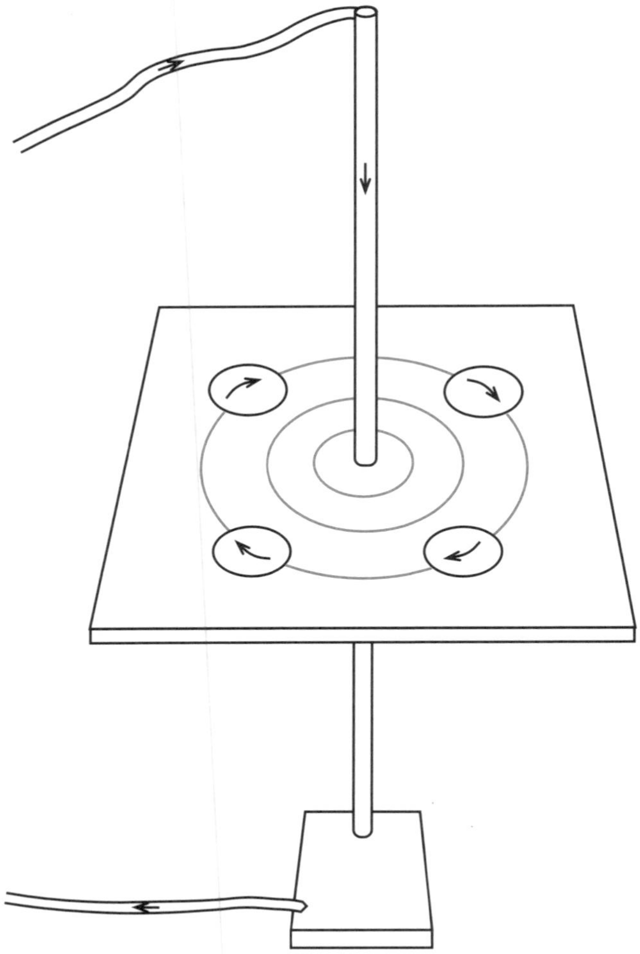

Fig. 23.1

The pattern of lines of force when a current is passed through a flat circular coil is shown in Fig. 23.2.

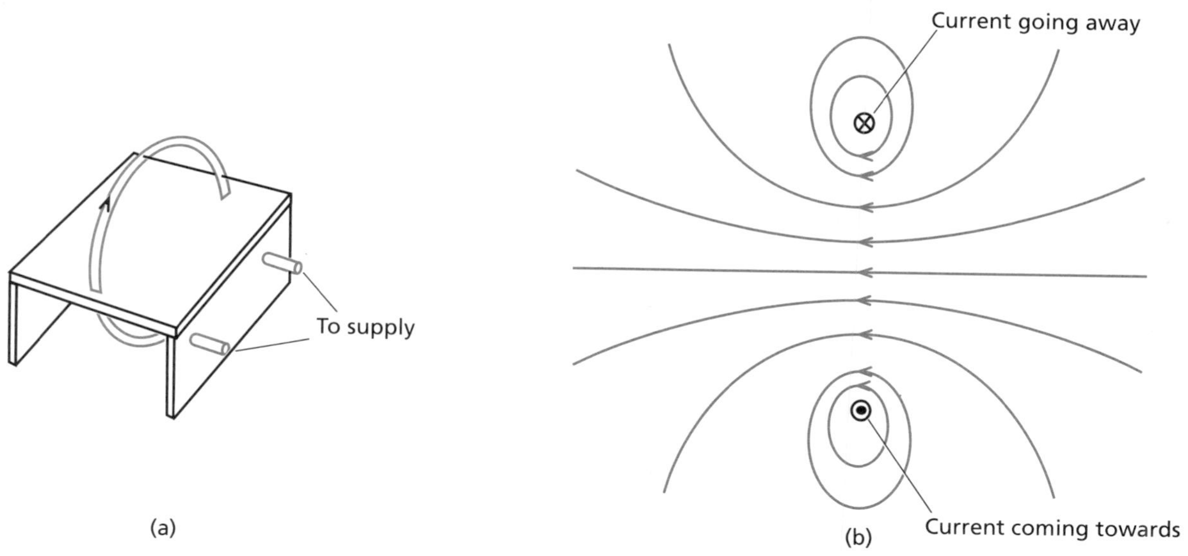

Fig. 23.2

Figure 23.3 illustrates the magnetic field due to a current in a solenoid.

If one considers the circular magnetic field round each short length of wire in the flat circular coil, it can be seen that the field adds up through the centre of the coil. This leads to a strong field through the coil but a weak one outside it (Fig. 23.2(b)). A solenoid may be considered as a series of flat circular coils, each a little spaced from one another on a common axis. Each turn of insulated wire gives a magnetic field similar to that of a flat circular coil. The fields between neighbouring turns oppose one another and cancel, but the fields along the common axis reinforce, producing the pattern shown in Fig. 23.3(b).

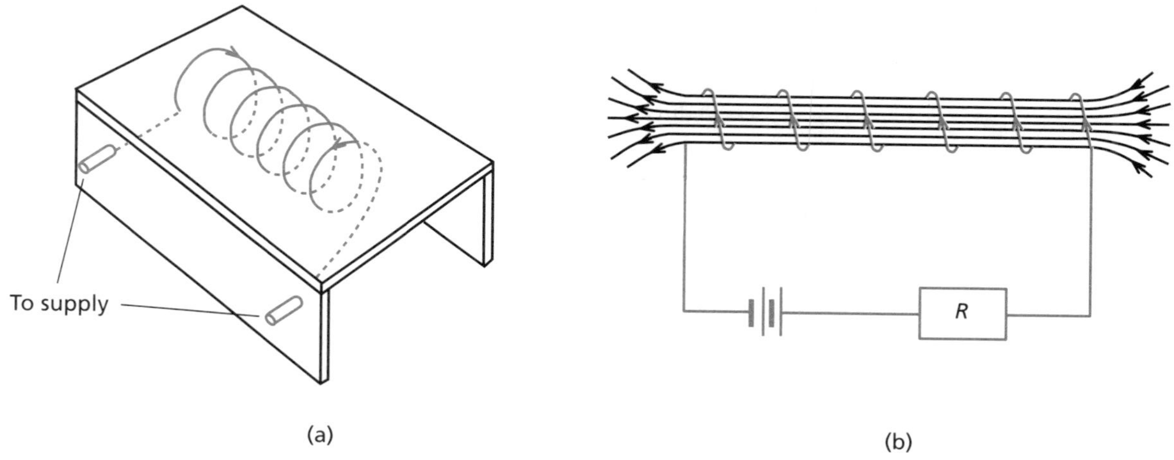

Fig. 23.3

The magnetic fields resulting from a current passing through flat coils and solenoids of square cross-sectional area are similar to those shown for circular areas.

23.1 The electromagnet

The use of a solenoid for making magnets has already been described in Unit 18.1. When a piece of steel is placed inside a solenoid and the current switched on, the steel becomes a magnet and remains one when the current is switched off. If a piece of soft-iron is used instead, the iron acts as a magnet only while the current is switched on. Figure 23.4(a) shows such an electromagnet. Sometimes the cores of electromagnets are U-shaped (Fig. 23.4(b)). This arrangement has the advantage that the attraction of both ends can be used simultaneously.

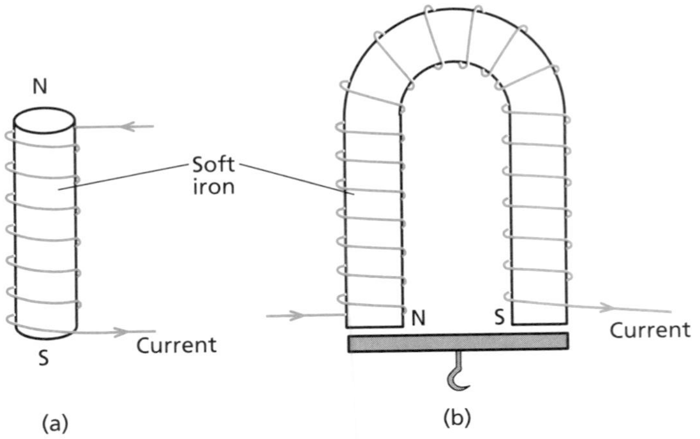

Fig. 23.4
Electromagnet

Electromagnets are very strong. A small one, made in a laboratory from a U-shaped core and a few turns of wire each carrying a current of a few amps, is capable of lifting several kilograms. Those used in industry can lift several tonnes, for example car and lorry bodies. Yet when the current is switched off, the magnetism ceases and the load is released.

23.2 The relay

Fig. 23.5 shows how a relay (e.g. used for starting a car) works. Inside it a solenoid is wound round an iron core. When the circuit is completed (ignition switched on), a small current magnetizes the solenoid and its iron core. The solenoid is attracted towards the heavy-duty electrical contacts. This completes the starter motor circuit and a current can flow to the motor from the battery. The advantage of this system is that a large current is switched on in the main (starter motor) circuit by the flow of a small current through the ignition switch and solenoid.

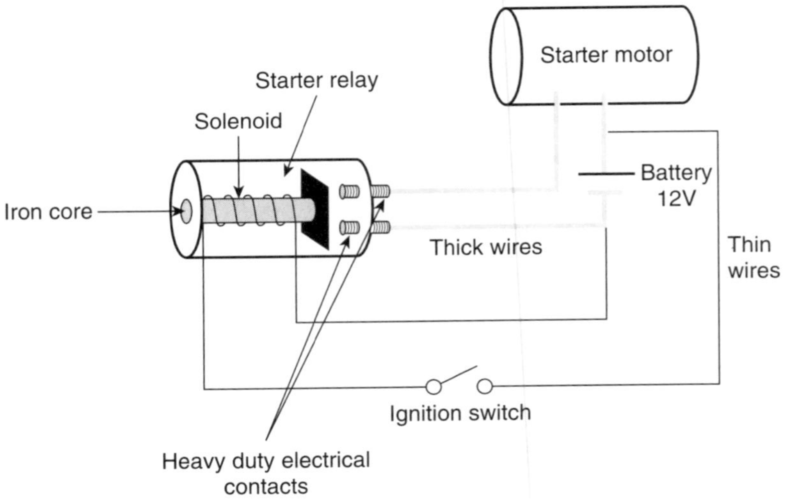

Fig. 23.5

23.3 The electric bell

The electric bell consists of two coils (solenoids) on two soft-iron cores joined by a soft-iron yoke (Fig. 23.6). One end of the windings is connected to the battery or other power supply and the other to a metal bracket which supports a spring-mounted soft-iron armature (moving part). The armature carries a light spring to which is soldered a small disc as contact. The disc presses against the end of the contact adjusting screw from which a wire goes to the push switch. When the switch is pressed a current flows through the circuit and the cores become magnetized. The resultant attraction of the armature separates the contacts and breaks the circuit.

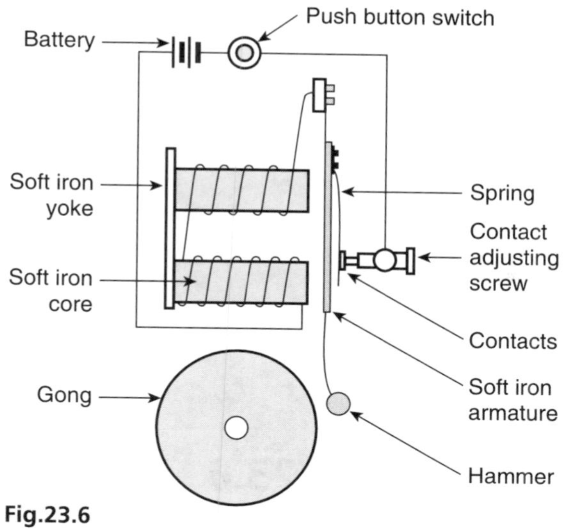

Fig.23.6

The cores become demagnetized and the armature is returned to its original position by the spring. Contact is remade and the action repeated. As a result the armature vibrates and a hammer attached to it strikes the gong.

23.4 The microphone

A common type of microphone consists of a thin sheet of plastic film, one side of which is coated with a thin film of metal which is charged (Fig. 23.7). When sound waves reach the microphone the plastic film vibrates at the same frequency. When the film is nearer to the metal plate it attracts more of the opposite charge to it and vice versa when it is further away. This makes a current which has the same frequency as the sound wave. This current is then amplified.

Therefore, a microphone transforms sound energy into electrical energy.

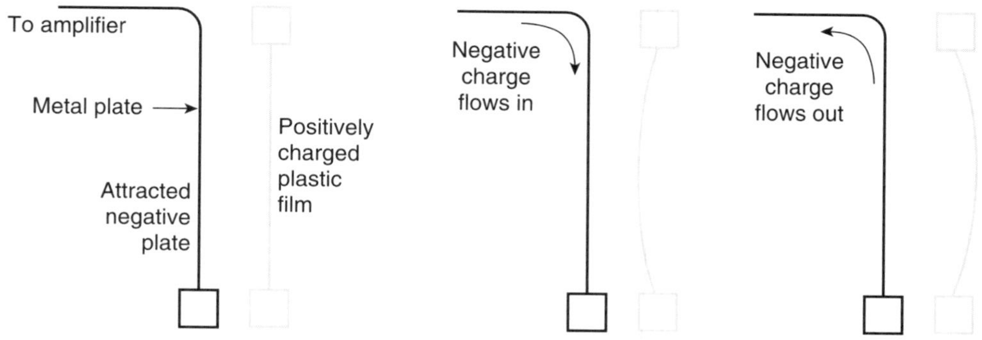

Fig.23.7

23.5 The loudspeaker

Varying currents from the amplifier at the output of a radio or cassette player pass through a short cylindrical coil. The coil's turns are at right angles to the magnetic field of a magnet with a central pole and a surrounding ring pole (Fig. 23.8). Thus a force acts on the coil which makes it move in and out. The paper cone attached to the coil moves with it and sets up sound waves in the air around the loudspeaker.

Thus a loudspeaker transforms electrical energy into sound energy.

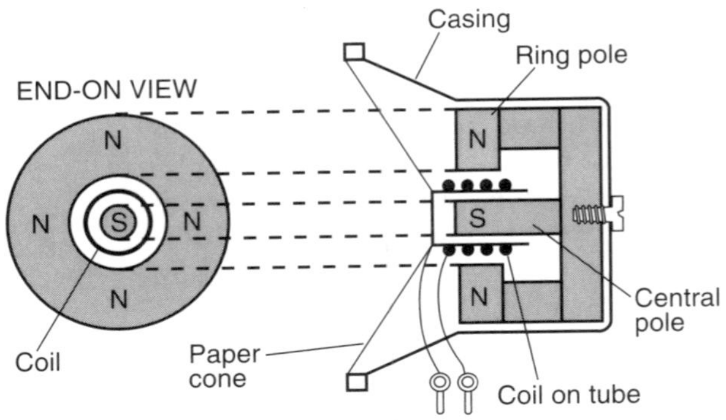

Fig. 23.8 A loudspeaker

23.6 The force on charges moving in a magnetic field

Figure 23.9 shows a current-carrying wire placed in a magnetic field. As soon as the current is switched on the length of wire *AB* moves horizontally on the other two pieces. The interaction of the magnetic field due to the current flow and that due to the magnets results in a horizontal force. The effect may be understood by reference to Fig. 23.10.

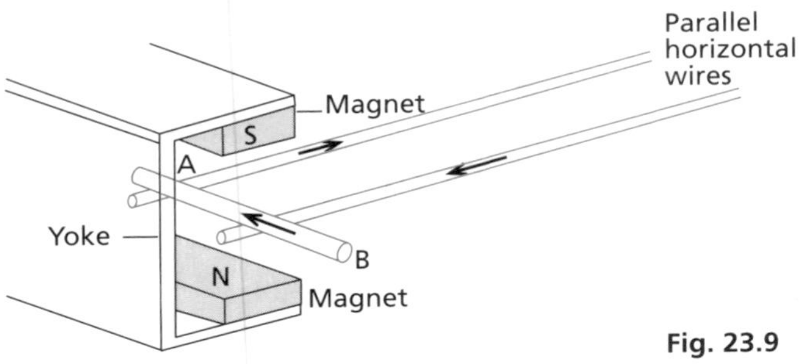

Fig. 23.9

The two fields shown separately in Figs. 23.10 (a) and (b) reinforce to the left and tend to cancel to the right of the wire when combined (Fig. 23.10(c)). A strong magnetic field results on the left with the lines in tension. The tension results in a force from left to right. If either magnetic field is reversed the force reverses.

It should be noted that the current, the magnetic field due to the magnets and the force produced are all three mutually at right angles. If the current is parallel to the field due to the magnets there is no force.

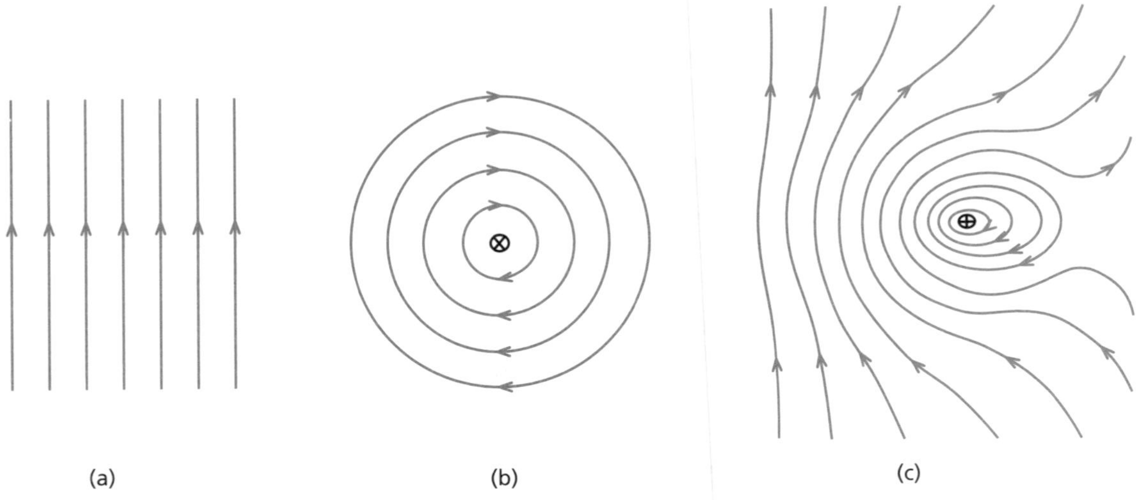

Fig. 23.10 (a) (b) (c)

If a stream of electric charges passes through a gas, as in a fine beam tube (Fig. 23.11), rather than a wire, the same force results. However, whereas in a wire the charges (electrons) are inhibited from moving by its stiffness, this is not so in a gas, where they are free to change their direction of motion as soon as the force acts. The force always remains at right angles to their direction of motion, as well as to the magnetic field, and so the charges move in the arc of a circle (see Unit 3.5).

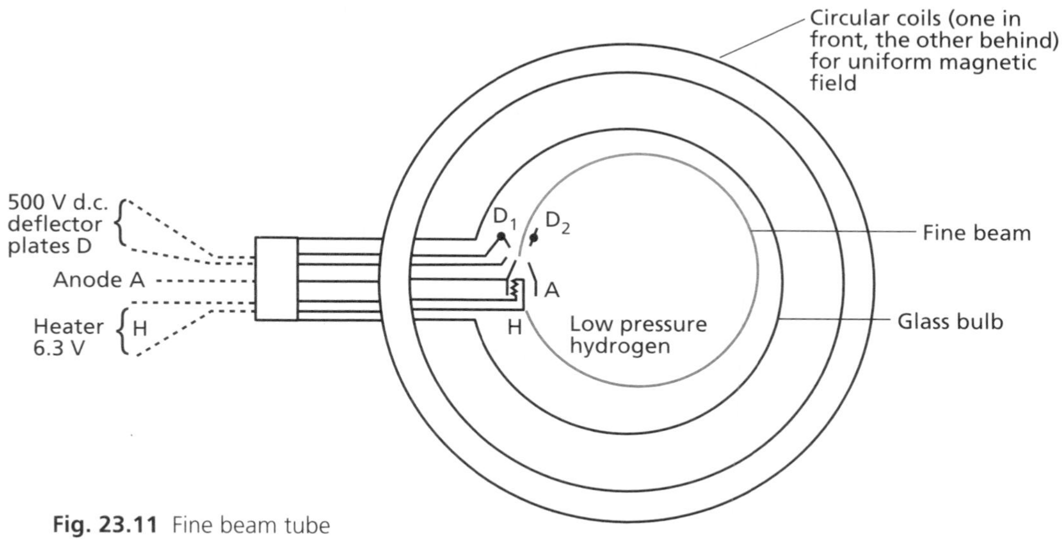

Fig. 23.11 Fine beam tube

23.7 The d.c. electric motor

Figure 23.12 shows the construction of a simple direct current (d.c.) electric motor. It consists of a rectangular coil of wire mounted on a spindle so that it is free to rotate

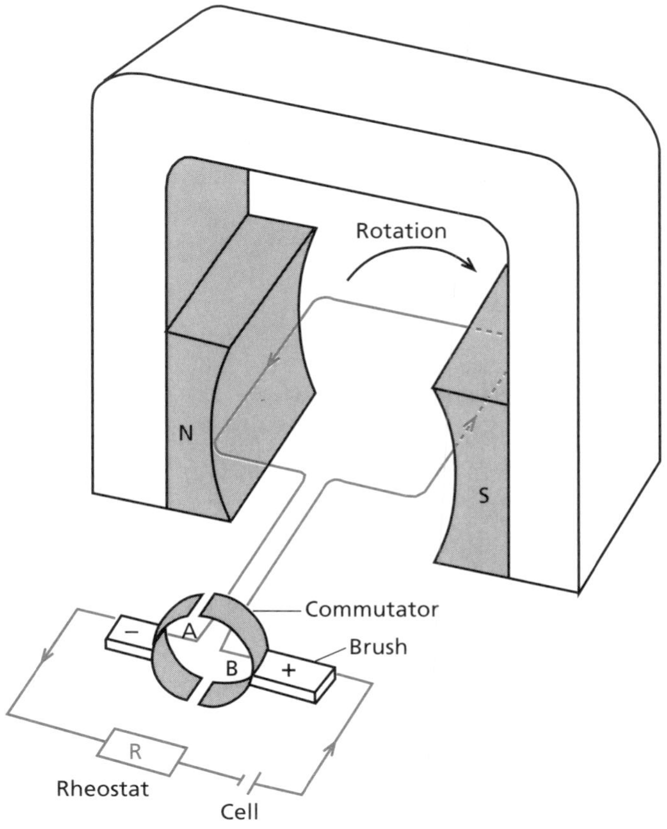

Fig. 23.12 Simple d.c. motor

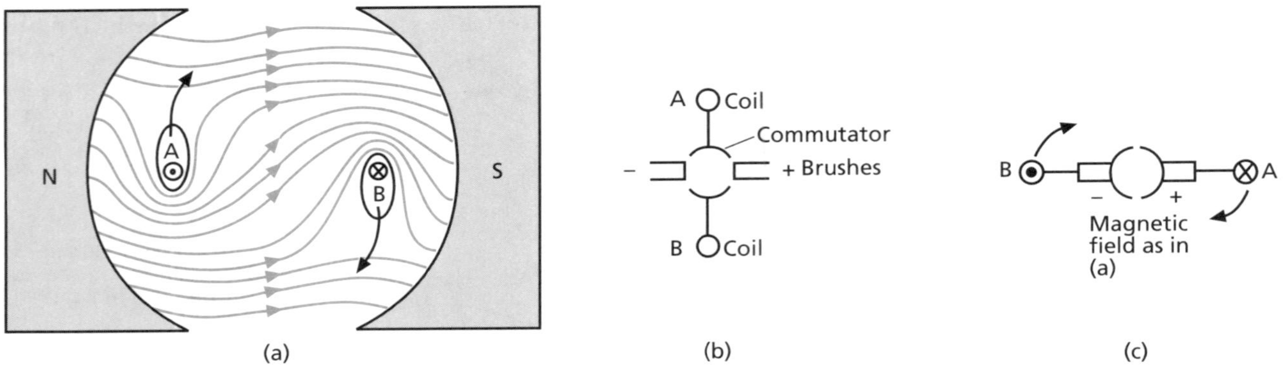

Fig. 23.13

between the pole pieces of a permanent magnet. The two ends of the coil are soldered to the two halves of a copper split ring or **commutator**, which is a device for reversing the direction of current flow in the coil every half turn. The two brushes press lightly against the commutator. When a current is passed through the coil it rotates. Figure 23.13(a) shows a cross-section through the coil together with the resultant magnetic field, which is strong above the right side and also below the left side. The coil therefore rotates clockwise.

When the coil is vertical the brushes touch the space between the two halves of the commutator. There is no torque (twist) at this position (Fig. 23.13(b)); however, the coil's momentum carries it past the vertical, and when this has occurred the commutator halves automatically change contact from one brush to the other. This reverses the current through the coil (Fig. 23.13(c)) and thus it rotates through the next half turn. The reversal of the direction of current flow by the commutator each half turn ensures the continued rotation of the coil. If the current is increased, the torque increases and the motor turns faster. Reversing the direction of current flow or swapping the magnets each result in the motor turning the other way.

The simple motor described is not very efficient or powerful, as the torque changes from a maximum when the coil is horizontal to zero when it is vertical. The motor can be improved by winding a number of coils, each of many turns, at different angles round a soft-iron armature. The greater number of turns in a coil gives a greater torque. Having a number of coils ranged at angles round the armature means that, when one is vertical another is horizontal thus resulting in an even torque. The iron armature becomes magnetized and increases the magnetic field through the coils, resulting in a greater torque. It is also usual for the magnetic field to be provided by electromagnets rather than permanent magnets.

Summary

1 Whenever an electric current flows in a conductor a magnetic field is present in the region of the conductor.
2 The magnetic field round a coil carrying direct current is similar in shape to that round a bar magnet.
3 When a steel bar is placed in a coil carrying direct current the bar becomes permanently magnetized.
4 When a bar of soft iron is placed in a coil carrying direct current the soft iron becomes a strong magnet only while the current flows.
5 A microphone transforms sound energy into electrical energy.
6 A loudspeaker transforms electrical energy into sound energy.
7 Charges moving at right angles to a magnetic field experience a force at right angles to both their direction of motion and the direction of the magnetic field.
8 The behaviour described in point 7 is the basis of an electric motor.

Quick test 23

1 The diagram below shows the strength of an electromagnet with a fixed number of turns of wire as a function of the current passing through the turns. Why can the strength of the electromagnet not be increased above the value of the line *PQ*?

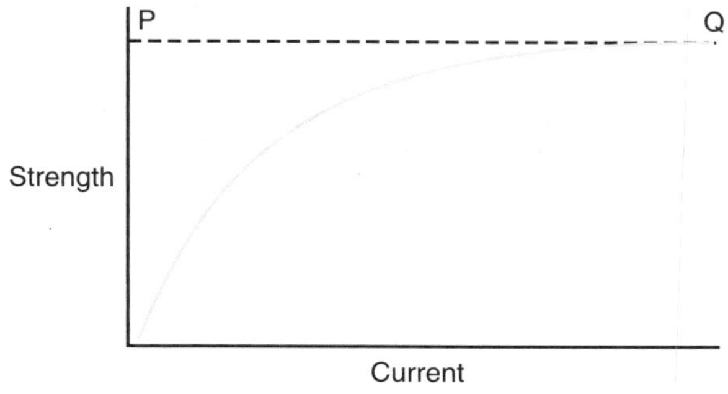

2 Briefly explain how a relay works. What is it used for?

3 Fill in the gaps in the following sentence. A microphone transforms .... energy into .... energy.

4 A loudspeaker transforms energy from one form to another. What are these two forms of energy?

5 Name the three factors which determine the size of the force on a current-carrying wire placed in a magnetic field.

6 List two ways of reversing the direction of rotation of a d.c. electric motor.

7 State three ways of increasing the rate of rotation of a simple d.c. electric motor.

Chapter 24
Electromagnetic induction

The magnetic field in a region is often referred to as **magnetic flux**.

24.1 Laws

1. **Faraday's. Whenever there is a change in the magnetic flux linked with a circuit an electromotive force is induced, the strength of which is proportional to the rate of change of the flux through the circuit.**
2. **Lenz's. The direction of the induced current is always such as to oppose the change producing it.**

The truth of these laws is best illustrated by considering a simple experiment. First a centre-zero meter is connected in series with a cell and a suitable high resistance, and the direction of movement of the pointer noted when a small current passes in a known direction. The meter is now connected to the ends of a straight wire placed at right angles to the lines of magnetic field between two opposite magnetic poles (Fig. 24.1).

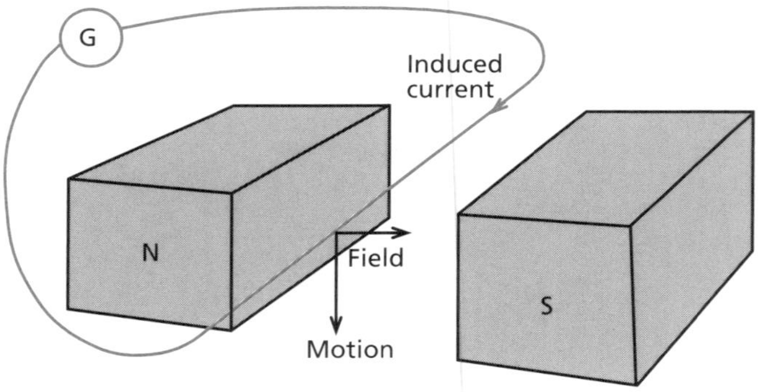

Fig. 24.1

If the wire is moved downwards the meter indicates that an induced current flows in the direction shown. If the wire is moved up the current flows in the opposite direction. The same results are obtained if the wire is held still and the magnets moved up or down, respectively. It is the relative motion between the wire and magnetic field which leads to the induced voltage and hence current. The quicker the relative motion takes place the greater the deflection (Faraday's law).

While the induced current flows there is a magnetic field around the wire. Consideration of the effect of this field and that of the magnets shows that it results in an upward force in Fig. 24.1. That is, the induced current leads to a force acting in the opposite direction to the movement of the wire and thus opposing it (Lenz's law).

24.2 Dynamos

The simple direct current electric motor described in Unit 23.7 may be used as a **simple d.c. dynamo**. The motor is connected in series with a resistance and a moving coil meter instead of a voltage source. When the coil is rotated the meter is seen to deflect in one direction, although the deflection is not a steady one. The commutator ensures that, although the current in the coil itself reverses during the second half of a rotation, the same brush always remains positive and the other negative.

The simple dynamo just described is not very efficient. A practical dynamo has a number of coils wound in slots cut in the armature. Each coil has its own pair of segments in a multi-segment commutator. This arrangement ensures that the e.m.f. obtained is fairly steady, as it is only the horizontal coils which are connected to the brushes at any given moment. The iron armature is built in layers, each one insulated from its neighbours. Although e.m.f.'s are induced in these layers of iron as they rotate in the magnetic field, very little current flows in the armature as a result, due to this insulation.

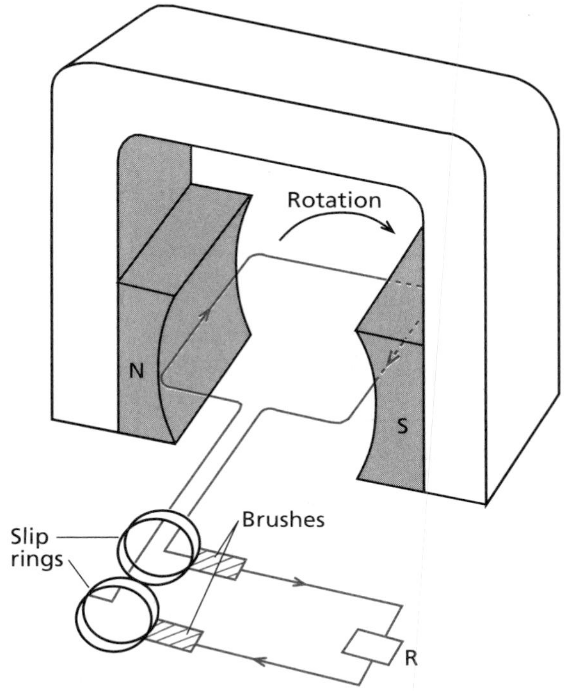

Fig. 24.2 Simple a.c. dynamo

The simple a.c. dynamo differs from the d.c. version described above only in its connections (Fig. 24.2). The ends of the coil are connected to two slip rings mounted on the coil spindle. One side of the coil is therefore always connected to the same brush. As it moves up through the magnetic field a potential difference is induced in it in one direction. As, on the opposite side, it moves down through the magnetic field a potential difference is induced in the opposite direction. This is an alternating voltage which will give an alternating current or a.c. as opposed to a direct current or d.c. which always flows in one direction. The same effect is obtained if magnets are rotated inside or outside a stationary coil.

Alternating current changes its direction many times a second depending on the speed of the dynamo or generator. In the United Kingdom, a.c. has a frequency of 50 Hz.

The outputs of both a simple a.c. and a simple d.c. dynamo are shown in Figs. 24.3 (a) and (b), respectively. In each case the coil starts from the vertical.

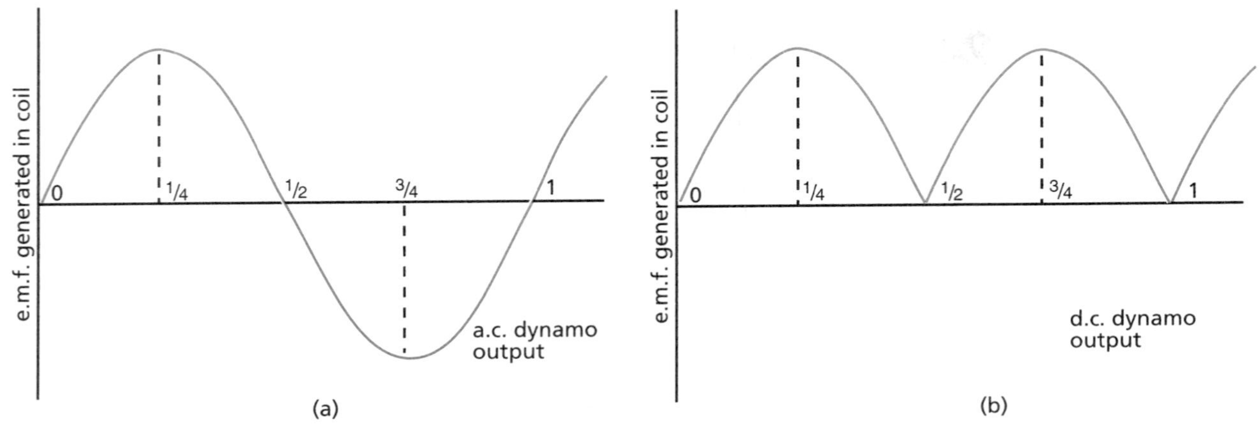

Fig. 24.3

24.3 The transformer

A transformer is illustrated diagrammatically in Fig. 24.4. The two coils shown are wound on a laminated soft-iron core. When an alternating current passes through the primary an alternating magnetic field is set up in the core. Since the magnetic flux through the secondary coil is changing, this induces an e.m.f. in it which is also alternating. The size of this induced e.m.f. will depend on the e.m.f. applied to the primary and on the relative numbers of turns in the two coils:

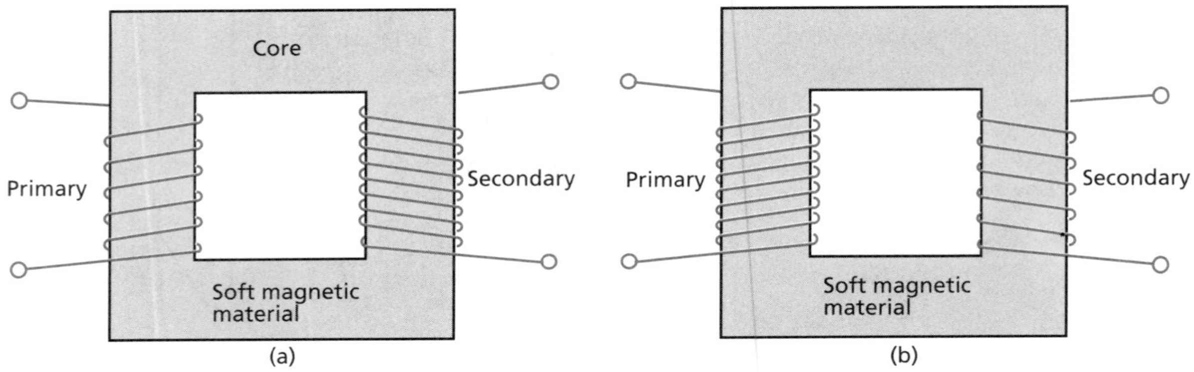

Fig. 24.4 Transformers: (a) step-up; (b) step-down

$$\frac{\textbf{secondary e.m.f.}}{\textbf{primary e.m.f.}} = \frac{\textbf{number of turns in secondary}}{\textbf{number of turns in primary}}$$

If the ratio of the number of turns is greater than one, the secondary e.m.f. will be greater than the primary and we have a *step-up* transformer. A ratio less than unity gives a *step-down* transformer.

A transformer is designed to minimize energy losses. The windings are made of low-resistance copper coils to reduce the heating losses. The core is laminated, that is it is constructed of layers of magnetic material fixed together and insulated from each other by varnish or oxide coatings. This ensures that, although e.m.f.s are induced in the core, as well as the secondary coil by the changing magnetic field, currents cannot flow between the laminated layers. Thus the total current in the transformer core is kept to as small a value as possible, as are the energy losses due to its heating effect.

Efficient core design also means that all the magnetic flux produced by the primary passes through the secondary. In practice this is best achieved by winding the primary and secondary on top of one another. The efficiency is given by:

$$\text{efficiency} = \frac{\text{power output at secondary}}{\text{power input at primary}} \times 100\%$$

In a good transformer energy losses are small and the efficiency is very close to 100%, i.e. power output at secondary = power input at primary.

24.4 Power transmission

One of the main advantages of alternating current is that it can easily be changed from one voltage to another by a transformer, with little loss of energy. For this reason, electric power is generally conveyed by alternating current, as it can be transformed to a very high voltage and transmitted over long distances, with small power losses as explained below. This has two advantages. Firstly, electricity can be generated where water power, coal and oil are easily available or at conveniently sited nuclear power stations, and conveyed to all parts of the country by high voltage overhead power lines. Secondly, power is easily made available wherever the peak demand occurs. For example, during the day power which has been generated in an area that has little industry may be used in a more industrialized area that has, at this time, a greater demand.

In Great Britain electricity is generated at 11 000 V and then stepped up to as much as 400 000 V by transformers. It is subsequently stepped down in stages at substations in the neighbourhood where the energy is to be consumed. The reason electrical energy is transmitted at such high voltages can clearly be seen from the following calculation.

Find the power wasted as heat in the cables when 10 kW is transmitted through a cable of resistance 0.5 Ω at (a) 200 V; (b) 200 000 V.

(a) The current is given by the equation:

$$\text{current} = \frac{\text{power}}{\text{voltage}} = \frac{10\ 000}{200}$$

$$= 50\ \text{A}$$

$$\text{Therefore the power lost in the cable} = I^2R$$

$$= 50^2 \times 0.5\ \text{W}$$

$$= 1250\ \text{W}$$

(b) $$\text{current} = \frac{\text{power}}{\text{voltage}} = \frac{10\ 000}{200\ 000} = 0.05\ \text{A}$$

$$\text{Therefore the power lost in the cable} = I^2R$$

$$= 0.05^2 \times 0.5\ \text{W}$$

$$= 0.00125\ \text{W}$$

At 200 V more than 10% of the energy transmitted is wasted in heating the cable. At 200 000 V this energy loss is reduced by a factor of a million and is negligible.

Summary

1 Whenever a conductor moves relative to a magnetic field an electromotive force (e.m.f.) is induced in the conductor. The strength of the e.m.f. is proportional to the strength of the magnetic field and the speed of the relative motion.

2 The effect outlined in point 1 is the basis of a dynamo.

3 A transformer changes the value of an alternating e.m.f. either up or down.

4 For a transformer

$$\frac{\textbf{secondary e.m.f.}}{\textbf{primary e.m.f.}} = \frac{\textbf{number of turns in secondary}}{\textbf{number of turns in primary}}$$

5 Power is transmitted over long distances at high voltage and low current. This reduces energy losses in the transmission cables.

Quick test 24

1 When a wire is moved through a magnetic field an e.m.f. (voltage) is induced between the ends of the wire. List two factors which determine the size of this e.m.f.

2 How true is the assertion that a dynamo is really an electric motor working in reverse? Justify what you write.

3 A step-down transformer has a turns ratio of 6:1. A 240 V alternating current supply at a frequency of 50 Hz is connected to the primary coil.
What is (a) the output voltage? (b) the output frequency?

4 Explain why a transformer works only if it is supplied with alternating voltage.

5 Why is it best to transmit electric power at high voltage?`

Chapter 25
Electron beams

25.1 Thermionic emission

Metals contain many electrons which are loosely attached to their atoms. If a wire is heated to a high temperature the extra energy given to the electrons enables them to break away from the metal structure and exist outside as an electron cloud. This is called **thermionic emission**.

Strontium and barium are good electron emitters but are not suitable to be made into a thin wire. Tungsten, however, can be made into a very thin wire and can withstand high temperatures without melting. Thus tungsten is used as the base of the wire and its surface coated with barium or strontium which emit well at these temperatures. The wire is heated electrically, usually by using a 6.3 V supply which can be obtained from either a d.c. or an a.c. source.

25.2 The diode

The electrons released from a wire by thermionic emission form a cloud around it which prevents further emission. This cloud may be removed by placing a plate near to the wire and connecting a steady voltage between them, so that the plate (anode) is more positive than the wire (cathode). It is necessary to place this whole arrangement in an evacuated tube so that the passage of the electrons is not impeded by the presence of air molecules. This arrangement is known as a **diode**.

The characteristic action of a diode may be investigated using the circuit shown in Fig. 25.1(a). The voltage applied to the diode is varied using the source *B*, and the resulting current is registered on the milliammeter. Figure 25.1(b) shows a typical set of results.

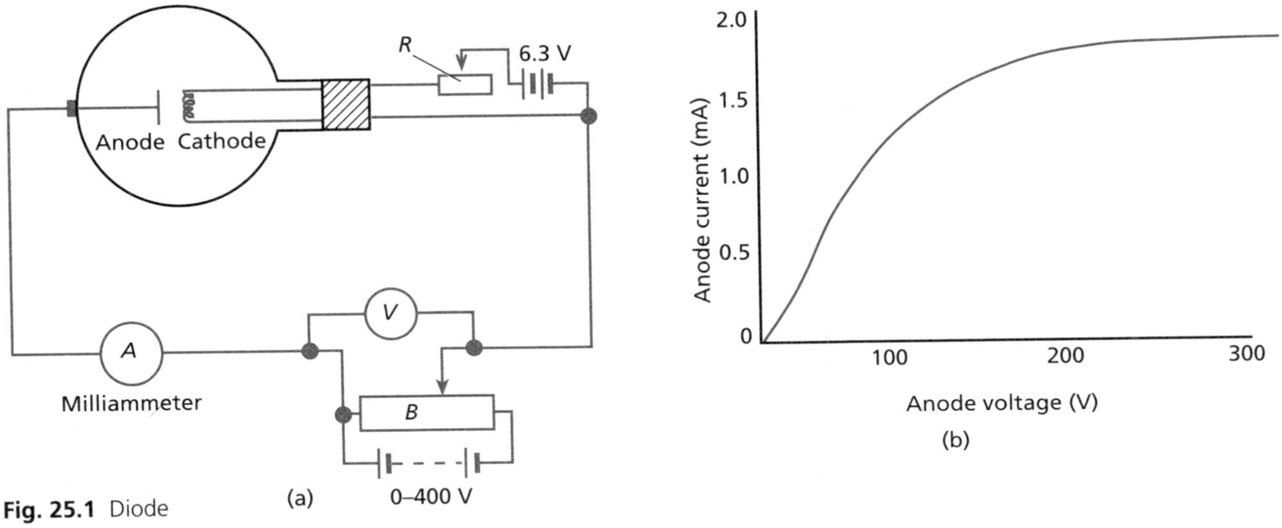

Fig. 25.1 Diode

The actual values of the voltage applied and the current obtained will depend on the actual diode used. However, the general shape of the graph will be similar in all cases. When no voltage is applied between the anode and cathode the electrons released by thermionic emission remain near the cathode. If a small positive potential difference is applied between the anode and cathode, some of the electrons in the cloud move across the empty space to the anode. Here they flow through the anode circuit back to the cathode, and a small current is registered.

The electrons crossing to the anode create a negative charge in the space between anode and cathode. This negative space charge repels some electrons back to the cathode. Thus not all the electrons emitted from the cathode reach the anode when the potential difference is small. However, as the potential difference increases, a larger proportion of the electrons emitted do reach the anode. At large voltages all the electrons emitted per second reach the anode and increasing the voltage further will not increase the current. The maximum current is known as the **saturation current**.

No current flows when the anode potential is negative with respect to the cathode. All the electrons emitted are repelled back to the cathode. The diode will thus only allow current to flow in one direction; for this reason it is known as a **valve**.

Suppose an alternating voltage is connected to a diode valve with a resistance R of a few thousand ohms in series with it (Fig. 25.2(a)). The diode will only pass current during the positive half of each cycle. An oscilloscope connected across the resistance R will show a voltage of the form illustrated in Fig. 25.2(b). The applied voltage has been rectified (converted from a.c. to d.c.) by the diode valve which has been used as a '**rectifier**'.

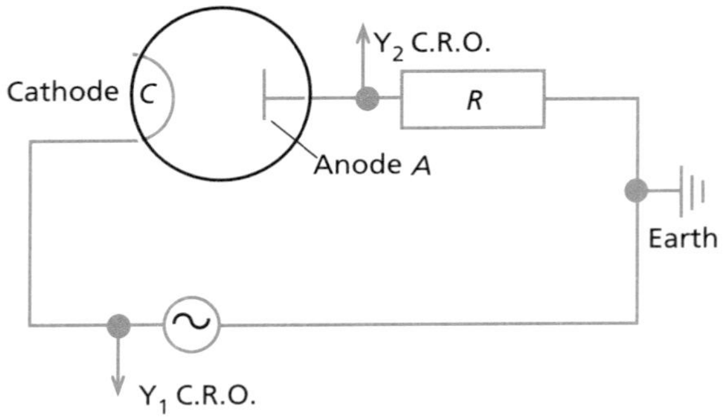

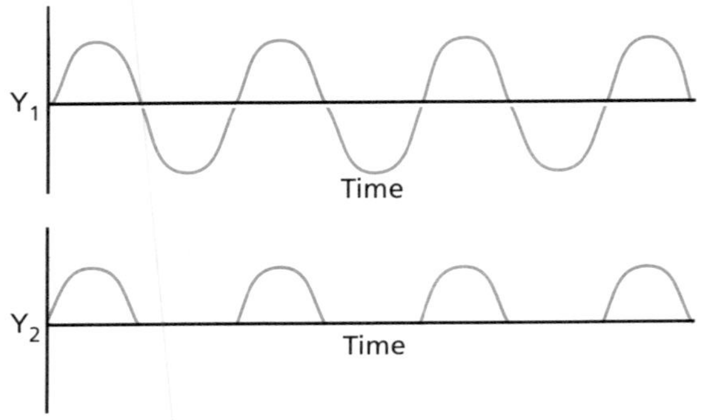

Fig. 25.2

One diode only allows half of an alternating current to flow through a load R; the other half is cut out. A more even supply of power can be obtained using the circuit in Fig. 25.3(a). This makes the whole of the alternating current flow one way through R. When terminal 1 is positive, current flows through diode A, the resistor R and diode C and returns to terminal 2. When terminal 2 is positive, current flows through diode B, the resistor R and diode D before returning to terminal 1. The output waveform is shown under the circuit diagram.

A smoother output may be obtained by using the circuit shown in Fig. 25.3(b). This is the same as that shown in Fig. 25.3(a) with the addition of a smoothing capacitor C in parallel with the resistor R. While the potential difference across R and C is rising to its peak value, the capacitor C is charged up. Then while the output of the rectifier drops rapidly to zero, the capacitor supplies charge, causing the current through R to fall more slowly. The larger the value of the capacitor, the smoother is the final output. The output waveform is shown under the circuit diagram in Fig. 25.3(b).

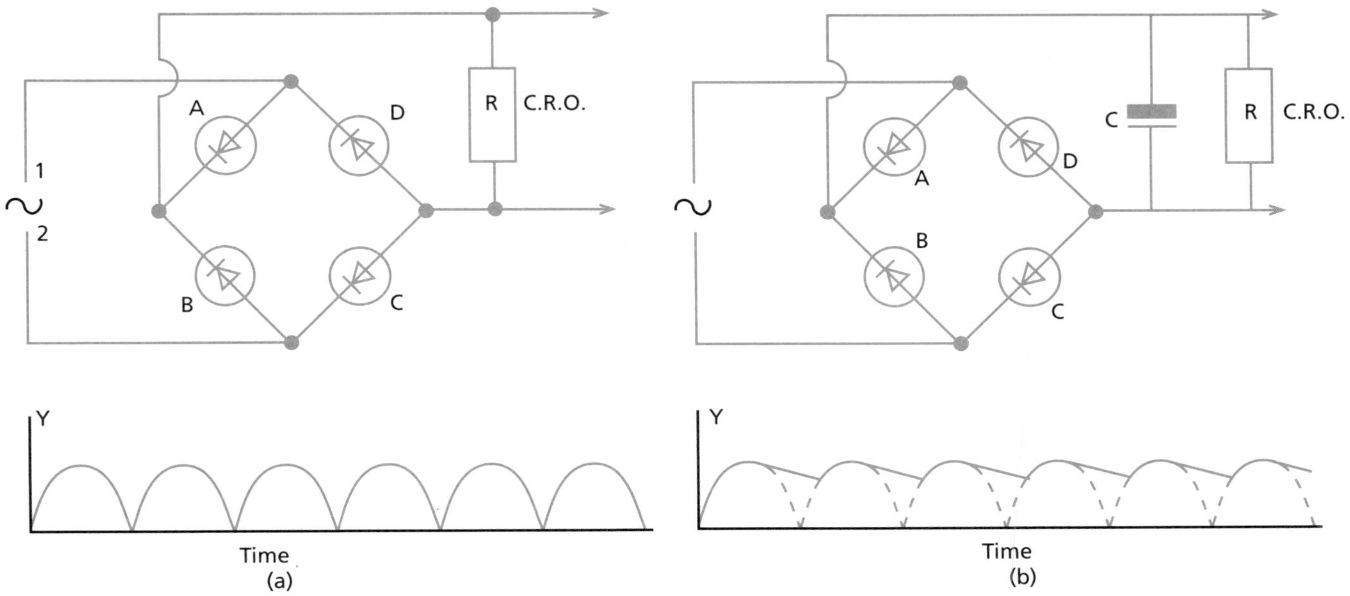

Fig. 25.3

25.3 Cathode rays

Since electrons are easily produced by thermionic emission, experiments on electrons can be conveniently carried out using this source.

In the Maltese cross tube illustrated in Fig. 25.4 the anode *A* is cylindrical and is maintained at a positive potential of a few thousand volts relative to the cathode *C*. This part of the apparatus is called an **electron gun**. The electrons are accelerated in the space between the cathode and anode and pass through the cylindrical anode. The Maltese cross shown is at right angles to the beam of cathode rays and is connected to the anode. The cross is thus at the same potential as the anode and the electrons move between the two at a constant speed (that is, they are not accelerated). When the electrons strike the screen some of their kinetic energy is converted into light, thus showing the position of the beam. A sharp shadow of the cross is seen on the screen, suggesting that the electrons emitted from the cathode travel in straight lines along the tube.

Fig. 25.4
Maltese-cross tube

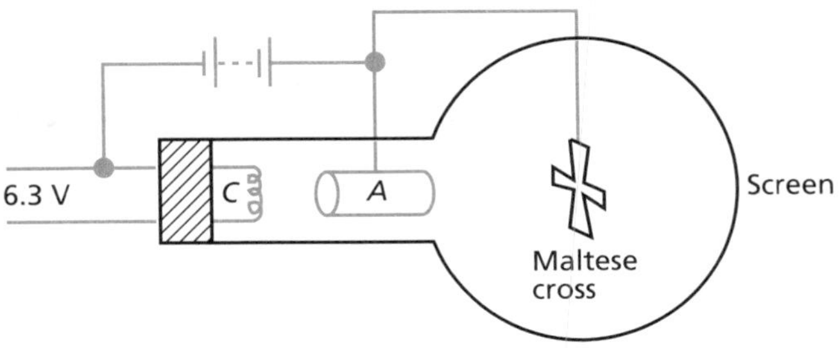

25.4 The effect of electric and magnetic fields

The deflection tube illustrated in Fig. 25.5 is similar to the Maltese cross tube, except that it contains two horizontal plates *P* and *Q* instead of the cross. The electrons emitted from the cathode are accelerated in the same way. They then pass between *P* and *Q* before striking the centre of the screen. However, if a large potential difference is connected between *P* and *Q*, the electron beam will be deflected. If, for example, *P* is positive relative to Q the electrons will be attracted to it and the beam will be deflected towards it. The beam is deflected downwards if Q is the more positive plate. The amount of deflection depends on the potential difference.

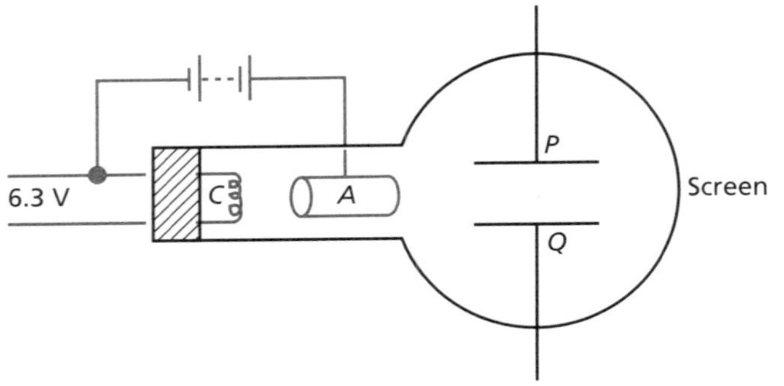

Fig. 25.5
Deflection tube

If two bar magnets are placed, one each side of the tube, with opposite poles facing, the beam will be deflected. This is the same effect as that responsible for the force on a current-carrying wire placed in a magnetic field, and thus for the rotation of an electric motor. In place of the bar magnets, the magnetic field may be produced by using two vertical coils, one each side of the tube. If a current of between one and two amps is passed through these coils, connected in series, a magnetic field results in the space between them. It has already been seen, in Unit 23.6, that a beam of charged particles passing through a magnetic field will experience a force at right angles to the field and their direction of travel. In the deflection tube the force acting on the electrons is initially either up or down, but, as the beam is deflected by this force, the force remains at right angles to the beam. The amount of deflection in a magnetic field depends on the strength of the field; in the case of the coils this depends on the current passing through them.

There is one further common type of deflection tube, known as the fine beam tube (Fig. 23.11). It contains a conical metal anode *A*, with a hole at the top over the cathode *C*. When a potential difference of a few thousand volts is connected between the two an electron beam is emitted vertically. The tube has a very small amount of hydrogen in it. The fast-moving electrons produce a fine beam of light as they ionize the hydrogen molecules. The beam shows the path of the electrons. The electrons may be deflected by connecting a potential difference between the two plates D_1 and D_2 just above the anode, or by passing an electric current through the two large coils placed one each side of the tube. In the latter case the beam of electrons may be deflected into a closed circle as the force is always at right angles to the direction of travel of the electrons.

25.5 The cathode ray oscilloscope

The cathode ray tube shown in Fig. 25.6 is very similar to the deflection tube illustrated in Fig. 25.5. It relies on exactly the same principle for its operation but has an

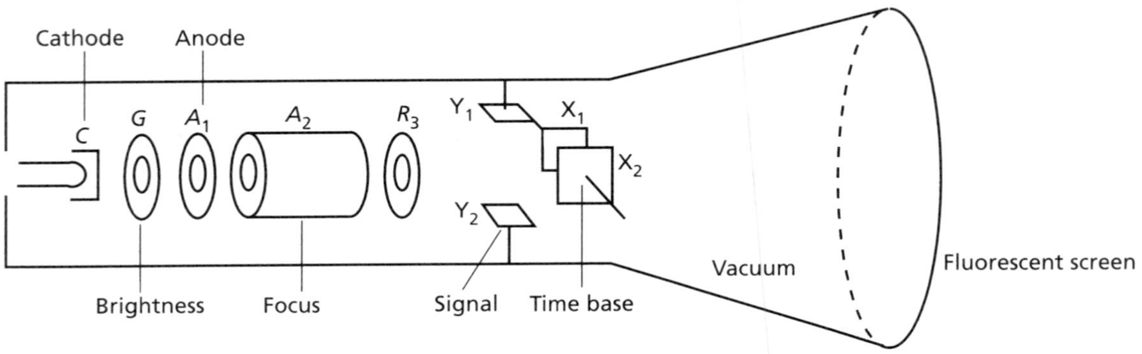

Fig. 25.6 Cathode ray oscilloscope

additional pair of plates X_1 and X_2 so that the electron beam may be deflected horizontally as well as vertically.

The cathode C emits electrons which are accelerated to the anode A by a high positive potential difference. In practice the anode usually consists of more than one plate or cylinder (A_1, A_2) so that it behaves like an electron lens and is able to focus the beam. The plate G is slightly negative compared to the anode. The number of electrons reaching the screen is controlled by how negative G is.

The cathode ray oscilloscope is excellent for use as a voltmeter. As no charge passes between the plates, when the beam is deflected, the tube draws no current from the component whose voltage it is recording; that is, it has an extremely high resistance.

If a d.c. voltage is to be measured it is connected between the plates Y_1 and Y_2. The spot on the screen will move a certain distance vertically which should be measured. If the oscilloscope has a calibrated scale this reading may immediately be converted to volts. If it is not calibrated a battery of known voltage should be connected to the oscilloscope and the deflection it causes recorded.

If it is required to measure an a.c. voltage, this should be connected to the plates Y_1 and Y_2. The length of the vertical line which results gives the value of the peak to peak voltage. However, if it is desired to see how the value of the voltage changes with time, the time base facility should be used. This provides a changing voltage connected to the X-plates, thus deflecting the beam horizontally. The spot thus repeatedly moves across the screen at a speed dictated by a switch controlling the time base frequency. Thus, as the spot moves up and down in response to the a.c. voltage connected to the Y-plates, it moves horizontally at a steady speed. A graph (Fig. 25.2(b) Y_1) is obtained with voltage as the Y-axis and time as the X-axis.

The cathode ray oscilloscope may be used to display any a.c. voltage; for example that across a resistor or that given by a microphone when sound falls on its diaphragm. It may also be used to examine the small voltage associated with the human heartbeat. The time base mechanism makes the oscilloscope suitable for use as a timing device. A pulse can be displayed on the screen at the instant it is emitted by a radar system and again when it is received back after reflection by an object in the Earth's atmosphere or in the space beyond. The distance between the two pulses on the screen gives the time taken for the return journey of the pulse. As the velocity of radio waves is known to be 3×10^8 m/s, the distance between the emitter and the reflecting object can be calculated.

The cathode ray tube is the basis of a television set. The time base causes the spot to cross the screen many times in quick succession, each time a little below the last, so that the whole screen is covered. In Great Britain and many other countries 625 lines are drawn on the screen in 1/25 second in this way. As the spot moves across the screen its intensity is varied by the incoming signal, thus causing a picture to be 'painted' on the screen. The whole process is then repeated. Thus 25 slightly different pictures appear on the screen every second, giving the impression of continuous movement.

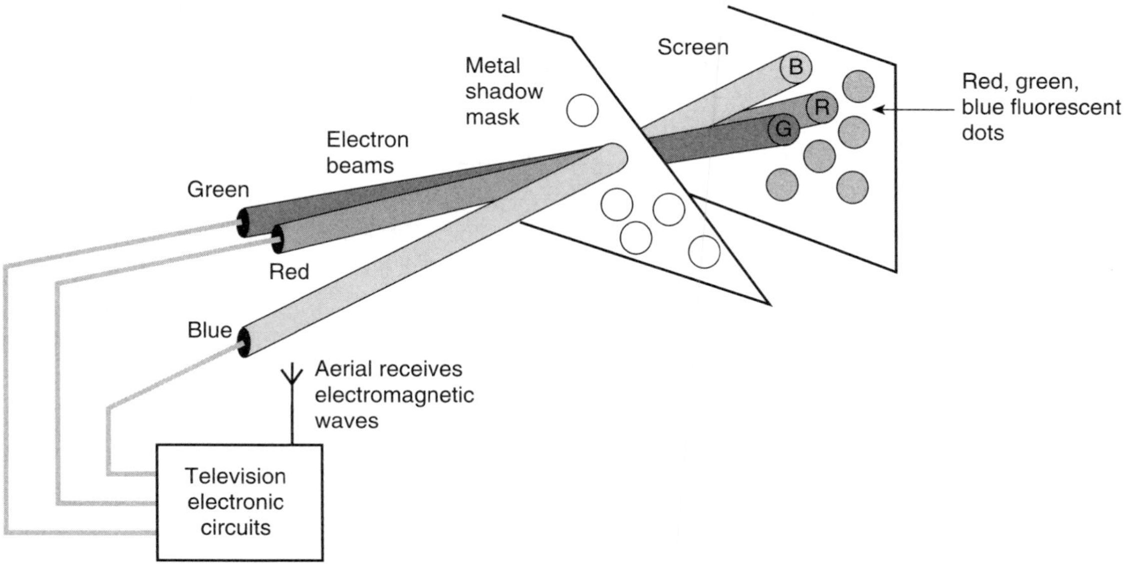

Fig. 25.7

To make a colour picture the television set needs three electron beams, as shown in Fig. 25.7. A beam of electrons leaves the 'red' gun, passes through holes in the shadow mask and then hits small spots on the screen which fluoresce, giving out red light. Similarly, electron beams leave the other two guns and hit spots that give out blue and green light. The human eye gets the impression of one coloured picture every 1/25 s. The shadow mask makes sure that the beams hit the right parts of the screen.

Summary

1 When a wire is heated electrons are released from the surface.

2 A thermionic diode contains a wire which is heated electrically (the cathode) and a metal plate (or cylinder) called the anode which is positive with respect to the cathode. Electrons released by the cathode are accelerated to the anode. Electrons cannot be made to flow in the opposite direction.

3 If a diode is connected in an a.c. circuit, the diode 'rectifies' (cuts out half of) the a.c.

4 The diode (or electron gun) is the source of the electron beam in a Maltese cross tube, a deflection tube and a cathode ray oscilloscope.

5 Beams of electrons are deflected by both electric and magnetic fields.

Quick test 25

1 What is meant by **thermionic emission**?

2 How is the electron beam produced in a **thermionic diode**?

3 A diode only permits a current to pass in one direction. Explain how it is that a thermionic diode will permit current to pass in only one direction.

4 What evidence is there for believing that electrons normally travel in a straight line in space?

5 In the diagram below a stream of electrons passes through a horizontal slit and strikes an inclined screen as indicated.
(a) Why has the beam bent downwards?
(b) What change could be made so that the beam bends more?
(c) What change could be made so that the beam bends upwards?

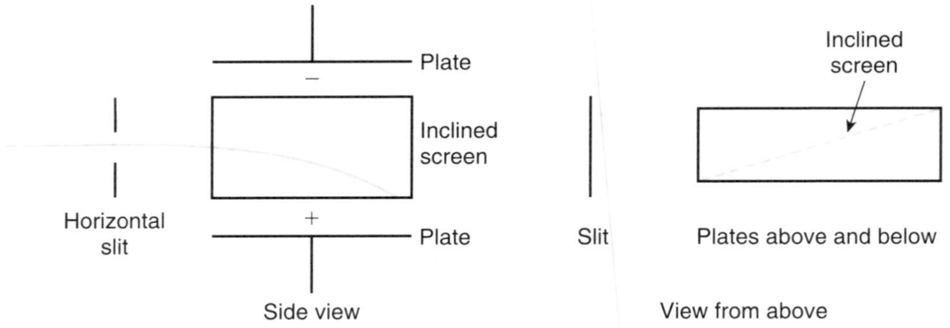

6 Write down the energy changes which occur in a television set between the current in the filament and the picture on the screen.

Chapter 26
Electronics

26.1 Semiconductor materials

Materials which allow electrons to flow through them are called **conductors**. Metals are the best conductors. The outermost electrons in each atom are so loosely attached that they are able to move freely between atoms. They are called '**free electrons**'.

Materials which do not conduct charge are called **insulators**. All their electrons are tightly held to atoms and are not normally free to move. Glass, rubber, polythene and plastics are good examples of insulators.

A few materials are neither good conductors nor good insulators, but have conducting properties between the two groups. These materials, which are known as **semiconductors**, contain a small number of free and mobile charges. The best known semiconductor material is silicon although there are others, such as germanium, lead sulphide and gallium arsenide.

In a pure semiconductor such as silicon, all the outer electrons of the atoms form bonds with neighbouring atoms and there are virtually no 'free electrons' left over for conduction. However, as the temperature is increased, the thermal energies of the vibrating atoms in the crystal cause some electrons to break free. More thermal electrons are freed as the temperature rises. Every electron that becomes free leaves a gap or hole in an atom. Since the atoms are normally neutral the hole behaves as if it has a positive charge. Like electrons these positive holes seem to move through the semiconductor material and form part of the electric current in it. Conduction in a semiconductor by means of thermal electrons and positive holes is called **intrinsic** conduction.

A thermistor is a piece of semiconductor material behaving in this way. When cold the thermistor has a high resistance. As its temperature increases more electrons and holes are released, improving the intrinsic conduction of the material and hence lowering its resistance. Thermistors are used to prevent large currents flowing through lamp filaments and electric motors at the moment of switching on. They can also be used to operate thermostats and fire alarms.

Cadmium sulphide is one of several semiconductor materials whose resistance varies with the amount of light falling on it. As light energy is absorbed, electrons and holes are released and become available for conduction. The brighter the light the more of these charge carriers are released and the further the resistance of the material falls. Such semiconductor materials are used in light-dependent resistors (LDR).

Small quantities of different elements can be added to a semiconductor material which greatly change its conduction properties. Conduction caused by these impurities is called **extrinsic** conduction or impurity conduction. Adding such impurities to semiconductor materials is called **doping**. Silicon atoms have four electrons in their outer shells and all are required for bonding with its four nearest neighbours. If some atoms with five electrons in their outer shells are added to the silicon crystal, they provide one spare electron each. Phosphorus, antimony and arsenic are used to dope silicon in this way and provide spare electrons for conduction. Such doped material is called **n-type** silicon as it has an excess of negative charge carriers.

If materials such as aluminium, gallium and indium, with three electrons in the outer shells of their atoms, are used to dope the crystal, it will have one electron missing in its structure for each impurity atom present. Semiconductor material with extra positive hole charge carriers (missing electrons) is called **p-type** material.

26.2 The p–n junction diode

Such a diode consists of a single crystal of silicon or germanium, part of which has been doped so that it contains an excess of positive charges (p-type). The rest of the crystal has had a different impurity added so that it contains an excess of electrons (n-type). It is the existence of the junction between the two types of material which enables the device to act as a rectifier. It is therefore called a p–n junction diode.

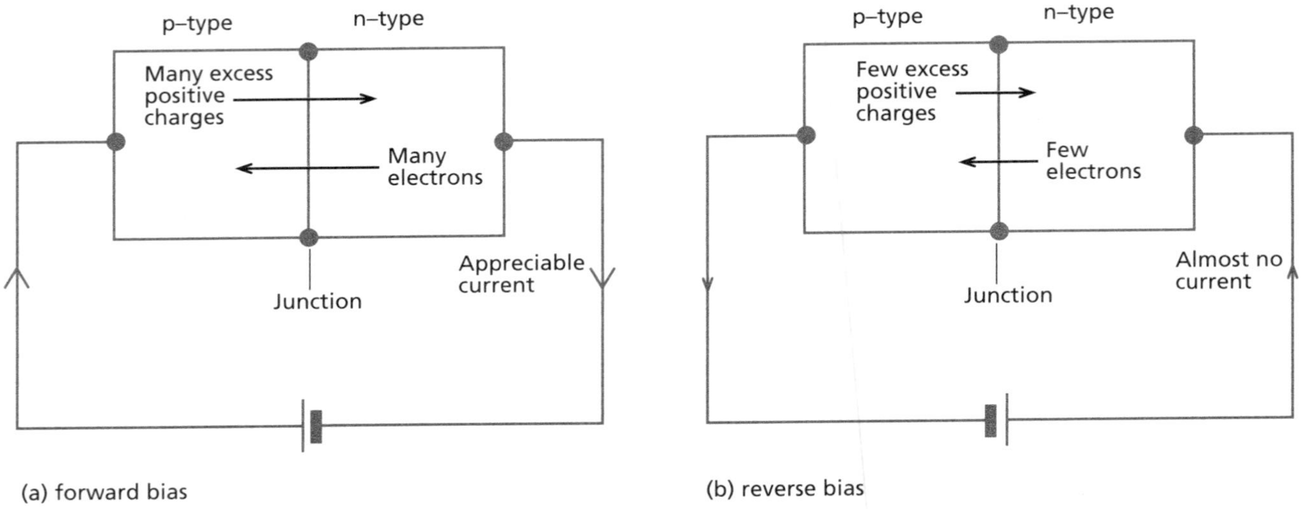

Fig. 26.1

Suppose that a battery is connected across a junction diode as in Fig. 26.1(a), the so-called forward bias connection. The battery urges the excess positive charges and the electrons to cross the junction and so constitute a current. When the battery is reversed the excess charges are discouraged from crossing the junction and no current flows (Fig. 26.1(b)). This one-way conduction property of a junction diode may be used to convert alternating current to direct current in the way described for the thermionic diode in Unit 25.2.

26.3 The light emitting diode (LED)

Examiner's tip

Remember that current in a diode flows in the direction of the arrow.

Junction diodes made of gallium arsenide and gallium phosphide emit light when a forward biased current flows through them. The colour of the light depends on the semiconductor material. The main advantage of the light emitting diode, compared to the filament lamp, is the low current and hence the low heat production. To limit the current to a low and safe value for the LED a protective resistor is connected in series with the diode (Fig. 26.2).

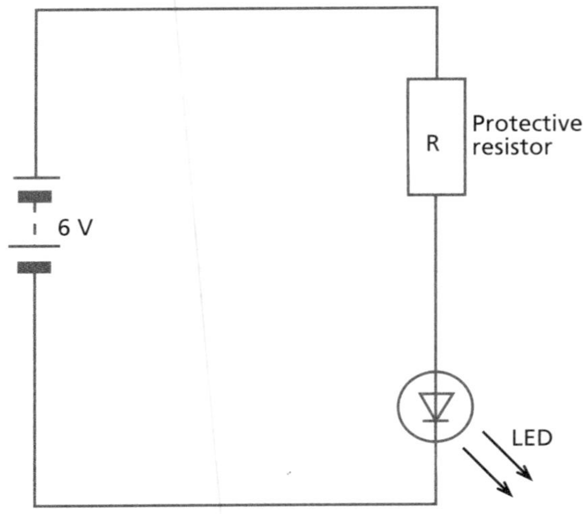

Fig. 26.2

26.4 The transistor

The transistor is a semiconductor sandwich usually made of silicon. A thin layer of p-type silicon sandwiched between two layers of n-type silicon forms an **npn transistor**. A **pnp transistor** has the types of silicon reversed.

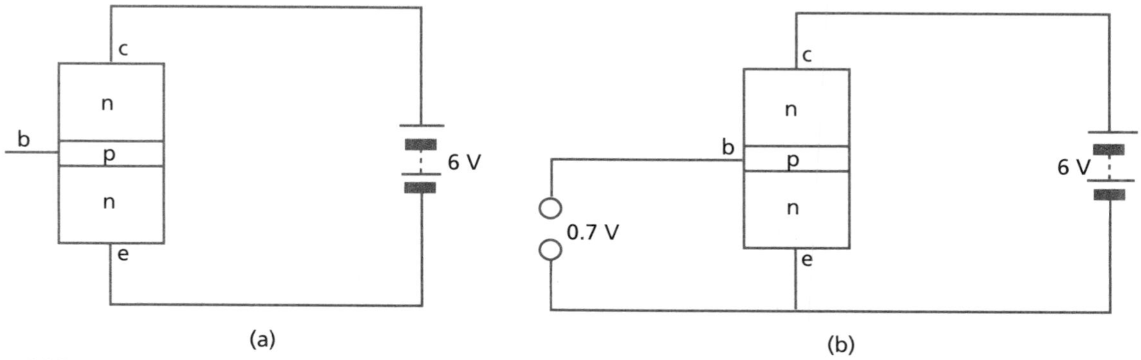

Fig. 26.3

Consider an npn transistor, shown diagrammatically in Fig. 26.3. The n-type regions are the emitter and collector; the thin p-type region is the base. If a potential difference is applied between the emitter and collector as shown in Fig. 26.3(a), the upper junction is reverse biased and no current flows through the transistor. If the lower junction is now forward biased by applying a small potential difference across it, as in Fig. 26.3(b), electrons flow from the emitter into the base. The base is so thin that most of these electrons drift across into the collector; the top junction is conducting and a current flows through the transistor as a result. A small current in the base or input circuit enables a much larger current to flow round the collector or output circuit. These results mean that:

1. The transistor can be used as a switch, because no current flows in the collector circuit unless a current flows in the base circuit.
2. The transistor can be used to amplify current changes as a small change in the base current produces a large change in the collector current.

In Fig. 26.3(b) note that the base and collector circuits share a common connection at the emitter. Used in this way the transistor is said to be in the **common-emitter** mode.

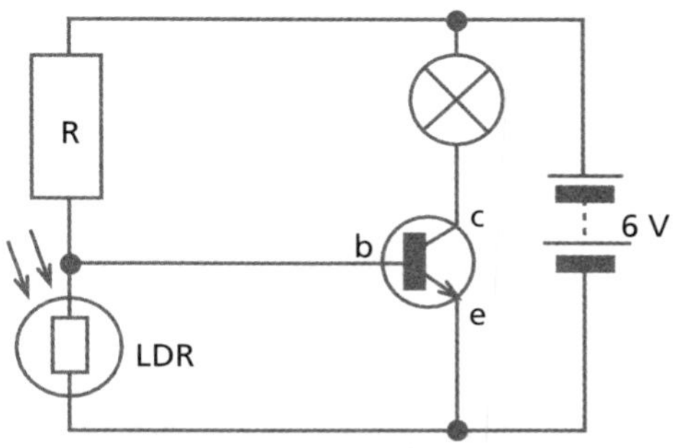

Fig. 26.4

Figure 26.4 shows an npn transistor being used as a light operated transistor switch. When light falls on the LDR its resistance is low, the input voltage to the base is below about 0.7 V, and the transistor is switched off. No current flows in the collector circuit and the lamp is off. When the LDR is shielded from the light its resistance rises. The input voltage to the base also rises above about 0.7 V, causing current to flow in the base circuit. A larger current flows in the collector circuit and the lamp comes on. The value of the resistor *R* is determined by the type of transistor and LDR used.

Figure 26.5 shows the transistor being used as a current amplifier. Small variations in the base current, caused by the microphone, lead to much greater variations in the collector current. The current amplification or gain of a transistor is given by the formula:

$$\text{current gain} = \frac{\text{collector current}}{\text{base current}}$$

The value of the current gain of a transistor can be anywhere between 10 and 1000 with a typical value of about 100.

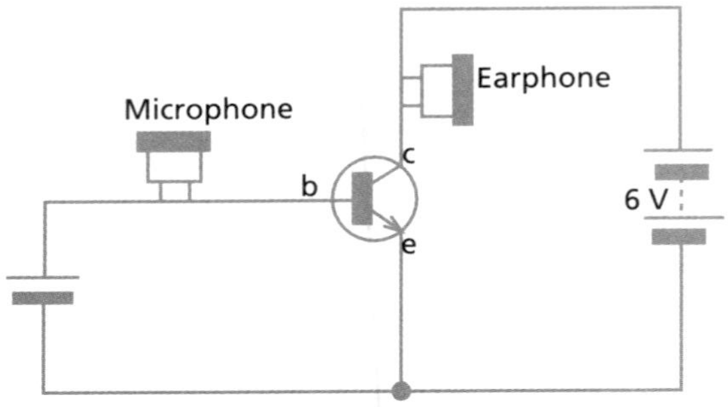

Fig. 26.5

This circuit is an example of an **analogue** circuit, where the output (collector current) can have any value and depends only on the value of the input (base current in this case).

26.5 The bistable

A bistable contains two transistors (Fig. 26.6). If lamp L_1 comes on when the circuit is first connected then transistor T_1 is 'on' and T_2 is 'off'. The circuit stays in this state, i.e. it is latched on. If switch S_1 is momentarily closed, the base of T_1 is connected to 0 V, i.e. it is no longer forward biased and switches 'off'. L_1 therefore goes off and L_2 lights up because T_2 comes on as its base is now connected to 6 V via R_1 and L_1, i.e. it is forward biased. The circuit will stay in this second stable state (bistable) until S_2 is closed momentarily, when L_1 lights again. A second type of bistable, made from two NOR gates, is described in Unit 26.7.

Fig. 26.6

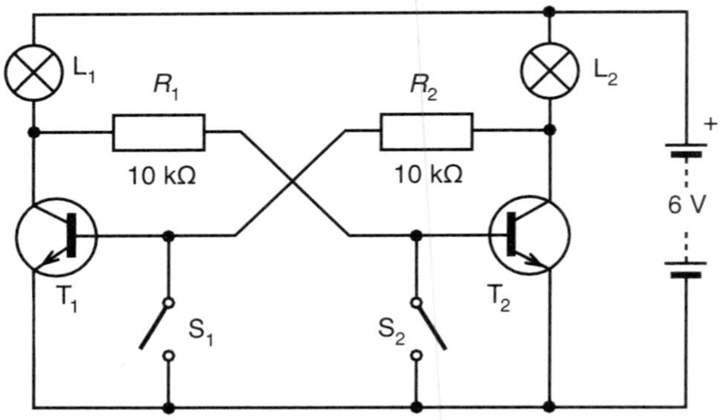

26.6 Electronic systems

Electronics systems are becoming increasingly more common and more important as time goes on. These systems can be described and understood in terms of building blocks and block diagrams. They handle and process two different kinds of information; analogue and digital. Here we confine our attention to digital systems.

In a **digital** system all information is processed in the form of digits: for example; 1996 has four digits and each digit tells us how many thousands, hundreds, tens and ones of years there are. Calculators and computers represent numbers by binary digits. There are only two digits, 0 and 1, in binary arithmetic, rather than the ten digits 0 to 9 that we are used to in our usual arithmetic. For example the number 6 becomes 110 when expressed in binary digits. 110 stands for 1 'four', 1 'two' and 0 'ones'. Each of the binary digits 110 is called a **bit** and an electronic system which handles information in this way is a **binary digital system**. Note that calculators and computers convert the binary numbers into normal arithmetic before displaying the answer.

26.7 Logic gates

The use of a transistor as a switch has already been described. A variety of switches or building blocks called logic gates are used in digital systems. These blocks are like 'gates' because they have to be opened to let information pass through to reach their outputs. Each type of gate is opened by a particular combination of information fed to its inputs in binary code.

There are five basic types of logic gate from which all the more complicated ones are constructed. They are shown in Fig. 26.7. A truth table is a very simple way of describing all the possible combinations of inputs and outputs produced by a particular gate or collection of gates. The name of a particular gate describes how it makes its decisions. It tells us which combination of high or NOT high (low) inputs produces a high output signal. Logic 0 represents a low input or output and logic 1 a high one. For example, an AND gate only gives a high output (1) when both inputs are high (1).

To prevent the circuits (gates) responding to 'spurious' (false) signals, their inputs are arranged to accept only voltages above a certain minimum (**threshold**) value.

Type	Symbol	Same as	Truth table	Output is high (1) when:
NOT	A  Y	INVERTER	Input: A / Output: Y 0 / 1 1 / 0	Input A is NOT high
OR	A, B 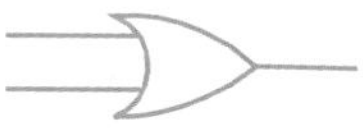 Y		A B Y 0 0 0 1 0 1 0 1 1 1 1 1	Input A OR B is high
NOR	A, B 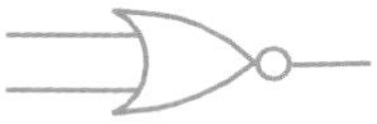 Y	OR–NOT	A B Y 0 0 1 1 0 0 0 1 0 1 1 0	Neither input A NOR input B is high
AND	A, B  Y		A B Y 0 0 0 1 0 0 0 1 0 1 1 1	Input A AND input B are high
NAND	A, B  Y	AND–NOT	A B Y 0 0 1 1 0 1 0 1 1 1 1 0	Input A AND input B are NOT both high

Fig. 26.7

Now, rather than manufacturing separate circuits containing individual transistors, integrated circuits (ICs) are used. Each integrated circuit consists of a very small single chip of silicon on which groups of components, including several transistors, are manufactured.

Each gate is referred to as a **processor**. Each of its **inputs** may be connected to a switch or to a sensor such as a light dependent resistor or a thermistor. The **output** is connected to a buzzer, lamp, LED or relay.

Two NOR gates may be used to make a bistable. The diagrams in Fig. 26.8 show how it works. The output of a NOR gate is 1 only when both inputs are zero.

In (a) the bistable is set with S = 1 and C = 0. Since S = 1, $\overline{Q} = 0$. As both inputs to the lower NOR gate are at 0, Q = 1. In (b), S has changed to 0. This does not affect $\overline{Q}$ or Q, so Q = 1 still.

However, in (c) S = 0 and C = 1. This means that $\overline{Q} = 1$ and Q = 0. In (d) C goes back to 0. This does not affect $\overline{Q}$ or Q.

The bistable remembers which of S or C was last in the logic state 1. The output Q of the bistable has two states, either 0 or 1. The bistable is the basis of the binary counting system.

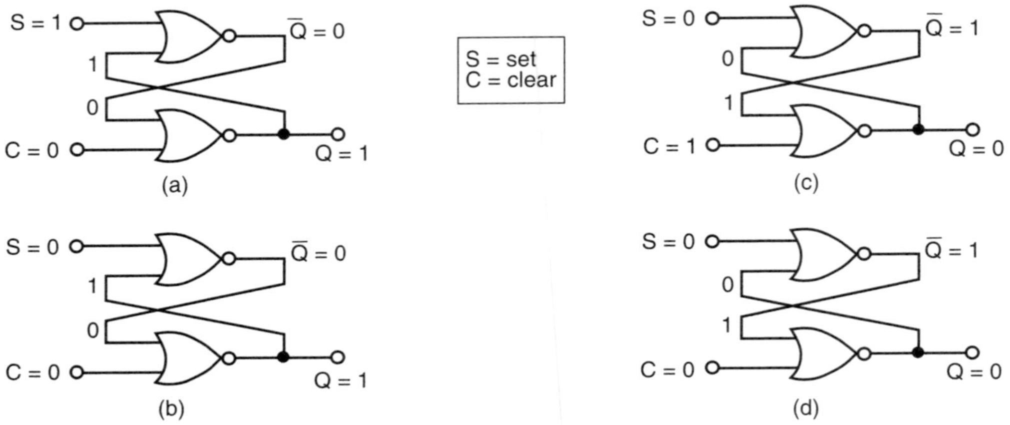

Fig. 26.8

Summary

1 Materials, such as metals, which readily allow electrons to flow through them are called **conductors**; materials which do not are called **insulators**. A few materials, such as silicon and germanium, have conducting properties between the two groups and are called **semiconductors**.

2 Some materials, cadmium sulphide for example, have less resistance when light falls on them. Such materials are used in light dependent resistors (LDRs).

3 A diode can be made from, for example, a single crystal of germanium which has been doped. Such a diode (**junction diode**) behaves in a circuit in a similar way to a thermionic diode.

4 Junction diodes made of gallium arsenide or phosphide emit light when a forward biased current flows through them. They are called light emitting diodes (LED).

5 A transistor is a semiconductor sandwich usually made from silicon. A thin layer of p-type silicon sandwiched between two layers of n-type silicon forms an **n-p-n transistor**. A **p-n-p transistor** has the types of silicon reversed.

6 A transistor is often used as a switch or to amplify a current. A transistor amplifier is an example of an **analogue** system where the output can have any value and depends only on the value of the input.

7 **Digital** electronic systems use binary arithmetic and are the basis of calculators and computers. Inputs and outputs of such systems can have only two values; high (1) or low (0).

8 There are many types of logic gate. Each type of gate is 'opened' by a particular combination of information fed to its inputs in binary code.

Quick test 26

1 What is meant by the term **semiconductor**?

2 Explain what is meant by **doping**.

3 Distinguish between **n-type** and **p-type** semiconducting material.

4 Explain the function of a **diode**.

5 What is meant by an **LED**?

6 A transistor may be used as a current amplifier. Explain the term current **amplifier**.

7 Explain the meaning of the word **bistable**.

8 What is a **digital** electronic system?

9 Write down 'truth tables' for the following.
(a) a NOR gate
(b) a NOT gate
(c) an AND gate

Chapter 27
Radioactivity and atomic structure

It has already been seen that electrons passing through a gas ionize the molecules of the gas (for example in the fine beam tube – Unit 25.4). Due to the electrical forces of attraction and repulsion, any charged particle passing near to a molecule will tend to ionize it – that is, split it into positively and negatively charged parts. This property of charged particles may be used to detect their presence.

27.1 Atomic structure

Atoms may be regarded as being like miniature solar systems. An atom is thought to have a central **nucleus**, consisting of tightly packed particles called protons and neutrons, with electrons revolving round it. Evidence for this model comes from a series of experiments carried out by Geiger and Marsden at Manchester University in 1911. Alpha particles emitted from a radioactive source were scattered by a thin foil of gold. A very small fraction of the particles were scattered through very large angles (some through more than 90°) and Rutherford suggested that these had come very close to a high concentration of positive charge (an atomic nucleus) and had been deflected by the large electrical force of repulsion.

In the nucleus of an atom each proton has a positive charge equal in magnitude to the charge on an electron, and the number of protons in the nucleus of an atom is equal to the number of electrons in the atom. The atom is therefore electrically neutral. The chemical properties of an atom and hence the element to which it belongs are dictated by the number and arrangement of electrons in it, and this in turn depends on the number of protons in the nucleus, known as the **atomic number**, denoted by Z.

Neutrons are similar in mass to protons, both being nearly 2000 times as massive as electrons. The mass of an atom is thus almost entirely due to the masses of the protons and neutrons contained in its nucleus. The total number of protons and neutrons in the nucleus of an atom is known as the atom's **mass number**, denoted by A. Thus if the number of neutrons is denoted by N we have

$$A = Z + N$$

It is possible for one or more of the peripheral electrons of an atom to become detached, thus leaving the atom with a net positive charge. It is then known as a positive ion. It is also possible for an atom to gain one or more electrons, becoming a negative ion. It is only in radioactive disintegrations that the number of protons or neutrons in an atom changes. All the electrical and chemical properties of an atom are explained in terms of the transfer of electrons.

Helium has a nucleus containing two protons and two neutrons, and two peripheral electrons. When an atom disintegrates by means of **alpha particle decay** (see Unit 27.3) it loses two protons and becomes an atom of the element two below it in the periodic table of elements. As it has also lost two neutrons, its mass number has fallen by four.

Examiner's tip

The electron comes from the nucleus and **not** from the electrons around the nucleus.

Beta decay seems to take place by a neutron changing to a proton, which remains in the nucleus, and an electron, which is emitted. The atom concerned has gained a proton and thus becomes an atom of the element one up in the periodic table. Its mass number has not changed.

As a result of either alpha or beta decay, a nucleus may undergo rearrangement, with a loss of energy as gamma radiation. Therefore, gamma emission also often occurs with either alpha or beta decay.

27.2 Isotopes

From the previous discussion it can be seen that two atoms of an element may exist (that is the atoms have the same number of protons) which have different numbers of neutrons and hence different mass numbers. These atoms are said to be **isotopes of the same element**.

At the lower end of the periodic table the number of neutrons present in an atom is equal to, or nearly equal to, the number of protons. Elements of high mass number consist of atoms with very many more neutrons than protons. It is these atoms which are more likely to disintegrate. It seems that a large number of excess neutrons in an atom leads to instability and the likelihood of spontaneous disintegration. Generally speaking it is the elements of high mass number which exhibit this property of radioactivity.

Also, any isotope of an element which has an excess number of neutrons will tend to be unstable and undergo beta decay.

27.3 Radioactivity

Examiner's tip

Make sure you know the properties of α, β and γ and how they can be distinguished.

A number of naturally occurring substances emit particles or radiations which ionize gases. Marie Curie and her husband did much of the early work on radioactive substances and showed that amongst the most active were those containing uranium, polonium and radium.

By 1899 Rutherford had shown that the particles or radiations emitted by radioactive substances fell into three categories which he called **alpha (α), beta (β)** and **gamma (γ) rays**.

Alpha rays are helium ions – that is, helium atoms which have lost two electrons, and hence have a positive charge. From a particular radioactive substance they are all ejected with approximately the same velocity and hence kinetic energy. They have a range of a few centimetres in air at atmospheric pressure, but most are stopped by a thick sheet of paper. Like all charged particles they lose their energy by continuous ionization and the fact that they produce many ions per centimetre of path means that they travel relatively short distances. Being charged particles they are deflected by both electric and magnetic fields.

Beta rays are streams of high energy electrons similar to cathode rays but travelling much faster. They are emitted with velocities approaching that of light (3×10^8 m/s) and, as they do not form such a high density of ions along their track, their range is greater than that of alpha rays. Beta rays are negatively charged and are thus deflected in the opposite direction to alpha particles in both electric and magnetic fields.

Gamma rays are very short wavelength radiations similar to X-rays, which can penetrate several centimetres of dense metal such as lead. They do not produce continuous ionization but lose their energy in one interaction with a molecule. The fact that they cannot be deflected by electric or magnetic fields indicates that they are not charged particles.

An idea of the range of alpha, beta and gamma rays may be obtained by placing sources emitting these separate rays in front of a Geiger-Muller GM tube connected to a scaler. The number of counts recorded by the scaler in a given time is noted with different absorbers (sheets of paper, aluminium or lead of different thicknesses) between the source and the tube. Alphas are stopped by a thin sheet of paper. It is found that gamma rays, in particular, and beta rays to a lesser extent, are very difficult to stop or screen, and thus may present a safety hazard. Gamma ray sources are kept in lead containers, the walls of which are often several centimetres thick.

If the GM tube and scaler are switched on, in the absence of a source and the absorbers, some counts will be recorded. This count rate, which is slow, is due to radiation which is always present in the atmosphere. It is called **background radiation**, and should be subtracted from the counts recorded when a source is present, to give the true count rate due to the source.

27.4 Uses of radioactivity

Radioactive materials have many uses in medicine, industry and agriculture.

In **medicine** iodine 131 is used to see if the thyroid gland is working properly. The thyroid gland absorbs iodine, so a dose of radioactive iodine (tracer) is given to a patient. Doctors then measure the radioactivity of the patient's throat, to see how well his thyroid is working. The tracer has a short half-life.

Cobalt 60 emits high-energy gamma rays and is used in the treatment of cancer. A strong beam of this radiation is directed onto the cancerous tissue to kill the cancer cells. The treatment has unpleasant side-effects but is often successful in slowing down the growth of, or even completely curing, the cancer.

Cobalt 60 is also used to sterilize medical equipment such as syringes, dressings and surgeons' instruments. These items are first packed into sealed plastic bags and then irradiated with gamma rays which kill any bacteria on them.

In **industry** radioactive tracers may be used to detect leaks in underground pipes. The tracer is fed into the pipe and then a Geiger (GM) tube is used above ground to detect any increase in the radiation level and hence the leak. This method is cheaper and quicker than digging up the entire length of the pipe.

A beta particle source may be used to automatically control the thickness of sheets of paper, plastic and metal being rolled in a mill. The source is placed on one side of the sheet and a Geiger tube on the other. If the count rate falls this means the sheet coming from the rollers is too thick and the rollers are automatically moved a little closer together by electronic means. The source should have a long half-life.

A radioisotope of iron is used in industry to estimate the wear on moving parts of machinery. For example, a piston ring made of radioactive iron is put into an engine and run for several days. At the end the oil from the engine is collected and, from the amount of radioactivity present, engineers can estimate the amount of wear of the ring.

An alpha particle source is used in some smoke detectors. The smoke prevents the alpha particles reaching the detector and this sets off the alarm.

Tracers are used in **agriculture**. Radioactive phosphorus is used as a tracer to show how well plants are absorbing phosphorus.

Sometimes gamma radiation is used to prolong the shelf-life of pre-packaged foods. Gamma rays kill the bacteria in the food and so eliminate the risk of food poisoning. As the gamma rays also kill some cells in the food itself such treatment can alter the taste of the food.

27.5 Radioactive decay

By 1903 Rutherford had come to the conclusion that radioactivity is the result of the spontaneous disintegration of an atom during which it emits an alpha or beta ray. Simultaneously the atom changes into one of another element which may itself be radioactive. The following are examples of such disintegrations.

$^{238}_{92}U \rightarrow {}^{4}_{2}He + {}^{234}_{90}Th$ α-decay

$^{234}_{90}Th \rightarrow {}^{0}_{-1}e + {}^{234}_{91}Pa$ β-decay

$^{234}_{91}Pa \rightarrow {}^{0}_{-1}e + {}^{234}_{92}U$ β-decay

The numbers above the symbols are the mass numbers of the atoms; those below are the atomic numbers.

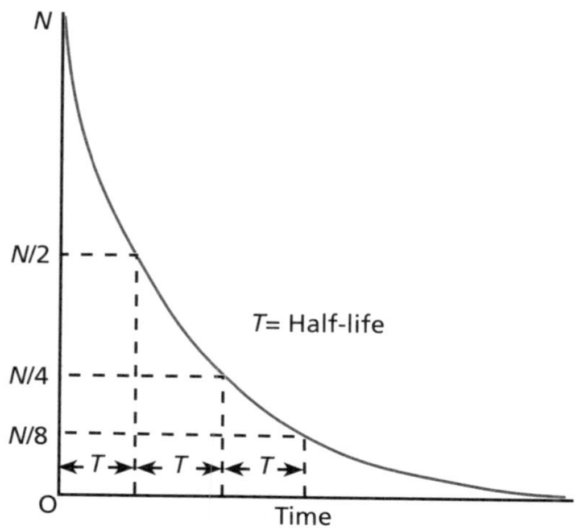

Fig. 27.1

It is impossible to predict which particular atom in a sample will change in this way; that is, the disintegration of an atom is a **random** event. However, in a sample containing a large number of atoms, the number which disintegrate each second will depend on the number of undecayed atoms left. Thus if the number of disintegrations per second is recorded (by counting the number of particles emitted), and plotted against time, an exponential graph results (Fig. 27.1).

As can be seen from this graph, an infinite time is taken for all the atoms of a sample to disintegrate. Therefore it is meaningless to talk about the 'life' of a sample. However, **the time taken for half the undecayed atoms in any given sample of the substance to disintegrate is finite, and the same whatever the number of undecayed atoms present initially**. This time T is known as the **half-life** of the substance. It is different for different radioactive materials.

This property of radioactive materials is used to date archaeological remains. Carbon 14 is a radioactive isotope; it decays to nitrogen with a half-life of 5500 years. All living things have a lot of carbon in them and a small fraction of this is carbon 14. For example, when a tree dies the radioactive carbon starts to decay. The fraction of carbon 14 in living materials does not change as time passes. After 5500 years the fraction of carbon 14 in the dead tree will be half as much as in a living tree. Thus by measuring the fraction of carbon 14 present at a later date, scientists are able to date ancient relics.

27.6 Safety

Exposure of the body to radiation from atomic disintegrations can have undesirable effects of a long- or short-term nature. The precise result of exposure depends on the nature of the radiation, the part of the body irradiated and the dose received. The hazard from alpha particles is slight, unless the source enters the body, since they cannot penetrate the outer layers of skin. Beta particles are more penetrating, although most of their energy is absorbed by surface tissues. Gamma rays present the main external radiation hazard since they penetrate deeply into the body.

Radiation can cause immediate damage to cells, and is accompanied by radiation burns (redness of skin followed by blistering and sores, the severity of these depending on the dose received), radiation sickness and possibly death. Effects such as cancer and leukaemia may appear many years later, due to the uncontrolled multiplication of some cells set off by exposure to radiation. Hereditary effects may also occur in succeeding generations due to genetic changes. The most susceptible parts of the body are the reproductive organs and blood-forming organs such as the liver.

Because of the hazards it is essential that the correct procedure be adopted when using radioactive substances. Briefly it is as follows:

1. Sources should only be held with forceps, never with the hand. This avoids any possibility of some of the substance transferring to the surface of the skin or lodging under a nail.

2. Any cuts on the hand should be covered before using sources.
3. Sources should not be pointed towards the human body.
4. Sources should be returned to their container as soon as they are no longer needed for an experiment. If possible, permanent storage should be within two containers.
5. A check should be made at the end of an experiment to see that all sources are present in their allotted containers.
6. Mouth pipettes should never be used with liquid sources.
7. Do not remain unnecessarily in the region of a radioactive source.

27.7 Nuclear energy

The nucleus of a $^{235}_{92}U$ atom splits into two parts with approximately equal masses when it captures a neutron. The splitting of the nucleus is known as **nuclear fission**. The products of the fission of one uranium-235 nucleus are:

1. Two new elements, known as fission products. A pair of examples is barium and krypton.
2. Two or three fast-moving neutrons.
3. About 3×10^{-11} J of energy. This energy is released as radiation and as kinetic energy of the neutrons. This kinetic energy is the source of the heat obtained from a nuclear reactor.

$$^{235}_{92}U + ^{1}_{0}n \rightarrow ^{144}_{56}Ba + ^{90}_{36}Kr + 2^{1}_{0}n$$

This nuclear fission equation shows that the number of nuclear particles (nucleons) is conserved. However, the total mass of the particles on the right-hand side of the equation is slightly less than the total mass on the left. This small mass difference is converted into energy according to the equation:

$$E = mc^2$$

where E is the energy released, m is the mass difference and c is the speed of light ($c = 3 \times 10^8$ m/s).

The fission of one uranium-235 nucleus gives off about 3×10^{-11} J of energy, which is far more than that released by natural radioactive decay.

If the neutrons released by the decay of one uranium-235 nucleus are captured by other nearby uranium-235 nuclei then more fissions occur, resulting in a **chain reaction**. About 85 per cent of the uranium-235 nuclei which capture a neutron, undergo fission, emitting two or three more neutrons. If all these neutrons were captured by uranium-235 nuclei a nuclear explosion would result. This does not happen because in a nuclear reactor it is possible to control the chain reaction. Natural uranium contains only about 0.7 per cent of the isotope $^{235}_{92}U$. 99.3 per cent of the atoms present are of the isotope $^{238}_{92}U$ which captures neutrons without fission resulting. Thus in natural uranium the chain reaction would quickly stop.

However, the probability of uranium-235 nuclei capturing neutrons can be increased by slowing the neutrons down. This also reduces the probability of capture by uranium-238 nuclei. The neutrons are slowed down by a material called a **moderator**, usually water or graphite. Neutrons which have been slowed down are known as thermal neutrons, because they have kinetic energies similar in value to the thermal (heat) energy of the surrounding material.

If the fission process is to be used in a power station, it is necessary to control the chain reaction so that exactly one neutron from the fission of each uranium-235 nucleus causes another similar nucleus to split. If, on average, less than one neutron does so, then the chain reaction will not be self-sustaining. If the number is above one the chain reaction will quickly get out of control and an explosion will result. This control is achieved by the use of **control rods** of boron, steel or cadmium, which absorb neutrons. The length of the control rods in the uranium core is continually adjusted automatically so that an average of one neutron per nuclear fission causes further splitting.

The heat produced by fission is removed from the reactor core by a coolant which is piped into the core. The pipe containing the coolant passes close to the hot uranium fuel rods and the moderator and much of the heat is absorbed. The heated coolant is then used to run a turbine. From this point onwards a nuclear power station works in the same way as power stations burning oil or coal.

27.8 More advanced ideas on nuclear structure and decay

Just as any isotope of an element which has an excess number of neutrons is unstable and undergoes beta($\beta-$) decay (see Unit 27.1), so an isotope which has too few neutrons decays by a proton changing to a neutron (which remains in the nucleus) and a positron($\beta+$) which is emitted.

Protons and neutrons are not fundamental particles but each contains three particles called **quarks**. There are two types of quark in protons and neutrons and beta decay occurs when one quark changes to the other type. This causes the neutron to become a proton ($\beta-$ decay) or the proton to become a neutron ($\beta+$ decay).

Summary

1. An atom consists of a central very small **nucleus** which contains all the positive charge and most of the mass of the atom. The nucleus is surrounded by electrons (negative charge) in motion. An atom contains an equal number of positive and negative charges.
2. When a substance decays it gives out **alpha**, **beta** or **gamma** radiation or a combination of these.
3. Alpha particles are helium nuclei, beta particles are electrons, and gamma rays are high frequency electromagnetic waves.
4. The **half-life** of a radioactive substance is the time taken for half the undecayed atoms to decay.
5. It is vital that correct safety procedures are followed when using radioactive materials.
6. The nucleus of a $^{235}_{92}U$ atom splits into two parts of approximately equal masses when it captures a neutron. In addition, two or three fast moving neutrons and about 3×10^{-11} J of energy are released.
7. If one or more of the neutrons released by the splitting of each $^{235}_{92}U$ nucleus are captured by other $^{235}_{92}U$ nuclei, more splitting (fission) occurs.
8. If, on average one of the neutrons released in the splitting of each nucleus causes another similar nucleus to split then a controlled **chain reaction** results.
9. There are few $^{235}_{92}U$ atoms in naturally occurring uranium. More than 99 per cent of natural uranium are $^{238}_{92}U$ atoms which tend to capture neutrons without fission resulting.

Quick test 27

1 What is meant by (a) **atomic number** and (b) **mass number**?

2 What is a particle with a mass of 1 atomic mass unit and a charge of +1 called?

3 What is (a) **an alpha particle**, (b) **a gamma ray**?

4 State what you understand by the term **isotope**.

5 Briefly describe two uses of radioactivity in each of (a) **medicine** and (b) **industry**.

6 What is meant by **half-life**?

7 A radioactive source gives a genuine count rate of 1000 per minute. Three hours later the count rate has dropped to 125 counts per minute. What is the half-life of the source?

8 Atoms of atomic number (proton number) 92 and mass number (nucleon number) 234 decay to form new atoms of atomic number 90 and mass number 230. What does the emission consist of?

9 Name four safety precautions that should be observed when using radioactive sources.

10 Explain what a moderator in a nuclear reactor does.

Chapter 28
The Earth's place in the universe

Astronomy, the study of the heavens, has always fascinated men and women. Early star watchers used their eyes. Later, binoculars and telescopes gave a clearer picture. Nowadays, telescopes that detect invisible radiowaves from outer space, are providing us with even more information. Since Ed Aldrin and Neil Armstrong landed on the Moon on 21 July 1969, our horizons have widened still further. Our colonization of other planets is becoming a possibility.

28.1 What are stars?

Looking up into the sky on a clear night you will see thousands of stars. Stars were formed and continue to be formed by the compression of gas and dust scattered throughout space. Stars emit light as a result of reactions like those in nuclear reactors.

The **Sun** is a **star**. It is the nearest star to Earth and is at the centre of our **solar system**.

Clusters of stars group together to form **galaxies** and billions of galaxies make up the whole **universe**. The Sun and the solar system are part of the **Milky Way** galaxy (Fig. 28.1). There are approximately 100 000 million stars in the Milky Way and the Sun is just one of them. It would take 100 000 light years to cross the Milky Way (i.e. 100 000 years travelling at the speed of light). Light can travel about 10^{16} metres in one year alone. Just imagine how small the Earth really is compared to the size of the universe.

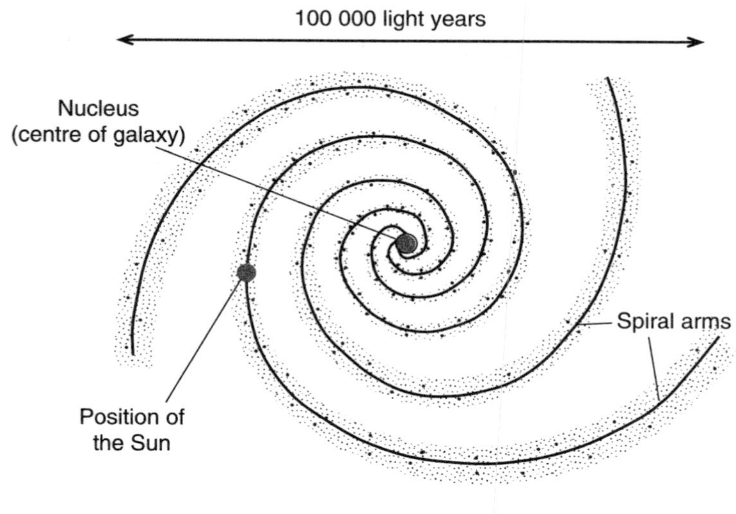

Fig. 28.1 The Milky Way galaxy

28.2 The Sun

Without the Sun there would be no life on Earth. The Sun provides light and warmth for photosynthesis, enabling plants to grow. Fig. 28.2 shows the structure of the Sun.

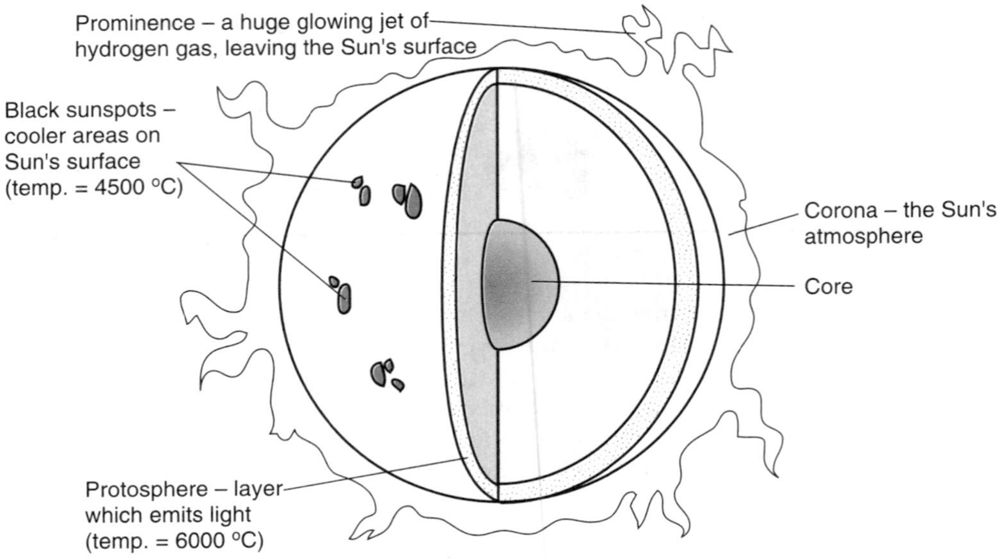

Fig. 28.2 The structure of the Sun

The high temperatures on the Sun are caused by nuclear fusion processes which occur in its core. During these nuclear processes heavy hydrogen (deuterium, ${}^{2}_{1}H$) atoms join together (fuse) to form helium (${}^{4}_{2}He$) atoms.

$$ {}^{2}_{1}H + {}^{2}_{1}H \rightarrow {}^{4}_{2}He + \text{heat} + \text{light} $$

At the same time, enormous amounts of heat and light are emitted and the temperature in the core of the Sun reaches 15 000 000 °C.

Theories about the solar system

Early Greek philosophers watched the Sun, the Moon and other planets carefully. They recorded their movements across the sky. In AD 150, Ptolemy suggested that the Earth was at the centre of the universe and the Sun and stars revolved around it.

A heliocentric theory, in which the Earth and planets revolve around the Sun, was proposed by Aristarchus in the third century BC. Copernicus provided some evidence for this theory in the fifteenth century. As more and more evidence was obtained, it became clear that:

- the Earth and other planets move around the Sun,
- the Earth rotates on a tilted axis once every 24 hours.

28.3 Days, nights and seasons

Day and night

As the Earth rotates on its axis (Fig. 28.3), different parts of the Earth face towards the Sun. When we are in the light, it is daytime. When we are on the side of the Earth away from the Sun, we are in darkness and it is night. It takes 24 hours for the Earth to rotate once on its axis. So, day and night are repeated every 24 hours.

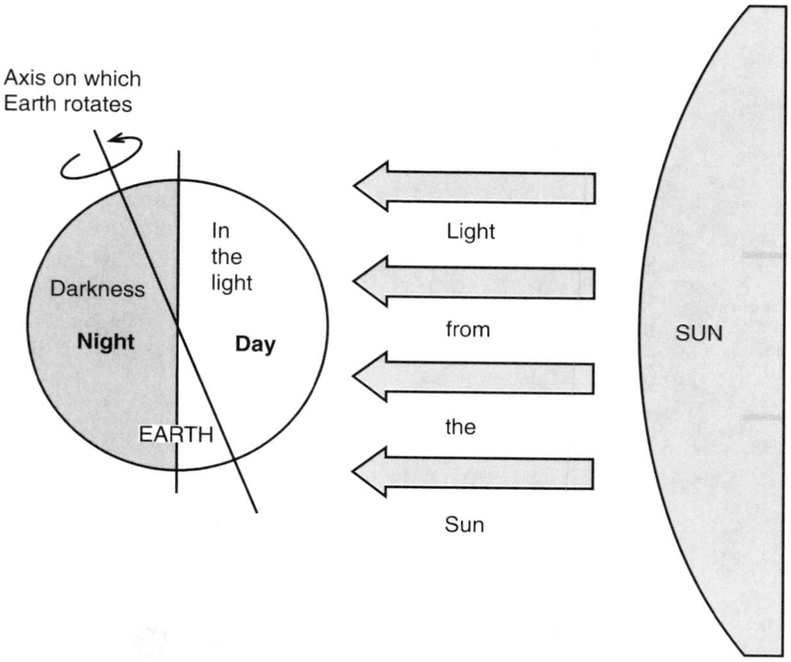

Fig. 28.3 Day and night

Seasons

The Earth revolves around the Sun as well as rotating on its axis. The seasons occur because the Earth's axis is tilted at $23\frac{1}{2}°$ to the vertical (Fig. 28.4). When the Northern hemisphere is tilted towards the Sun, it is summer there and winter in the Southern

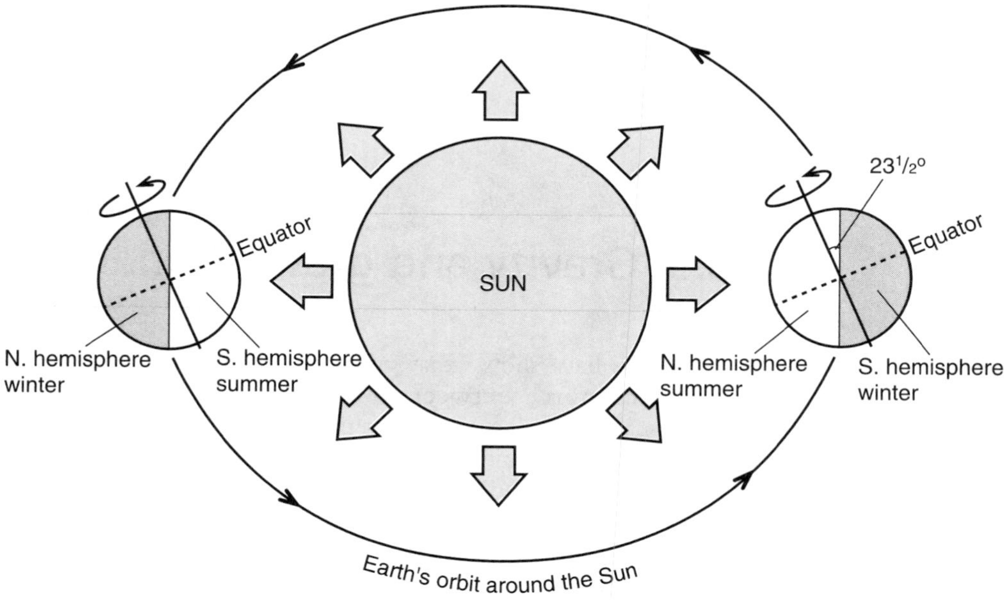

Fig. 28.4 Explaining the seasons

hemisphere. When the Northern hemisphere is tilted away from the Sun, it is winter there and summer in the Southern hemisphere.

It takes $365\frac{1}{4}$ days for the Earth to travel in orbit once around the Sun. So, $365\frac{1}{4}$ days is one **year**. After one year, the seasons are repeated.

Day length

Notice in Fig. 28.4 that when the Northern hemisphere has its summer, the days are longer as more of it is in sunlight than the Southern hemisphere. At this time, more of the Southern hemisphere is in darkness so it has long winter nights.

28.4 Planets and the solar system

Examiner's tip

You may be asked to suggest what conditions are like on other planets based on data about their distance from the sun, size and density.

Our solar system consists of the Sun and nine planets (Fig. 28.5). There are four planets (Mercury, Venus, Earth and Mars) relatively close to the Sun, and five planets (Jupiter, Saturn, Uranus, Neptune and Pluto) further away. All of the planets move in elliptical orbits in the same direction around the Sun. With the exception of Pluto, all the planets lie in much the same plane. Pluto's orbit is at an angle to this plane. The greater the planet's distance from the Sun, the greater the orbit time.

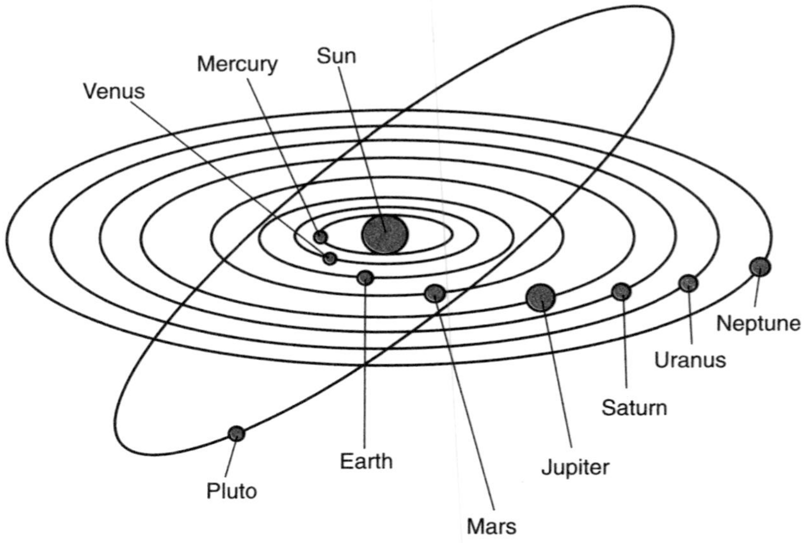

Fig. 28.5 The planets in our solar system

28.5 Gravity and gravitational forces

Experiments have shown that gravitational forces act between all masses. So, there is a gravitational force between you and everything else in the universe. However, gravitational forces get stronger if the objects involved have larger masses or if they are closer. The largest object, close to you, is the Earth. Because of this, the gravitational force between you and the Earth may be 500 N or more. This is your **weight**. Even if you sit close to one of your friends, the gravitational force between the pair of you will only be about one millionth of a newton because you both have very small masses.

The Sun contains 99.8% of the mass of our solar system. Because of this, it exerts very strong gravitational forces. These forces are strong enough to hold the planets in orbit even though they are moving at high speed.

28.6 The Earth

The Earth is shaped like an orange and its structure is like a badly cracked egg. The 'cracked shell' is the **crust**, the 'white' is the liquid **mantle** and the 'yolk' is the **core**. Evidence for the layered structure of the Earth (Fig. 28.6) comes from the study of earthquakes and the Earth's magnetic field.

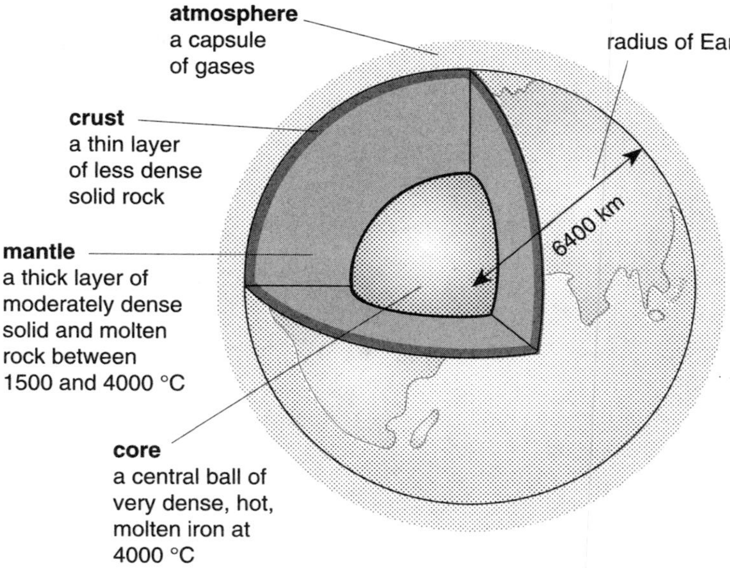

Fig. 28.6 Layers of the Earth. Note how the temperature and density of the layers decrease as you move towards the Earth's surface

When an earthquake occurs, three kinds of shock waves (**seismic waves**) travel outwards from the centre of the quake (**epicentre**).

1. **Surface waves** roll around the surface of the Earth like waves on the ocean. Surface waves are *transverse* waves. They do most damage to buildings.
2. **Primary waves** or **p-waves** go through the Earth. p-waves are *longitudinal* waves. p-waves travel through the mantle and the core at 5 km/s.
3. **Secondary waves (shear waves)** or **s-waves** also go through the Earth. s-waves are *transverse* waves. They travel through the mantle at 3 km/s, but are reflected when they hit the core.

Seismic waves can be detected using a **seismometer**. A large mass is suspended from a beam. Even a slight earth tremor will cause some movement of the suspended mass. This movement can be charted using a pen recorder. Scientists have obtained evidence for the Earth's internal structure from the records of p-waves and s-waves on seismometers.

s-waves are not detected by seismometers at an angle greater than 105° from the epicentre of the quake. p-waves are also *not* detected after 105°, but they reappear again at 140° (Fig. 28.7). This suggests that;

- s-waves cannot pass through the Earth's dense core.
- p-waves are refracted by the core.

The Earth has a strong magnetic field. Scientists think that this magnetism exists because the Earth's core is made of iron. Rocks in the Earth's crust and in lava, which contain iron, also take on this magnetism as they solidify.

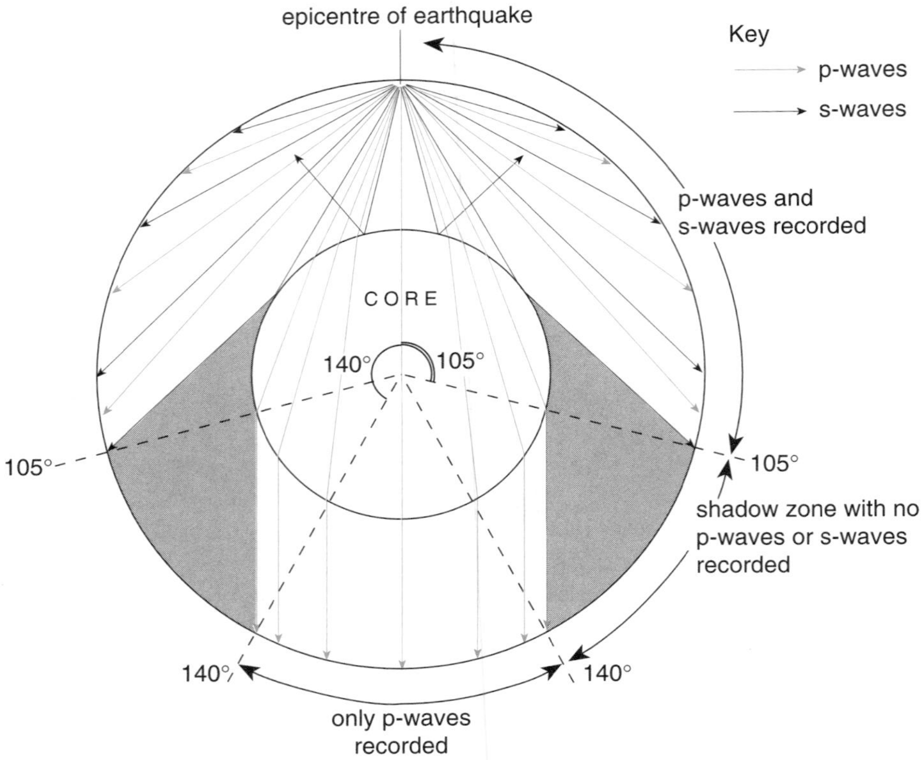

Fig. 28.7 Recording p-waves and s-waves after an earthquake

28.7 The origin of the solar system

It is difficult to imagine how our solar system came about. Astronomers now agree that the Sun and planets were formed about 4600 million years ago. Fig. 28.8 shows the main stages in the process which lasted millions of years.

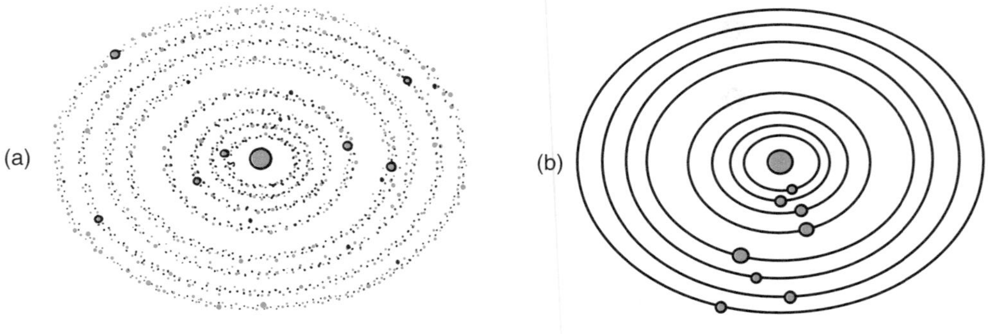

Fig. 28.8 Stages in the formation of our solar system

At first, a cloud of gas and dust rotated around a central heavy core like a flat disc. Dust particles attracted each other by gravity, building up the core and other large spheres within the disc (Fig. 28.8(a)).

Eventually, a small number of dense spheres resulted (Fig. 28.8(b)). The central sphere with the greatest concentration of mass was the Sun and the remainder gave rise to the planets. Gases formed in the atmospheres surrounding these planets.

On planets close to the Sun, where it is hotter, most of the gases have evaporated. This has left small rocky planets (Mercury, Venus, Earth and Mars) with iron cores (Table 28).

Further from the Sun, where it is colder, the gases have not evaporated fully, leaving crystals of methane, ammonia and ice with the gases helium and hydrogen. Because of this, Jupiter, Saturn, Uranus and Neptune are much larger planets with small rocky cores surrounded by vast quantities of gas (Table 28).

Examiner's tip

You are not expected to learn the data in this table.

Table 28 Data concerning the planets in our solar system

Planet	Average distance of planet from the Sun (millions of km)	Diameter of planet relative to diameter of the Earth	Average surface temp (°C)
Mercury	58	0.4	450
Venus	108	1	500
Earth	150	1	20
Mars	228	0.5	−40
Jupiter	778	11	−150
Saturn	1427	9.4	−160
Uranus	2870	4	−220
Neptune	4497	3.9	−230
Pluto	5900	0.5	−230

Pluto, furthest from the Sun, is thought to be a satellite of Neptune which has escaped and moved into its own orbit. It is very small and rocky.

The conditions on a planet depend on two key factors:

- **its nearness to the Sun**, which determines the surface temperature and the evaporation of volatile substances,
- **its relative size**, which determines the gravitational pull on any atmosphere it might have.

In general, the small planets have little or no atmosphere due to their small gravitational attraction. A planet which does have an atmosphere is cooler than it would be without it.

28.8 The Earth and its Moon

The Moon orbits the Earth once a month. It is therefore a satellite or planet of the Earth. Experiments during the American Apollo missions to the Moon in the 1960s have shown that there are no living organisms on the Moon.

At any moment, half of the Moon is lit up by the Sun, and the other half is in shadow. From the Earth we can see only the illuminated side. That is why we see the Moon in various phases or shapes (Fig. 28.9).

Along the line dividing the illuminated and dark sides of the Moon, the Sun's rays cast long shadows. These shadows highlight details of the lunar landscape such as craters and mountain ranges. The craters were caused by meteors (rocks in space) colliding with the Moon whilst it was still molten.

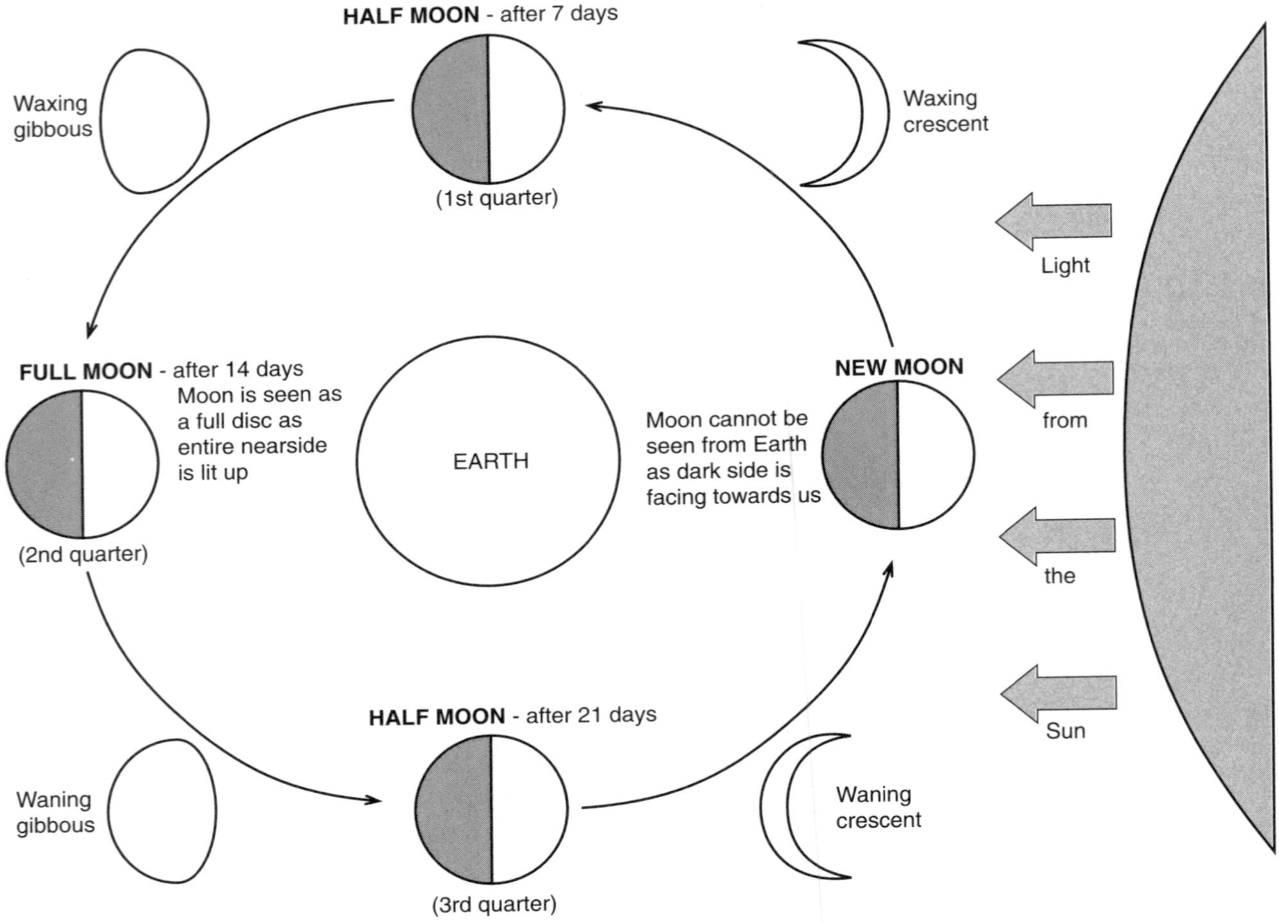

Fig. 28.9 Phases of the Moon

Tides

Tides occur due to the gravitational pull of the Moon (and to a lesser extent the pull of the Sun on the oceans). As the Moon orbits the Earth, its gravitational pull draws the oceans towards it (Fig. 28.10). This causes the sea to rise giving high tides at points A and B and low tides at points X and Y.

At certain times (Full and New Moon), the Sun and Moon are both in line with the Earth (Fig. 28.9). When this happens, the high tides are extra high and the low tides very low. These are called **spring tides**. Halfway between Full and New Moons (Half Moon), the Sun and Moon are at right angles (Fig. 28.9). When this happens, their gravitational pulls tend to cancel each other out. This produces lower high tides and higher low tides called **neap tides**.

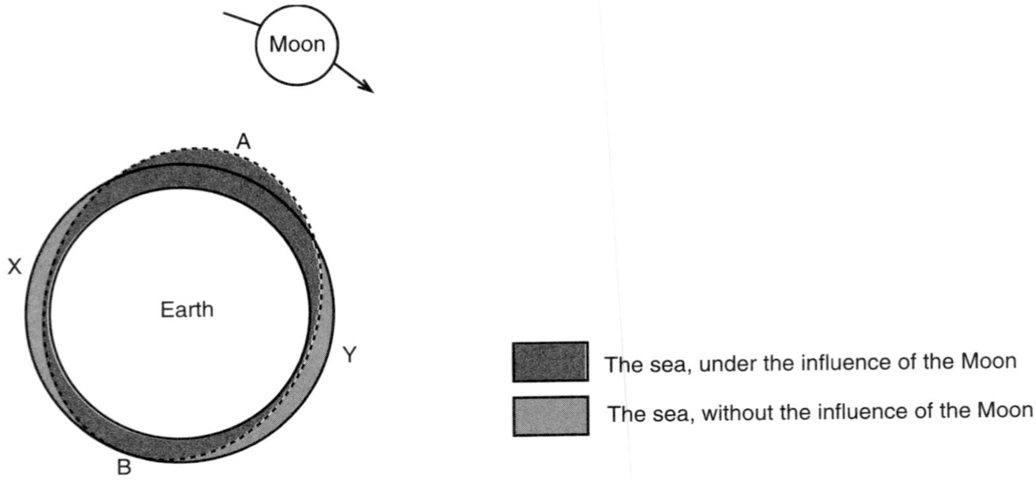

Fig. 28.10 The effect of the Moon on our tides

28.9 Comets

The movements of comets can also be explained using the idea of gravitational forces. Comets travel around the Sun in very long, elliptical orbits. They move fastest when near the Sun (and thus the Earth) where the gravitational forces are greatest and much more slowly when far out in space. Therefore, they spend most of their time well away from the Sun and Earth and we cannot see them. They reappear every few years. Their orbits can be plotted and their arrival in our sky can be predicted by astronomers. Often they are spectacular to look at with bright heads and long sparkly tails, thousands of kilometres long (Fig. 28.11).

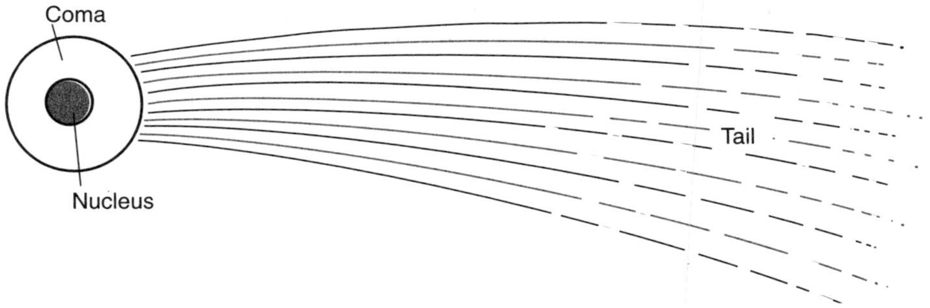

Fig. 28.11 The appearance of a comet

The comet's nucleus is thought to be rocky material covered with vast amounts of frozen gases. The coma is produced when the comet gets close to the Sun, causing some of the frozen gases to vaporize.

Each comet is named after the person who discovered it. The most famous comet is probably Halley's Comet, named after Edmond Halley in 1720. Halley used the idea of gravity and the movement of planets to predict when his comet would be visible from the Earth. He was widely acclaimed when the comet reappeared almost exactly on the date he had predicted.

28.10 Our exploration of space

Over the centuries, astronomers have obtained much information about planets and stars by observing them from the Earth. More detailed information is now obtained by launching rockets into space. The launch and the orbit of any spacecraft are governed by the laws of gravity. Fig. 28.12 explains how a rocket can be launched to orbit the Moon.

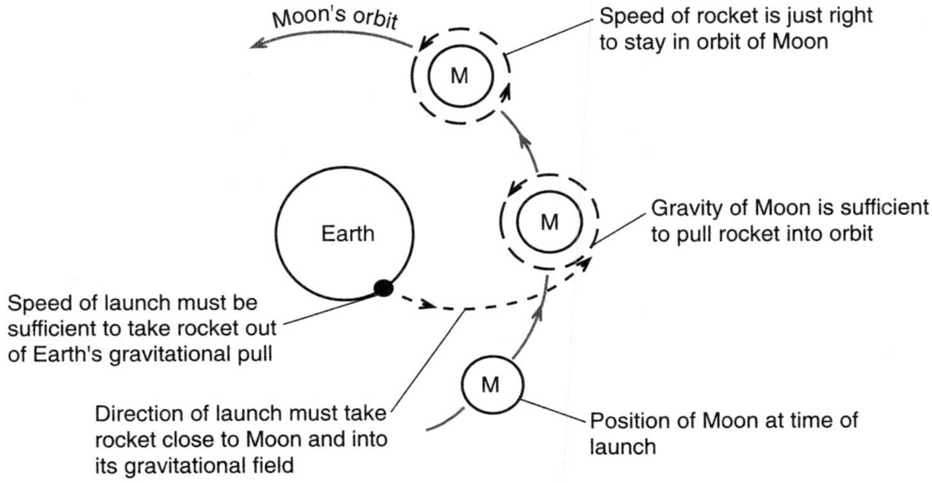

Fig. 28.12 Launching a rocket to orbit the Moon

Rockets have enabled scientists to study 'near space' very successfully. However, astronomers soon realized that artificial satellites would be a more thorough and economical way of studying space. These satellites could be carried into space by rockets and then set in stable orbits around the Earth or other planets. Satellites have already provided detailed photographs of the planets.

Satellites which remain stationary over one place on the equator (that is they orbit the Earth at the same rate as it rotates on its axis) are called **geostationary** and are very useful for transmitting information between two points on the surface of the Earth.

More recently space stations have been built and launched. Scientists can live in these for several months, carrying out experiments which could not be done on Earth. The American Space Shuttle has reduced the cost of sending crews to space stations. It flies back to Earth like an aeroplane and can be used again and again.

Scientists in space stations have studied the Sun and stars in detail. They have also used the weightless conditions in space to purify vaccines and to make ultralightweight foamed steels from metals and glass.

Although colonization of the Moon is possible, there are many problems to overcome:

- There is no air and no water on the Moon.
- The expense of travelling to the Moon would be considerable. Colonists would need to spend significant lengths of time there before returning to Earth.
- Food supplies could not be carried to the Moon from the Earth. It would be necessary to grow plants and produce food there.

Ideally a lunar station would be self-supporting, recycling air, water and food.

28.11 The life cycle of stars

Stars are not permanent. They have 'birth', 'life' and 'death'. Our Sun is a middle-aged star which is about ten thousand million years old. In another ten thousand million years, it will stop emitting light and die.

A piece of coal is normally black. When it is heated it gradually changes colour to dull red and then bright yellow. In the same way, stars indicate their temperature and age by their brightness and colour (see Fig. 28.13).

28.12 The origin of the universe

The presently accepted '**Big Bang**' theory envisages the universe as having begun by the explosion of one large mass about 50 000 million years ago. This theory is supported by our observations of the galaxies. The particular wavelengths of the light arriving from these is typical of the spectrum of hydrogen but with all the values increased by the same proportion. Because the wavelengths are apparently increased they are said to have undergone a **red shift**, i.e. towards the red end of the spectrum. The red shift is greater the further away the galaxy.

The apparent increase in wavelength of light arriving from galaxies is explained by the expanding theory of the universe, that is by thinking of the galaxies moving away from an observer on the Earth as they emit light. The galaxies furthest away from us are moving fastest. All this is consistent with the big-bang idea of its origin.

The ultimate future of the universe depends on the quantity of mass in it and the speed with which the galaxies are moving apart. If these values are sufficiently large, the Universe will go on expanding for ever, if not the galaxies will eventually start to move inwards again and the universe will ultimately implode.

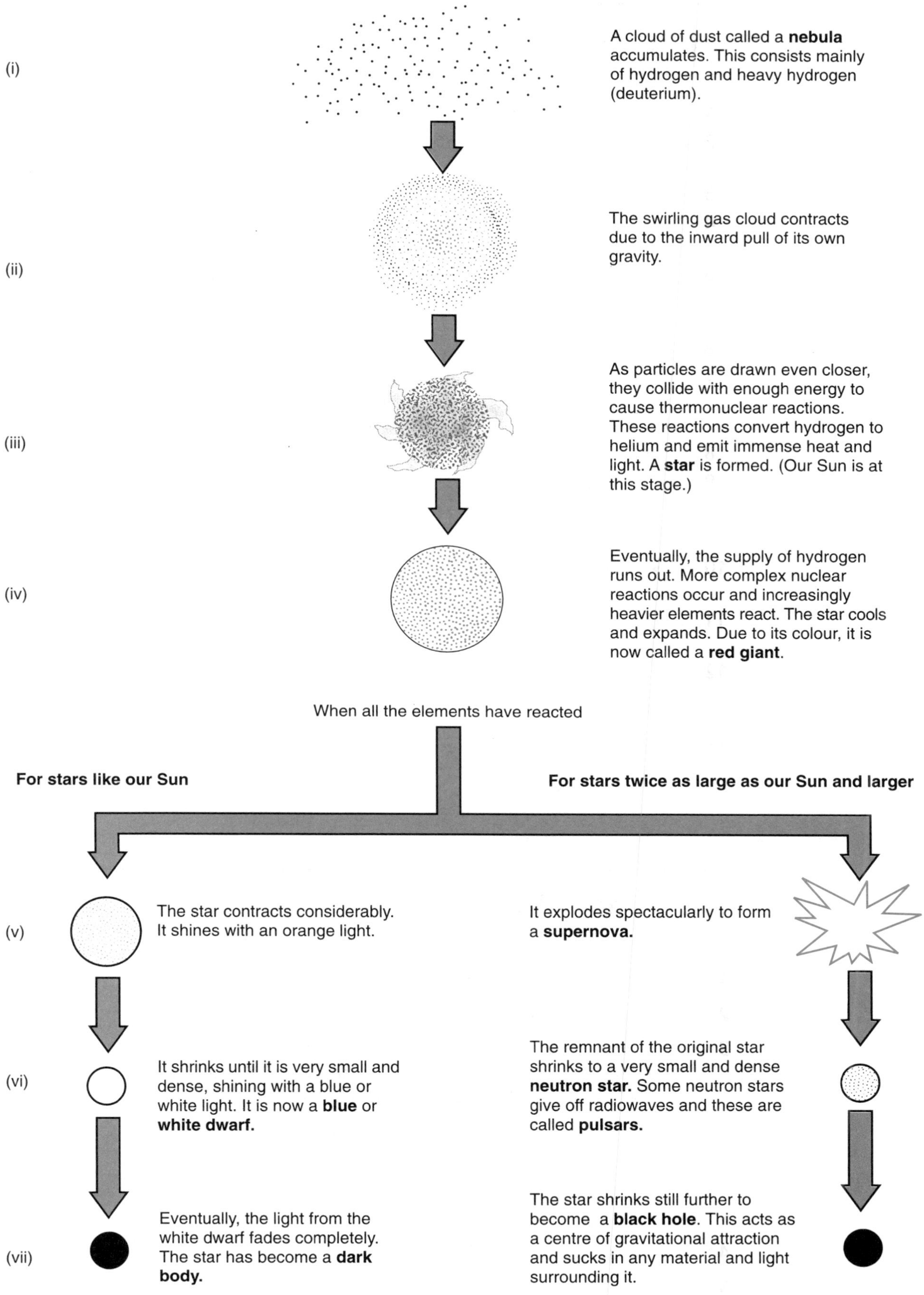

(i)
A cloud of dust called a **nebula** accumulates. This consists mainly of hydrogen and heavy hydrogen (deuterium).
(ii)
The swirling gas cloud contracts due to the inward pull of its own gravity.
(iii)
As particles are drawn even closer, they collide with enough energy to cause thermonuclear reactions. These reactions convert hydrogen to helium and emit immense heat and light. A **star** is formed. (Our Sun is at this stage.)
(iv)
Eventually, the supply of hydrogen runs out. More complex nuclear reactions occur and increasingly heavier elements react. The star cools and expands. Due to its colour, it is now called a **red giant**.
When all the elements have reacted
For stars like our Sun
For stars twice as large as our Sun and larger
(v)
The star contracts considerably. It shines with an orange light.
It explodes spectacularly to form a **supernova.**
(vi)
It shrinks until it is very small and dense, shining with a blue or white light. It is now a **blue** or **white dwarf.**
The remnant of the original star shrinks to a very small and dense **neutron star.** Some neutron stars give off radiowaves and these are called **pulsars.**
(vii)
Eventually, the light from the white dwarf fades completely. The star has become a **dark body.**
The star shrinks still further to become a **black hole**. This acts as a centre of gravitational attraction and sucks in any material and light surrounding it.

Fig. 28.13 The stages in the life cycle of a star

Summary

1 The Sun is a **star**. Stars are immense volumes of hot reacting gas and dust.
2 Clusters of stars make up **galaxies** and billions of galaxies make up the whole **universe**.
3 **Day and night** result from the Earth's rotation on its axis.
4 **Seasons** and the varying lengths of days result from the tilt of the Earth's axis and the Earth's movement around the Sun.
5 Our **solar system** consists of the Sun and nine planets. In order from the Sun these planets are Mercury, Venus, Earth, Mars, Jupiter, Saturn, Uranus, Neptune and Pluto.
6 **Gravitational forces** hold the planets in orbit around the Sun.
7 The Earth has a dense **core** of molten iron at 4000 °C. This is surrounded by less dense, rocky material in the **mantle** at temperatures between 1500 °C and 4000 °C. Lighter materials form a thin surface **crust** about 50 km thick.
8 **Stars** are immense volumes of hot reacting gas and dust.
9 The **conditions on a planet** depend on two key factors:
- its nearness to the Sun and
- its relative size.

10 **The phases** (shapes) **of the Moon** result from the Moon's movement around the Earth.
11 Tides occur due to the gravitational pull of the Moon (and to a lesser extent the Sun) on the oceans.
12 Stars have a life cycle. They begin as a cloud of dust (**nebula**) which contracts, causing thermonuclear reactions, to form a **star**. Eventually the supply of hydrogen runs out and the star cools and contracts.
13 The presently accepted '**Big Bang**' theory envisages the universe as having begun by the explosion of one large mass about 15 000 million years ago. This theory is supported by our observation of the **red shift**.

Quick test 28

1 What causes **day** and **night**?

2 Explain how the **seasons** of the year occur.

3 The sketch shows the masses and positions of two moons relative to planet X. The gravitational force between $4m$ and X is F. Write down the value of the gravitational force between m and X in terms of F.

4 What is a **seismometer** used for?

5 Explain why **tides** occur.

6 Describe the relative positions of the Earth, the Moon and the Sun at (a) **Full Moon** and (b) **New Moon**.

7 What is meant by the **red shift**?

Chapter 29
Communication systems

29.1 A brief history of telecommunications

Man has been inventing methods of sending messages over distances for thousands of years. These early methods all relied on sound or light, for example the North American Indians used smoke signals, early shipping used semaphore flags and later lamps with shutters but all these methods of sending messages relied on good visibility and 'line of sight'.

The first practical telegraph was developed by **Charles Wheatstone** and **William Cooke** in 1837. It was designed to signal the presence of trains on the Euston to Camden Town railway. It was also used to send messages for the public. At the same time **Samuel Morse** developed a system in the USA but Morse's code was much better than Wheatstone's as it allocated the shortest codes to the most frequently used letters of the alphabet. The first commercial telegraph opened in 1844. In 1851 the first successful underwater cable was laid from England to France and in 1858 the first transatlantic cable was laid although it only worked for a short time and had to be replaced in 1866.

The telephone was invented in 1876 by **Alexander Graham Bell** and in 1877, **Thomas Edison** invented the Carbon Microphone for use in telephones. This type of microphone works by changing its resistance as the diaphragm moves. It was modified and refined but the basic design was still widely used until the late 1980s.

The existence of electromagnetic waves was first predicted by **James Maxwell** in 1867 and in 1888 **Heinrich Hertz** successfully transmitted and received electromagnetic waves. These became known as radio waves. The original apparatus was crude and did not work over more than a few metres. The significance of Hertz's experiments was realised by a number of people but it was **Guglielmo Marconi** who developed transmitters and receivers to work over long distances. This became known as 'wireless' telegraphy and culminated in the famous 1901 transmission from Cornwall to Newfoundland in Canada, a distance of 3500 km. The first transmissions were by Morse code. Rapid developments in electronics allowed the first successful speech broadcast in 1906 in the USA.

John Logie Baird's invention of the television was first demonstrated in 1926. It was electromechanical and was not really suitable for domestic use. A completely electronic version was developed by **EMI** and in 1936 the BBC started simultaneous broadcasts using both standards. The electronic version was more satisfactory and was adopted.

By 1949 microwave links were being used to transmit information between London and Birmingham. These links require 'line of sight' between transmitter and receiver but are very reliable and now form part of the telephone and television networks.

In 1962, **Telstar** was launched from Cape Kennedy, USA. This was the first satellite to transmit live television signals. The day after launch, viewers in Europe saw the first live TV broadcast from the USA. The satellite was not in geostationary orbit and could only be used for about 20 minutes in each orbit. The first satellite in geostationary orbit was SYNCOM II which was launched in 1963.

In the 1960s optical fibres were developed. These could carry far more information much further than wires. The main problem that had to be overcome was that of developing a pure enough glass. The first optical fibre to be part of the British telephone network started service in 1977. Now almost all long-distance telephone traffic is carried by optical fibre.

29.2 Communication systems building blocks

Examiner's tip

Sometimes these building blocks are combined in a question.

All communication systems have common elements; these elements, which are the basic building blocks of any system are described below.

- **Encoder** This takes the signal or message and converts it into a code that is suitable for transmission. For example, a message could be put into Morse code for sending down a telegraph or into digital code for transmitting by an optical fibre.
- **Modulator** The coded signal has to be placed onto the carrier. This is done by the modulator. For example a coded message might be used to switch on and off a light beam; in this case, the carrier is the light wave and the modulator is the switch.
- **Transmitter** The modulated carrier has to be transmitted from one place to another. For example, a modulated radio wave is transmitted from an aerial. The power of the transmitter determines the distance from the transmitter that the carrier can be detected.
- **Receiver** The transmitted signal will be detected by the receiver. A radio will receive radio waves. Usually the receiver is combined with a decoder.
- **Decoder** This deciphers the message or signal from the carrier so that the original message can be read. For example, a human might be the decoder for a Morse code message.
- **Storage** Often the message needs to be stored before it is used. For example, a human might write down a decoded Morse message, a tape recorder could be used to store a sound, and a computer disk drive could be used to store a digital message.
- **Transducer** This is a device that changes a signal or message from one type to another. For example, a microphone changes a sound into an electrical signal, a loudspeaker changes an electrical signal into a sound.
- **Amplifier** When signals are transmitted, they are often *attenuated* (reduced in strength). An amplifier is needed to restore the signal to its original strength. The problem with amplifiers is that they generally increase the level of the wanted signal and unwanted background noise, so making it more difficult to distinguish the correct signal.

A typical communication system will be made up of most of the building blocks listed above. It is easier to see how these all relate to each other by using a *system diagram*. (Fig. 29.1)

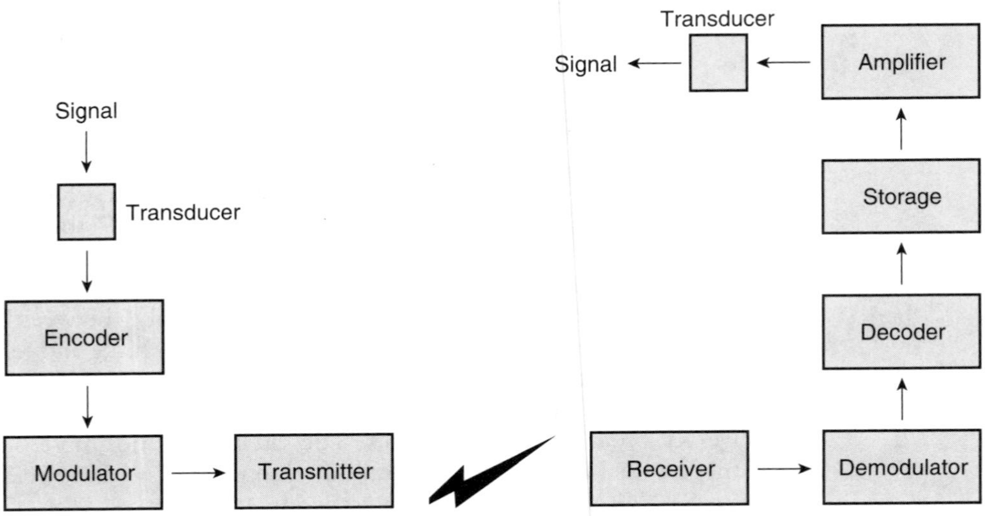

Fig. 29.1

29.3 Transducers

The working of some transducers has been covered elsewhere in this book. The loudspeaker is covered in Unit 23.5 and a moving coil microphone is the reverse of a loudspeaker as vibrations of the diaphragm cause a coil to vibrate in a magnetic field so causing a varying current (Fig. 29.2).

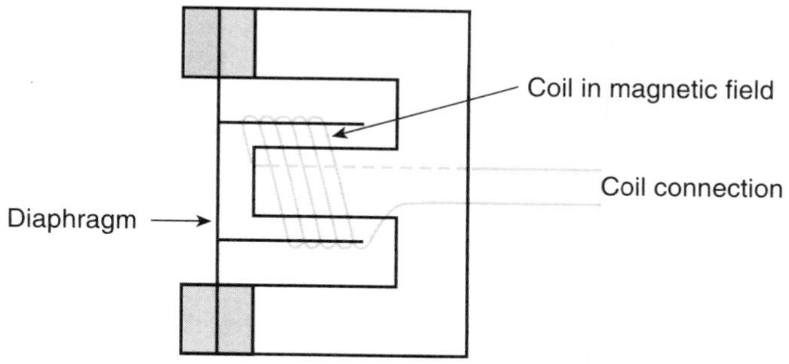

Fig. 29.2

The LED (light emitting diode) is an output transducer. Like all diodes, it only conducts when current flows in one direction. When it does conduct, it emits light. Because it does not rely on a filament getting hot, it is possible to pulse the light emitted so that it can be used to send a signal. LEDs are also used in numerical displays and as indicators.

The photodiode works in the opposite way to the LED. When light falls on the diode, it allows a current to flow in one direction. The size of the current depends on the amount of light. In a circuit, the photodiode is able to produce a changing voltage for a changing light signal and it is used to receive the signals from a LED or from a laser.

The semiconductor laser is similar to the LED but produces intense, coherent light of very precise wavelength. It is able to be switched millions of times per second and the output beam is very narrow. It is ideal for use in optical fibres because of the very narrow range of wavelengths produced.

29.4 Codes

Most signals from transducers are **analogue**. An analogue signal is one where the voltage varies continuously. For example, the electrical signal from a microphone might look like Fig. 29.3

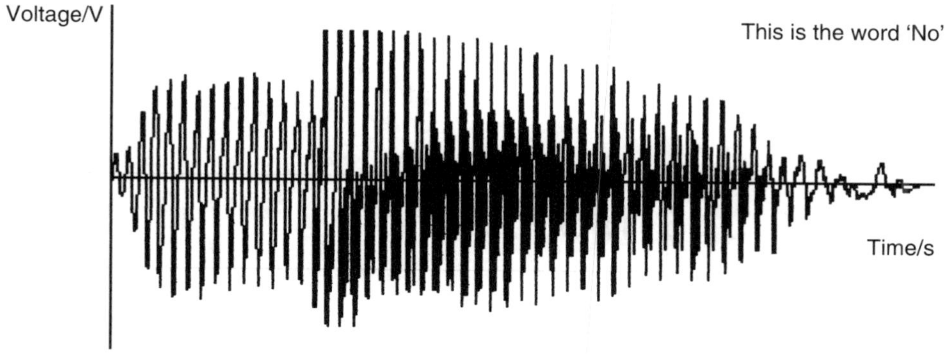

Fig. 29.3

You may have seen an analogue signal like this displayed on an oscilloscope.

Data from a computer or from some transducers is **digital**. A digital signal consists of a voltage that changes only between two levels; zero volts and high voltage (usually 5 volts). A voltage of 0 V represents the binary digit 0 and a high voltage represents the binary digit 1. Therefore any binary number can be represented by a series of pulses of 0 V and a high voltage (Fig. 29.4).

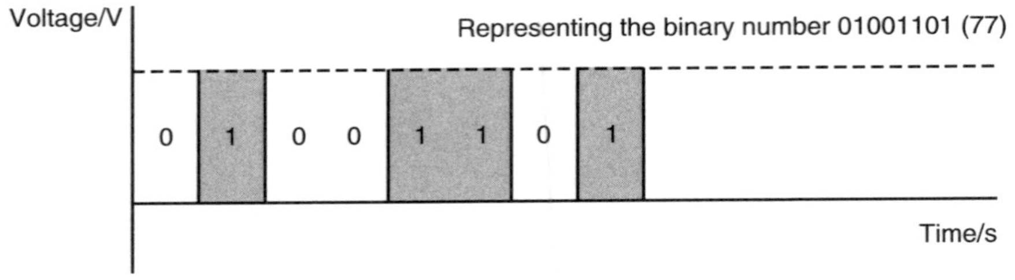

Fig. 29.4

Increasingly, analogue signals are being converted to digital signals before being transmitted. This process is carried out by an electronic circuit called an analogue to digital converter (ADC)

In order to convert from analogue to digital code, the analogue signal is *sampled* at regular time intervals. The instantaneous value of the signal at the sampling time is given a binary code. An 8-bit (binary digit) code is often used. Thus 00000000 would be the code for the lowest voltage possible and 11111111 would be the code for the highest voltage possible. Fig. 29.5 shows a simplified analogue to digital conversion using just 4 bits

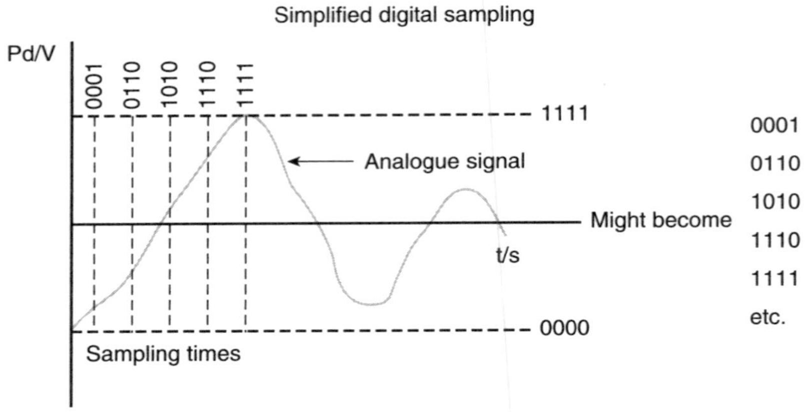

Fig. 29.5

This is how most telephone conversations are transmitted over long distances and how the music is stored on a CD or DAT (digital audio tape). The sampling frequency should be at least twice the maximum frequency of the highest analogue frequency to be reproduced.

New mobile phones are using digital code to transmit voices and soon television will be transmitted in this form.

Digital code is secure and almost immune to interference and noise since the receiver only has to distinguish 0 or 1 and there are complicated error correction codes included with all signals.

29.5 Modulation

In order for information, digital or analogue, to be transmitted over a distance, a carrier has to be used. This is for two reasons: the low frequency speech or music would not travel very far in space and only one signal could be transmitted and received at a time in any one place. A carrier is a higher frequency wave that can be *modulated* in order to transmit the information. There are two basic forms of modulation; frequency modulation (FM) and amplitude modulation (AM).

Both of these forms of modulation are used in radio broadcasting; FM is used in the higher frequency ranges, it is more reliable and gives better reproduction than AM but uses a lot of the available frequency range. If FM were used on the medium waveband, there would only be room for 3 or 4 radio stations. AM is used for transmission down optical fibres but when used in optical fibres, the information is first converted into a digital code.

AM is the simplest modulation system to understand. Medium and long wave radio, television pictures, older mobile phones, optical fibres all use AM.

The original signal (analogue or digital) is made to modulate or change the amplitude of a carrier (radio waves or light)

Examiner's tip

Make sure you can sketch an amplitude modulated signal.

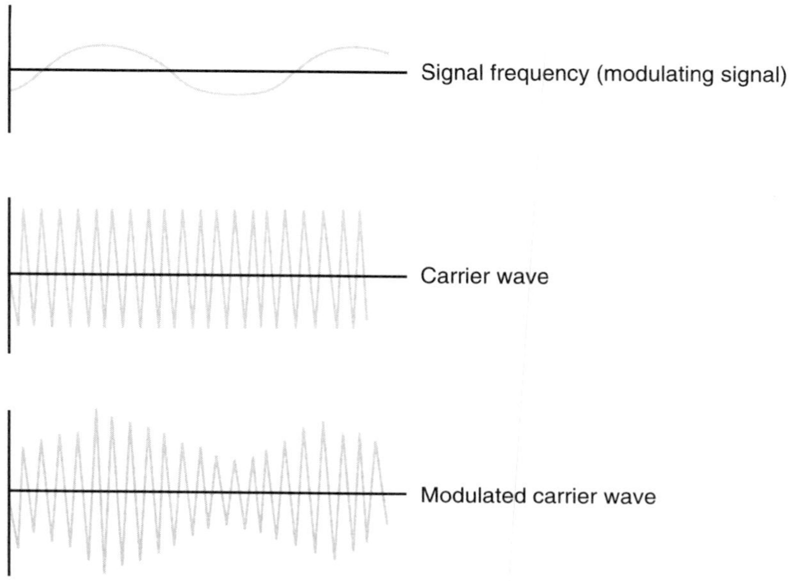

Fig. 29.6

In Fig. 29.6 it can be seen that the amplitude of the final signal follows the original signal. This signal could have just as easily been a digital signal. To decode this signal in the receiver the bottom half of the signal is removed and the 'humps' of the carrier smoothed out (Fig. 29.7).

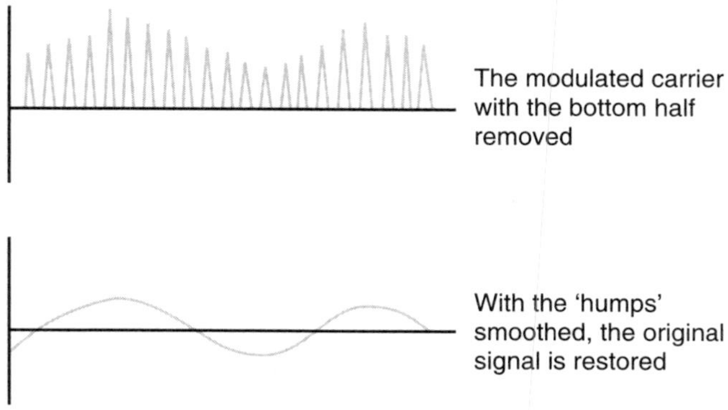

Fig. 29.7

FM is achieved by making the modulating signal change the frequency of the carrier wave (Fig. 29.8).

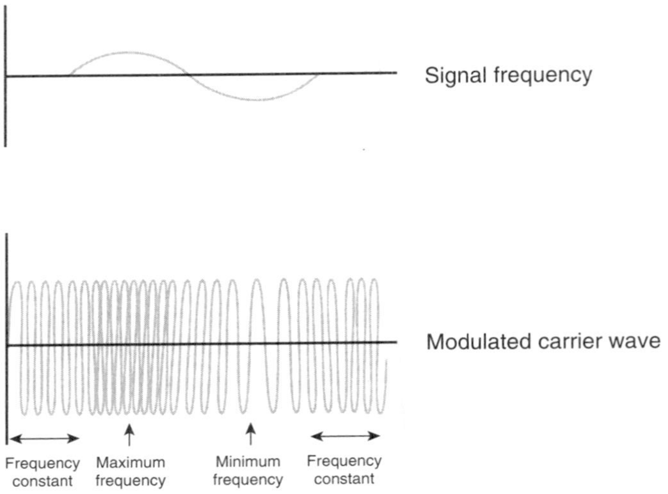

Fig. 29.8

Examiner's tip

Make sure you can sketch a frequency modulated signal.

Decoding the information again is more complicated than for AM.

Summary

1. The development of electronic telecommunications started from the need for reliable communication that was more than 'line of sight'.
2. Efficient communication requires the signal to be coded.
3. Analogue signals are ones that continuously vary.
4. Digital signals only have two allowed values: high or 1 and low or 0.
5. Analogue signals can be coded as a digital signal.
6. Transmission of a digital signal is more reliable and accurate than an analogue signal.
7. All communication systems can be broken down into a number of basic building blocks.

Quick test 29

1. The signal received at the end of the first transatlantic cable was very weak. Give a reason for the loss of energy.
2. Draw a system diagram for a ship to ship signalling system using lamps. Name the devices that perform the following:
   (a) the transmitter
   (b) the carrier wave
   (c) the decoder
   (d) the information storage
3. Explain what is meant by:
   (a) an analogue signal
   (b) a digital signal
4. Why is digital code being used increasingly for communications?
5. Explain with the help of a diagram what is meant by amplitude modulation.

Chapter 30
Information storage

Information can be stored in two basic forms: analogue and digital. Records and most recording tape use analogue storage. CDs, computer discs, some recording tape and solid state memory all store digital information.

30.1 Analogue recording

This relies on a continuously varying signal stored as some continuously varying property of the recording medium.

Records

For a record, the continuously varying property is the shape of the sides of a groove in a plastic disc. The electrical gramophone, introduced in the 1920s revolutionized recording techniques.

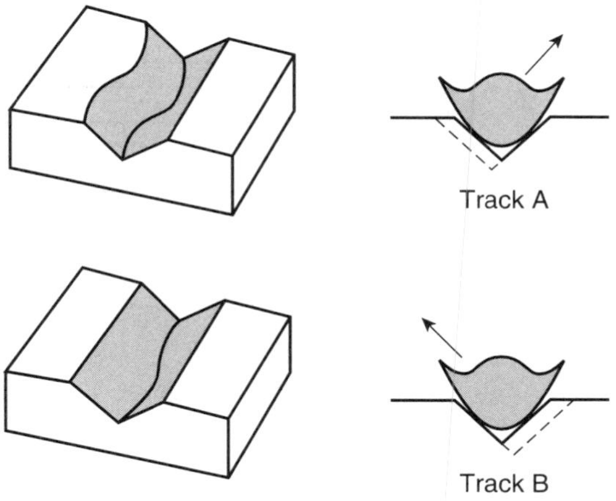

Fig. 30.1 Soundtracks on a stereo disc showing the movements of the stylus on each track

The stereo disc carries two soundtracks, each of which is recorded by a separate microphone. The two separate soundtracks are built on the sides of the groove. The angle between them is 90° (Fig. 30.1). As the disc turns, the stylus is pushed in two directions perpendicular to each other. The movements of the stylus in these two directions is detected by two separate coils and magnets, converted to an electrical signal and fed to the two amplifiers. The problem with records is that any dirt on the record or damage to the surface is also detected by the stylus and amplified. The disc turns at a constant speed, therefore the outer tracks play at a greater linear speed than the inner tracks.

Recording tape

The continuously varying medium is the magnetization of a layer of magnetic material such as ferric oxide. This contains millions of magnetic 'particles' that behave like tiny magnets. Normally these are all jumbled up so that their effects cancel out and the tape is unmagnetized.

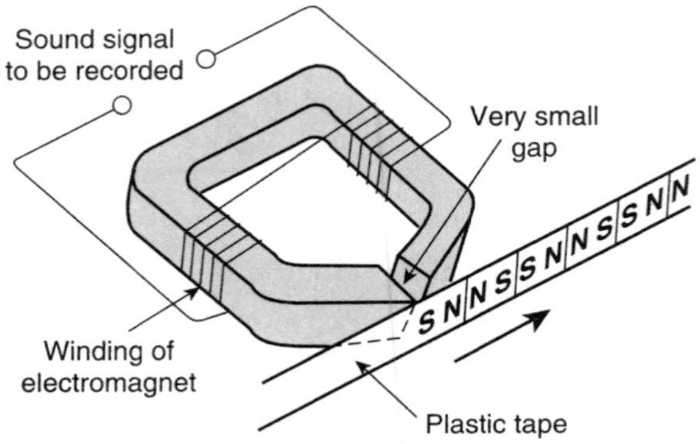

Fig. 30.2

The recording head is an electromagnet with a tiny gap in it and as the analogue signal is fed to the head, the tape is passed, at a steady speed, across the gap. The changing magnetic field is 'captured' by the magnetic particles on the tape (Fig. 30.2).

Passing the tape back over the head induces a small current in the electromagnet which is amplified and fed to a loudspeaker. Normally a different head is used for recording and playback. Stereo signals are recorded as two different 'channels' (Channels 1 and 2) on the tape.

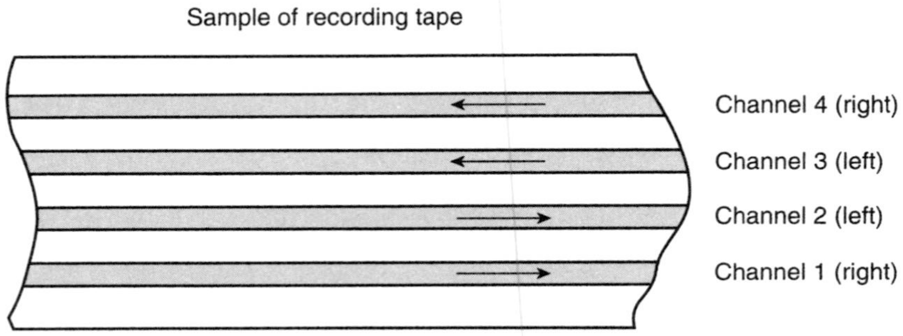

Fig. 30.3

When the tape is turned over, the tape goes the other way and the sound is recorded on channels 3 and 4

30.2 Digital recording

Computer disk

The principle behind storage of information on a computer disk, hard or floppy, is similar to magnetic tape. The disk is coated with a magnetic material and, as it rotates, the disk is written to and read by a recording head. The computer controls where the head looks for the information and the information itself is stored as a digital code rather than an analogue signal.

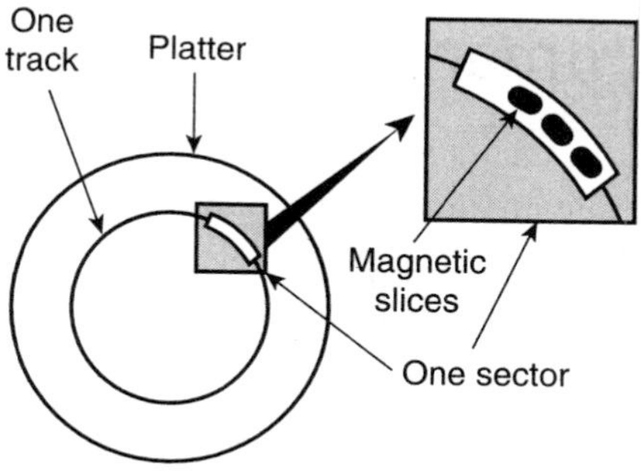

Fig. 30.4 How information is recorded onto a magnetic disk

When a disk is formatted, tracks are recorded which can receive information. More importantly, the directory is created. In the directory the computer stores information about where particular files are located on the disk. When a file is deleted, the computer simply removes the information about it from the directory.

Compact disc

The analogue signal is sampled at 44.1 kHz. The digital code generated is recorded on the surface of the compact disc by making a series of 'pits' in the surface. A pit is a '1' and no pit is a '0'.

The pattern of pits is read by a laser that is focused to a tiny beam by a lens. The beam has to be tiny as the pits on the disc are only separated by a distance of about 1μm (1×10^{-6} m). A laser has to be used as the information is detected by measuring the interference between the reflected beam and the original beam. Because the surface of the disc is read only by a light beam, it does not become damaged with use, unlike a record. Also small amounts of dirt on the surface will not affect the data read by the laser and so will not cause a problem. The disc spins at a variable rate as the data is read at a constant linear speed. This means that the disc has to spin slower when reading the outside tracks than when reading the inner tracks. Another difference between a CD and a record is that the spiral track starts at the centre rather than at the edge. Fig. 30.5 provides a simplified diagram of the reading mechanism of a CD player.

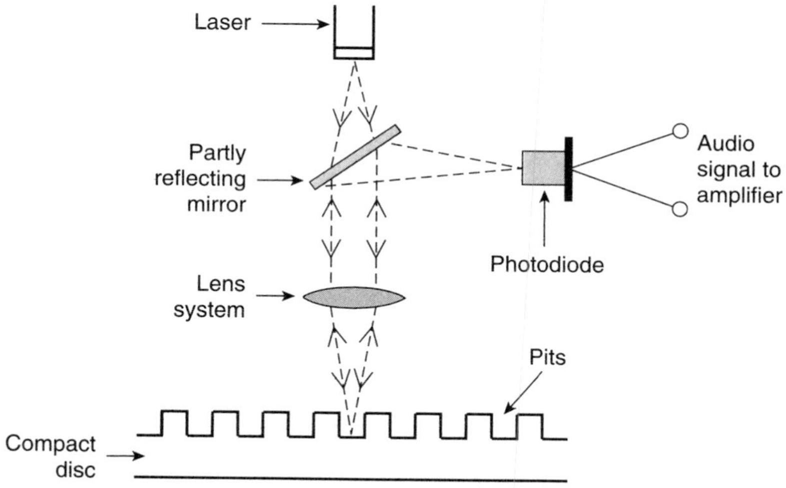

Fig. 30.5

The digital signal output has to be converted back into an analogue signal to be amplified and fed to the loudspeaker. This process is carried out by an electronic system called a Digital to Analogue converter (DAC).

Summary

1 Information can be stored either as an analogue signal or as a digital signal.

2 Records and magnetic tape store analogue signals. The signal is stored by means of a continuously varying property; in the case of a record this is the shape of the groove.

3 Digital signals are stored on tape, on discs, on CD or in solid state memory. The signal is stored as a series of 1s and 0s.

4 Analogue signals are more likely to have noise with them when they are replayed.

Quick test 30

1 How is the analogue signal stored on a record?

2 Why are records and analogue tapes noisy when played back?

3 How does the recording head of a tape recorder store the signal on the recording tape?

4 Digital recording is more reliable than analogue. Why is this?

Chapter 31
Radio waves

Radio waves are part of the electromagnetic spectrum (see Unit 16.2). Like all waves, radio waves can be reflected, refracted, diffracted and can show interference effects. All these wave effects are particularly important for the reception of radio signals. The speed of all radio waves in air is the same, 3×10^8 m/s. Since for all waves, $v = f\lambda$, a long wavelength means a low frequency and a short wavelength means a high frequency.

31.1 How radio waves travel

Radio waves travel in straight lines. The curvature of the earth prevents a radio wave travelling in a straight line without going off into space but it soon became clear from the experiments of Marconi and others that long distance radio communication is possible. The reason is the ionosphere; this is a layer of reflecting ions starting about 50 km above the surface of the earth. This layer bounces radio waves back down to the surface of the earth. Radio waves are also reflected from the surface of the earth and under the right conditions can propagate all around the world by successive reflections (Fig. 31.1(b)).

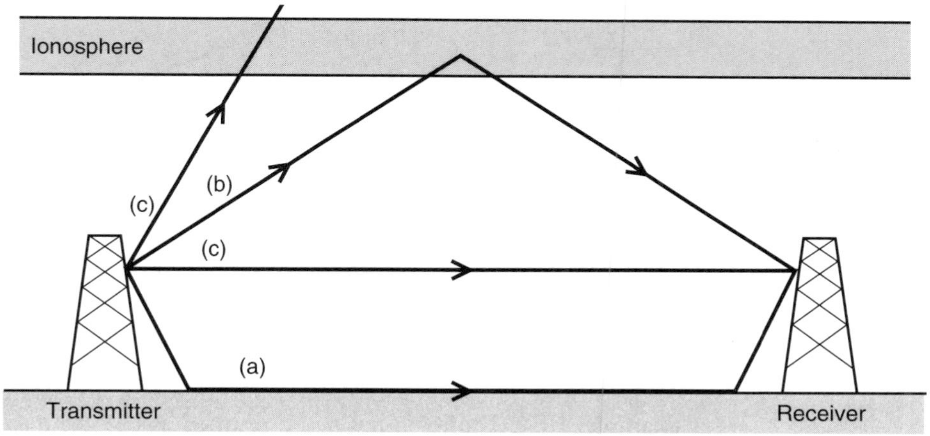

Fig. 31.1 The propagation of radio waves (a) ground waves (b) sky waves (c) space waves

Although the ionosphere plays an important part in the propagation of radio waves, it is not the only method. The method of propagation depends on the frequency of the carrier wave:

- For waves up to about 2 MHz (150m) waves follow the surface of the earth due to diffraction. These are known as ground waves and their range is of the order of 1000 km.
- For waves between 3MHz and 30MHz (100m–10m) the waves travel around the earth by reflecting off the surface of the earth and the ionosphere. This is used for worldwide radio communications. These waves are known as sky waves.

Examiner's tip

You need to be able to work out frequency when given the wavelength (and the reverse) by using $v = f \times \lambda$.

- For frequencies above 30 MHz, the waves pass straight through the ionosphere. This is used for short range communications and 'line of sight' communication, e.g. microwaves. These waves are known as space waves and are ideal for communicating with aircraft, satellites and space craft.

Features on the ground can absorb, reflect, or diffract radio waves. The short radio waves associated with FM broadcasts are space waves and so should obey the 'line of sight' rule. In built-up areas, reflections off buildings and hills can allow reception without a direct 'line of sight' to the transmitter. However, for television reception, these reflections are a nuisance, resulting in double images or 'ghosting' on the screen.

Long wave radio transmissions, e.g. Radio 4 1500m, diffract sufficiently to follow the curvature of the earth. Also, in the shadow of a hill or a large building, long wave reception is usually much better than short wave reception because the longer waves are diffracted more by the obstacles. This helps to explain why they have a greater area of coverage than FM broadcasts (Fig. 31.2).

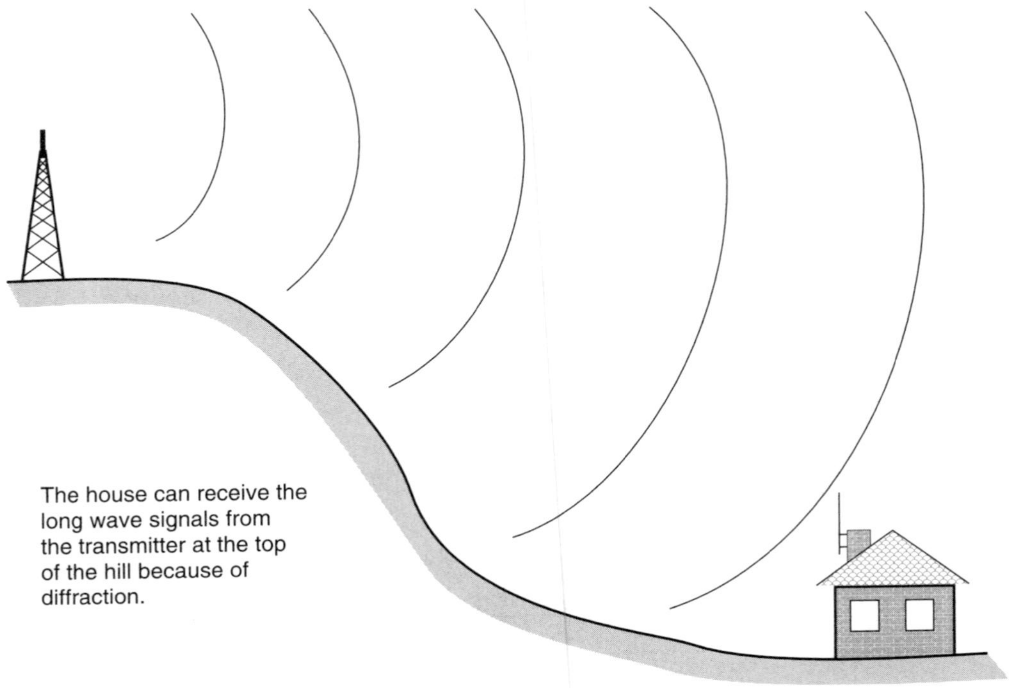

The house can receive the long wave signals from the transmitter at the top of the hill because of diffraction.

Fig. 31.2

Interference effects are a constant problem for broadcasters; if two radio or television transmitters, transmitting on the same frequency, overlapped their coverage area, some receivers could be in positions of destructive interference and receive no signal at all. In order to reduce this problem, national FM radio transmitters have to broadcast their signals with different carrier frequencies in different areas; this is why a car radio set to, for example, BBC Radio 1, has to be retuned as the car travels to different parts of the country. The same is true of television broadcasts but the reception problems are helped by having aerials that only receive signals from one direction and which are pointed at the transmitter (Fig. 31.3).

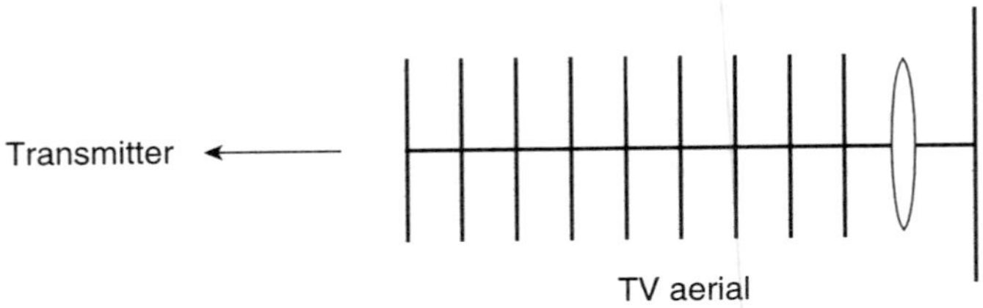

Fig. 31.3

Summary

1 For radio waves $v = f\lambda$.

2 Radio waves can be reflected, refracted, diffracted and undergo interference.

3 Radio waves travel differently depending on their wavelength:

- ground waves are long wavelength and diffract around the curvature of the earth.
- sky waves have wavelengths 100–10m and reflect off the ionosphere around the earth.
- space waves have wavelengths shorter than 10m and have to have 'line of sight'.

4 Diffraction around obstacles allows good coverage by long waves.

5 Interference causes problems for broadcasters and this is why national FM stations have to have different frequencies in neighbouring areas.

Quick test 31

1 BBC Radio 4 broadcasts on long wave with a frequency of 200 kHz. Calculate the wavelength of the carrier waves.

2 Explain why BBC Radio 4 on long wave has good coverage, even in valleys and under bridges where other signals are too weak.

3 Two local radio stations use the same high frequency radio waves to broadcast their FM programmes. The local stations are in York and Newcastle. How can they both use the same frequency?

4 Radio waves transmitted from a ground-based transmitter can be used to provide worldwide communication by reflections from the ionosphere. Why are some places on the earth not able to receive some transmissions?

Chapter 32
Satellites

32.1 Developments

The early communications satellites worked in the passive mode. This means that they simply reflected signals back down to earth. The signals could be received over a very wide area but were weak, needing a large receiving dish. The transmitters had to be very powerful.

All satellites are now active devices. The signals are beamed up to the satellite on a high frequency carrier. The received signal is then processed within the satellite and returned to earth in a narrow beam and at a lower frequency.

Telstar, launched in 1962, was designed to relay signals between the United States, Europe and Japan. It was put into a low elliptical orbit and could only relay signals during short periods of each orbit. This was clearly a disadvantage and in 1967, INTELSAT 2B, the first geostationary communications satellite was launched. Geostationary satellites have the advantage that the transmitter and receiving dish aerials can be permanently pointed in one direction and the satellite can relay signals continuously.

A large number of other satellites have been launched. Some are geostationary and provide communications and satellite television, others have remote sensing equipment and monitor atmospheric and surface conditions on earth, others are equipped to look out into space and provide information on the nature of the universe that would be difficult or impossible to gather from the earth's surface.

32.2 Geostationary satellites

A geostationary satellite is one which stays above the same place on the surface of the earth. It must be above the equator (Fig. 32.1).

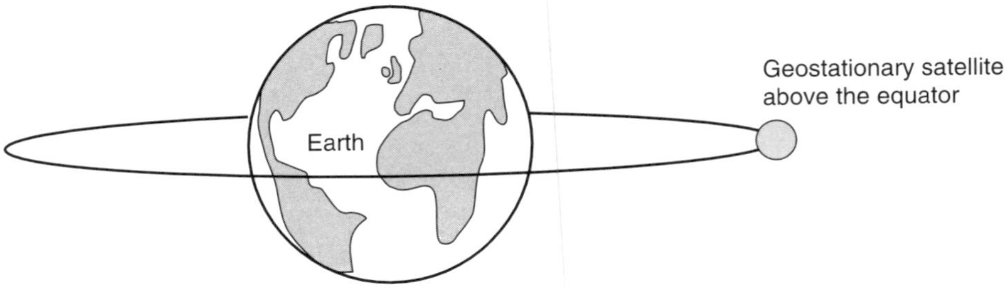

Fig. 32.1
Geostationary satellite above the equator

As the satellite is performing circular motion, there must be a centripetal force (see unit 3.5). This force is provided by gravity. Newton's law of gravitation states that the gravitational force F acting on a satellite at a distance R from the centre of a planet, depends on the mass of the planet M and the mass of the satellite m

$$F = \frac{GMm}{R^2}$$

G is the Universal Gravitational constant and is equal to 6.67×10^{-11} N m^2/kg^2

Since this force provides the centripetal force:

$$\frac{mv^2}{R} = \frac{GMm}{R^2}$$

$$\text{so, } v^2 = \frac{GM}{R^0}$$

but the satellite must travel round its orbit once per day with the rotation of the earth, so it travels at a distance $2\pi R$ in a time $T = 24 \times 3600$ s

$$\text{so, } v = \frac{2\pi R}{T}$$

$$\text{and therefore } v^2 = \frac{4\pi^2 R^2}{T^2}$$

The mass of the Earth is about 6×10^{24} kg and using these expressions, it is possible to work out that the radius of the orbit of a geostationary satellite is about 42 400 km and since the radius of the earth is 6400 km, the height of a geostationary satellite must be 36 000 km. This means that there is only *one* orbit that is geostationary.

32.3 Polar orbits

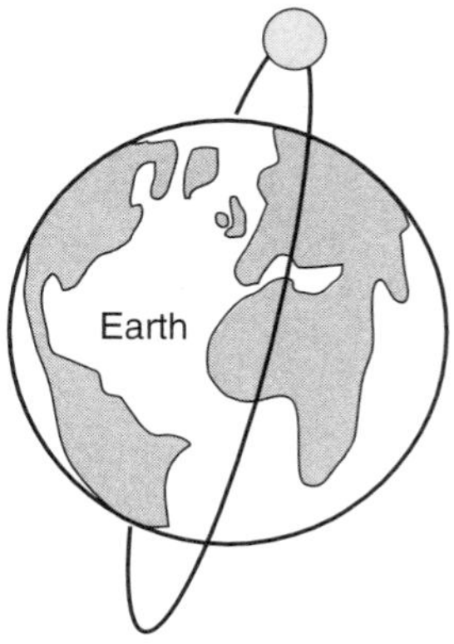

Polar satellites orbit while the earth rotates below them

Fig. 32.2 A satellite in polar orbit

A polar orbit allows a satellite to be closer to the surface of the earth. As the satellite orbits, the earth rotates below. The result is that the satellite covers the surface of the earth in a long, continuous strip. Spy satellites and remote sensing satellites orbit in this way so that they can cover the whole surface of the earth.

Summary

1. Communications satellites are active devices and are most useful when in geostationary orbit.
2. A geostationary orbit is above the equator with an orbital time of 24 hours. There is only one possible geostationary orbit.
3. Gravity provides the centripetal force needed to keep a satellite in orbit.
4. The gravitational force depends on $\frac{1}{R^2}$
5. Not all satellites are geostationary, many remote sensing satellites are in polar orbits or orbits inclined to the equator.

Quick test 32

1. Why is it not possible to have a geostationary satellite above London?
2. Why do all the satellite television dishes in this country point roughly South? Which direction would they point in Australia?
3. What is the advantage of a polar orbiting satellite? What is a disadvantage?
4. A polar satellite orbits at a distance of 12 800 km from the centre of the earth. How long does it take to orbit the earth once?

The examination

Technique

Success in any examination for which you have been entered depends on good examination technique. The best way of developing this technique is by practising answering sample examination questions. Many such questions follow later in this section. Whenever you are answering examination questions, either as practice or when taking the real examination, apply the following points:

- **Arrive in plenty of time** so that you are unhurried and therefore calm.
- **Come fully equipped** with pen, pencil, rubber, ruler, calculator, watch and coloured pens or pencils.
- **Read the examination instructions carefully**.
- **Plan your time for answering** according to the marks allocated to each part of the question. If you are stuck on part of a question, leave it and come back to it at the end.
- **Do the correct number of questions** (often all of them). Usually, you will have plenty of time to finish the required number of questions. Always check right through the paper for any parts of questions that you may have missed.

  Never leave any section blank. Write in as sensible an answer as you can. Any reasonable answer will score some marks, whereas leaving a blank will gain you no marks.
- **Understand and answer the question asked**. Never twist the examiner's words into a meaning that was never intended. It is no use answering a completely different question from that written on the examination paper. This will earn you no marks.
- **Plan before writing** your paragraph and experimental answers. Organize key words or thoughts into a *logical order* or pattern. This is particularly important when you have been asked to design an experiment. Use *short, concise* and *clear* sentences, each one explaining a single step in the procedure.

  The number of marks available for each part of a question gives an indication of the number of different points you should make. The space provided is usually more than enough for the length of answer required.
- **Use large labelled diagrams** in your answers if they make your answers clearer. Descriptions of experiments are almost always clearer, and much shorter, when diagrams are included. Diagrams save words.
- **Set out your work neatly**. An examiner is human. If your written answers are neatly set out, he is much more likely to give you the benefit of the doubt where your answers are not entirely clear. *Illegible answers gain no marks.*
- **Check your spelling, punctuation and grammar**. This may affect your marks.
- **Keep a cool head**. You can only do this by getting plenty of sleep and regular meals and exercise during the examination period. Take sufficient exercise each day so that you are tired enough to sleep soundly.

Tackling questions

Short or structured

Short answer questions are usually easy questions requiring only writing one or two words, choosing words from a list, finishing a table or labelling a diagram. They give good coverage of the syllabus. As the syllabuses for GCSE require two-thirds of the questions to consist of non-short answer questions, the number of these questions will be limited.

Most questions are 'structured' into sections. In each section the examiner is looking for a small number of definite points or facts – just how many is often indicated by the mark allocation. Recall the relevant points/facts (jot them down in pencil, if necessary), arrange them in order and then write them down. In this way your answer will be logically arranged and nothing will be left out. Do not include irrelevant information. Sheer length of answer will not gain any more marks.

The following is an example of this type of question.

On a hot day in summer a cool breeze often sets in from the sea on to the land around midday.

(a) Explain how this breeze happens. (4)

(b) Could the reverse happen, i.e. a breeze from the land to the sea? If so, at what time of day is this most likely to happen? Explain how it happens. (3)

A good answer would be.

(a) The specific heat capacity of the land is much less than that of the sea. Therefore, by the middle of a sunny day, the land gets hotter than the sea. The air above it becomes less dense and rises. It is replaced by cooler air flowing in from the sea.

(b) Yes, in the middle of a clear night, the land will be colder than the sea. The relatively warm air over the sea will rise. It will be replaced by cooler air from over the land.

Note that:

- There are four sentences in the answer to part (a), each containing a vital piece of physics. There is one mark for each piece. Similarly there are three sentences and three marks in part (b).
- There is no mark for 'Yes' in part (b).
- All the information given in the answer is not only *relevant* but *vital.*
- In the answer to both parts, the pieces of information are given in a *logical* order.

In both Foundation and Higher tier examinations at least 25% of the marks must be allocated to questions requiring either **Extended** or **Continuous** writing. Continuous writing is defined as an answer needing one or two sentences. Extended writing is defined as an answer needing three or more consecutive sentences. The balance between extended and continuous writing is different in the two tiers.

Foundation tier	5% extended writing
	20% continuous writing
Higher tier	10% extended writing
	15% continuous writing

Although the specification for questions mentions numbers of sentences, you will not be penalized if you do not write in sentences. Particularly if you are short of time near the end of the examination, concise notes will be acceptable.

The important thing to remember is that your answer must be well structured. When you have written your answer, read it through critically. Do not be tempted just to add extra words to make your answer look longer. Your answer can still score full marks if it is short, providing it correctly answers all aspects of the question.

Examination terms

- '**State**' or '**list**' means put down as simple words or facts – nothing more. '**Name**' is a similar instruction; no explanation is required.
- '**Explain**' requires not only the facts but also the reasons behind them. When you are answering an 'explain' question, ask yourself 'which?', 'what?', 'where?', 'why?' and 'when?' about the subject. This will help you to avoid leaving out information that you know. However, you *must* only give the information that is asked for; for example 'which?' and 'when?' may be irrelevant in a particular question.
- '**Calculate**' usually means not only give the numerical answer but show your working. Often marks are awarded if the method is correct even though the answer is wrong.
- '**Suggest**' means that there may be a number of 'correct' answers. You are required to reason or to apply scientific knowledge to the information given. You may not have met the answer before: an hypothesis is required.

Graphs and diagrams

- **Graphs**: If you are asked to put information onto a graph you must:
  1. Label both axes with both the quantity and its unit, e.g. 'mass in kg' or 'acceleration in cm/s^2'.
  2. Plot all the points accurately with the help of a ruler to lead your eye to the precise spot. Mark each with a neat cross.
  3. Finally plot a line of 'best fit' either by eye or with the help of a computer. This line should be continuous, smooth and visible but not too thick.
- **Diagrams**: Whenever you have to draw one (usually in writing up an experiment) always:
  1. *Draw in pencil.* This is in case you need to rub out anything.
  2. *Draw large* within reason. This is for clarity and easy labelling.
  3. *Rule lines for labels* in ink or biro, using a ruler. The lines should end on the part indicated, not stop short of it.
  4. *Label* each line neatly in ink or biro. In a 'block' or circuit diagram you should put the labels/symbols in or next to each box or component.

Common errors

- Giving too many answers and hoping that the examiner will give you marks for the correct ones and ignore the wrong ones, e.g. 'light, sound and ultra-violet' in answer to a question (2 marks) which asks you to list two types of transverse wave.
- Imprecise answers, e.g. 'the resistance changes' rather than 'the resistance increases (or doubles)'.
- Leaving out the unit in numerical answers.
- Inaccurate spelling. In particular, learn the correct spelling of technical terms.
- Inaccurately labelled diagrams, either because some labels are left out or because it is not clear what the line(s) is/are pointing to, or both.
- Not labelling axes of graphs with both the quantity and the unit.
- Not showing working in calculations.

Practice exam questions

Questions of the short answer or structured type are used most by the Examining Groups. The answer can be a single word, or number, a phrase or several sentences. A space is usually left for the student's answer; this is often an indication of the length of answer required.

Chapter 2 (answers – page 198)

1 Fig. 1 shows the distance against time graph of a journey made by two trains.

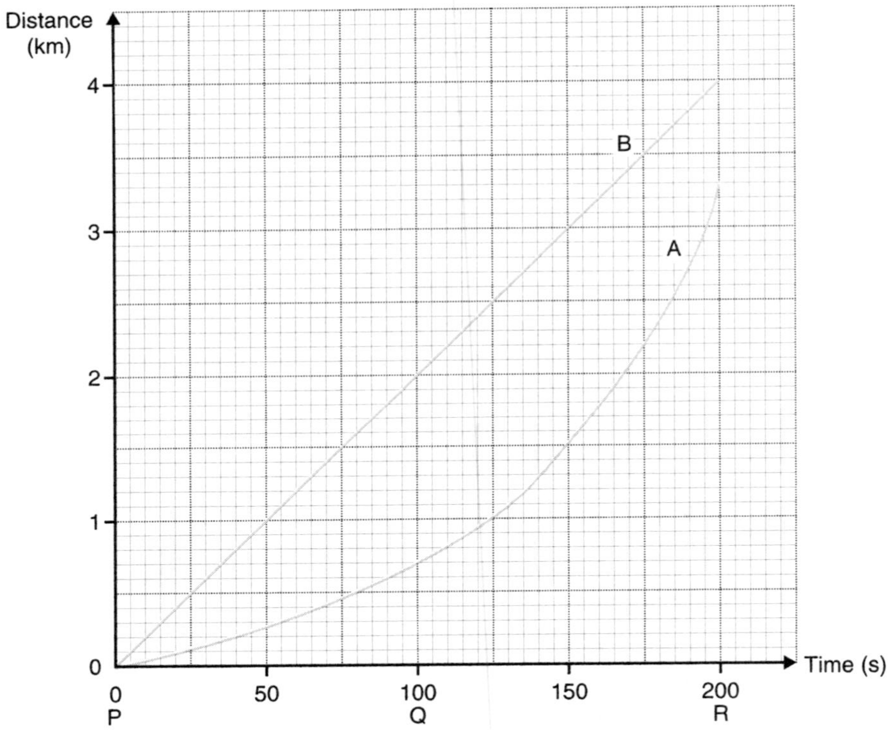

Fig. 1

(a) What is the greatest speed reached by train A? (2)

(b) How is train A moving during the time PQ? (1)

(c) How is train B moving during the time QR? (1)

(d) At what time are the two trains moving at the same **speed**? (2)

(e) Estimate the total distance travelled by train B. (2)

2 A child steps out into the path of an oncoming car. The graph in Fig. 2 shows how the speed of the car changes from the moment the driver sees the child until the car stops.

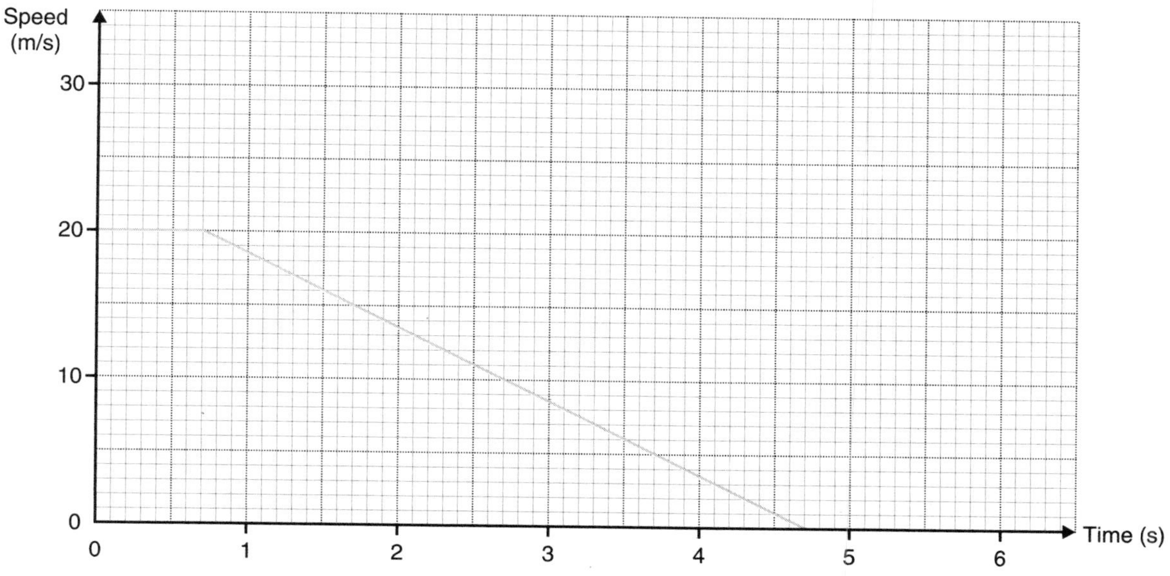

Fig. 2

(a) (i) After 0.7 s the brakes are applied and the car slows down. Calculate the value of the deceleration of the car while the brakes are applied. (2)
(ii) Calculate the distance travelled by the car from the moment the driver first sees the child until the brakes are applied. (1)
(iii) Calculate the distance travelled by the car while it is slowing down. (2)
(iv) What is the value of the total stopping distance of the car? (1)

(b) State and explain what difference it would make, if any, to your answers to (a) (i), (ii) and (iii) if the road was wet. (3)

Chapter 3 (answers – page 198–9)

3 Fig. 3 shows emergency food supplies falling with a parachute attached. The arrows show forces acting on the food supplies and the parachute.

(a) Give the name of each force: force A; force B. (2)

(b) The food supplies are falling with a maximum speed.
(i) What do we call this speed? (1)
(ii) What can you say about the forces acting on the food supplies at this time? (1)

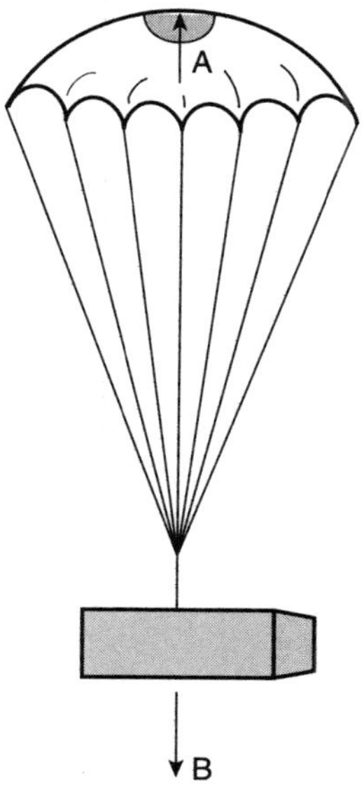

Fig. 3

(c) Fig. 4 shows how the speed of the food supplies changed as they fell from the delivery plane.
(i) When did the parachute open?
(ii) What was the fastest speed reached by the food supplies?
(iii) How far did the supplies fall between times D and E? (4)

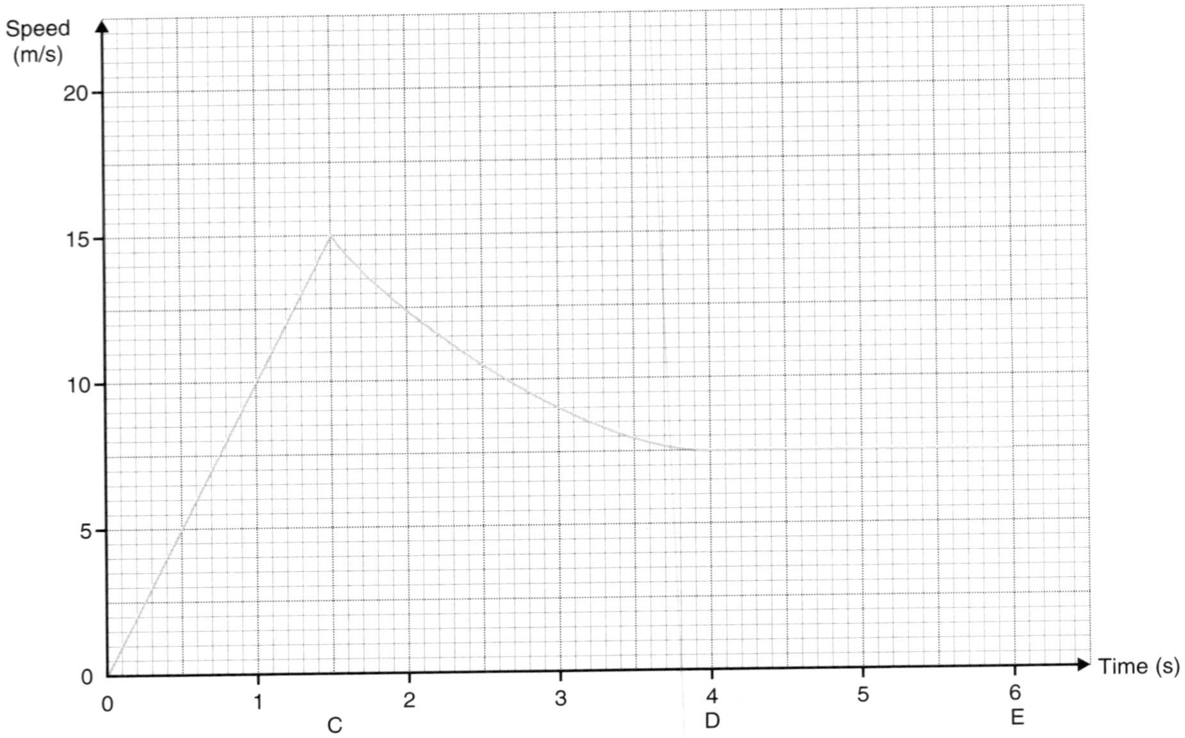

Fig. 4

4 (a) The graph in Fig. 5 below shows how the velocity of an aeroplane changes with time as it moves along the runway and takes off.

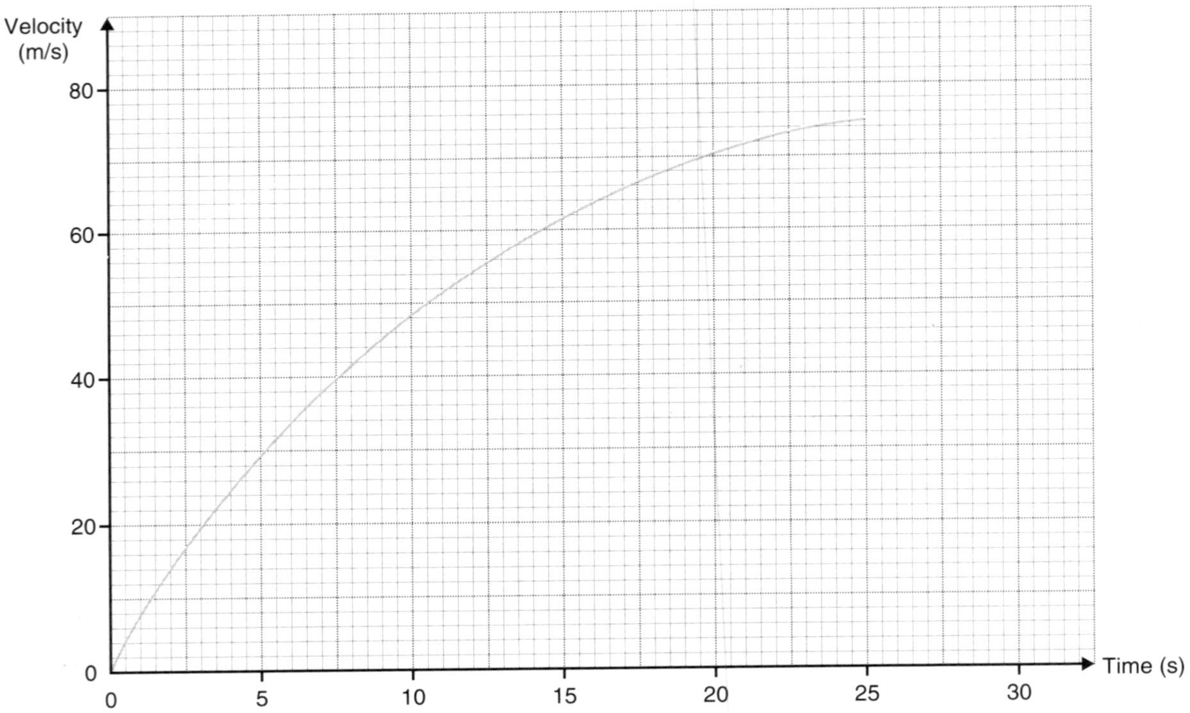

Fig. 5

If it is airborne after 25 seconds, calculate

(i) its velocity as it becomes airborne, (2)

(ii) the acceleration of the plane as it starts to move along the runway. (3)

(b) Explain why the acceleration of the aeroplane gets less as it moves along the runway. (3)

(c) Estimate the length of the runway. (2)

5 (a) A car of mass 1000 kg is being towed at a constant speed of 5 m/s by a breakdown lorry. The force of friction on the car at this speed is 500 N. What size of force is exerted by the tow rope on the car? (1)

(b) The force exerted by the tow rope on the car is increased to 1000 N. Assuming that the force of friction on the car remains constant at 500 N, find the acceleration of the car. (3)

6 (a) In each of the following situations name the force which keeps the object moving in a circular path (i.e. say what provides the centripetal force).

(i) The Moon moving round the Earth. (1)
(ii) A mass swung in a horizontal circle on the end of a string. (1)
(iii) A car moving round a corner. (1)

(b) In what direction does the centripetal force always act? (1)

7 (a) Explain what is meant by the 'law of conservation of momentum'. (2)

(b) How is this law applied in the case of the propulsion of a rocket. (2)

(c) To increase its velocity a space rocket uses a total of 20 kg of hydrogen and oxygen producing steam moving at 10 000 m/s. If the mass of the space rocket is 50 000 kg, calculate its increase in velocity. (3)

(d) A delivery van and a car crash head-on and instantly stop. The van has a mass of 1500 kg and was travelling at a speed of 10 m/s. The car has a mass of 900 kg.

Fig. 6

(i) Calculate the momentum of the van just before the collision. (2)
(ii) What was the momentum of the car just before the collision? (2)
(iii) Calculate the speed of the car just before the collision. (2)

Chapter 4 (answers – page 199)

8 Fig. 7 shows the forces acting on a lorry as it travels along a level road.

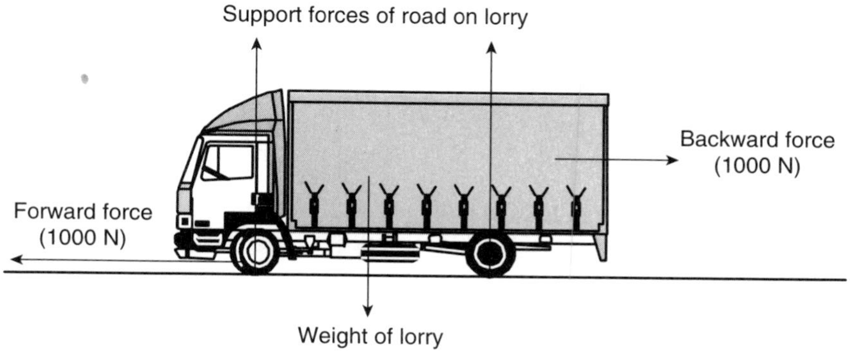

Fig. 7

The backward force opposing its motion is 1000 N.
The forward force exerted on the lorry is 1000 N.

(a) The speed of the lorry is 15 m/s. Calculate the work done by the forward force of 1000 N in 20 seconds. (4)

(b) The petrol supplies 1000 kJ of energy to the engine in 20 seconds. Calculate the efficiency of the engine. (2)

9 Fig. 8 shows the overall stopping distance needed for a car travelling in a straight line at 15 m/s.

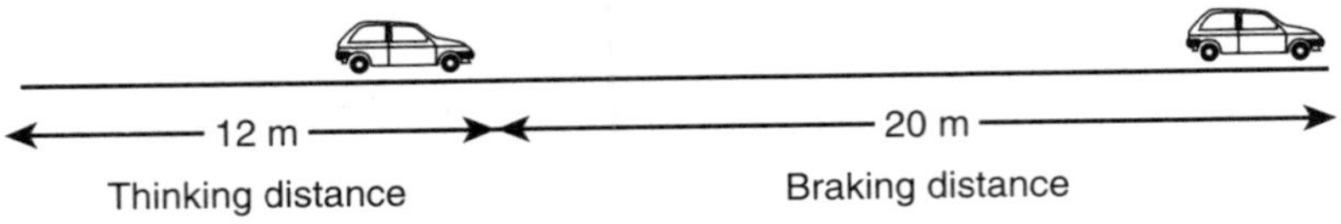

Fig. 8

The thinking distance is the distance travelled by the car in the time it takes the driver to react and put on the brakes (reaction time).

(a) Calculate the reaction time of the driver. (1)

(b) The mass of the car is 1000 kg.

(i) Calculate the kinetic energy of the car when it is travelling at 15 m/s.

(ii) What is the work done in stopping the car?

(iii) Calculate the average braking force needed to stop the car in a distance of 20 m.

(iv) Describe what has happened to the kinetic energy of the car when it has stopped. (6)

(c) When a car travels round a corner at a constant speed, passengers in the car feel as though they are being forced outwards. Explain why they feel this force, and describe fully what is really happening to them. (4)

(d) Car makers build a number of safety features into their cars. One of these is a crumple zone. Crumple zones are designed to collapse in a serious collision. These are shown in Fig. 9. Explain clearly, in terms of momentum, the physics behind this safety feature. (4)

Fig. 9

10 Fig. 10 shows a gymnast on a trampoline. He reaches a height of 3.2 m above the trampoline.

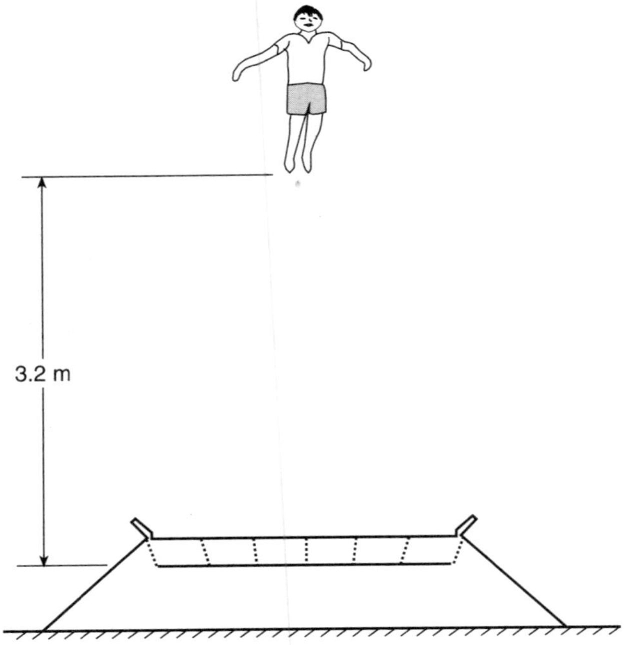

Fig. 10

Fig. 11 shows how the speed of the gymnast changes as he exercises on the trampoline.

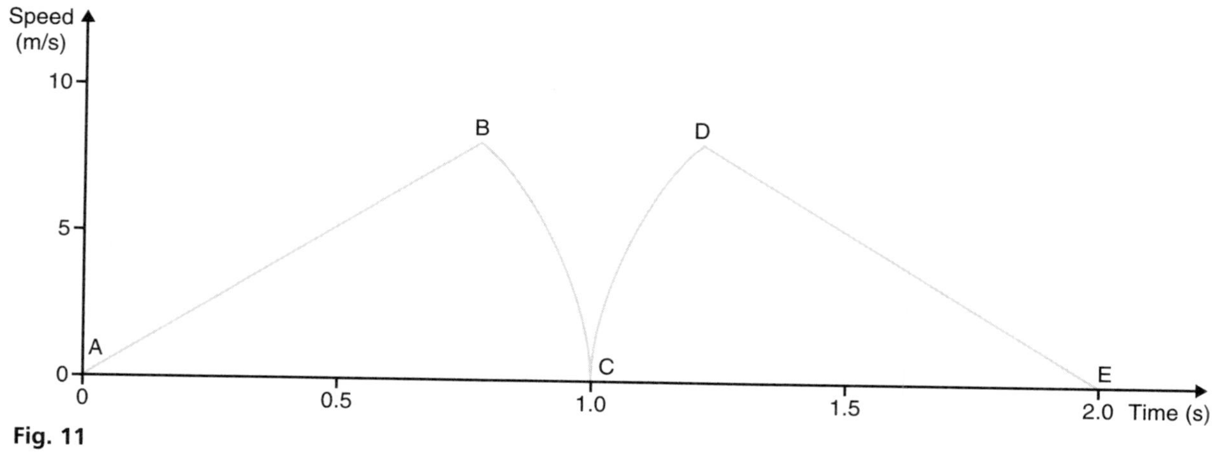

Fig. 11

(a) Describe in words what is happening to the gymnast between points
  (i) C and D.
  (ii) D and E. (4)

(b) At which point of the graph is the gymnast at his lowest position? (1)

(c) Calculate the acceleration of the gymnast when he is falling. (2)

(d) The mass of the gymnast is 70 kg.
  (i) Use Fig. 11 to calculate the maximum value of the kinetic energy of the gymnast. (2)
  (ii) How does your answer compare with the maximum potential energy of the gymnast? (3)

11 A rocket is moving from the Earth towards the Moon.

(a) What is happening to the gravitational potential energy of the rocket as it moves from the Earth to the Moon?

(b) Explain why it is necessary for fuel to be used to enable the rocket to get from the Earth to the Moon.

(c) Astronauts in orbit around the Moon experience 'weightlessness'. Explain the meaning of this word. (7)

12 An electric motor is used to lift a mass of 1 kg through a height of 3.2 m at a constant speed in a time of 8 s.

(a) Calculate
  (i) the potential energy gained by the mass. (2)
  (ii) the useful work done by the motor. (2)
  (iii) the useful power output of the motor. (1)

(b) When the mass reaches 2.45 m above the floor the string breaks.
  (i) How much kinetic energy does the mass gain in falling to the floor? (1)
  (ii) What is the speed of the mass just before it reaches the floor? (2)

13 (a) Explain the difference between a vector and a scalar quantity. (2)

(b) Give two examples each of vector and scalar quantities. (2)

14 Fig. 12 shows three spring balances, all pulling on a knot at P. The strings are at in line with each other.

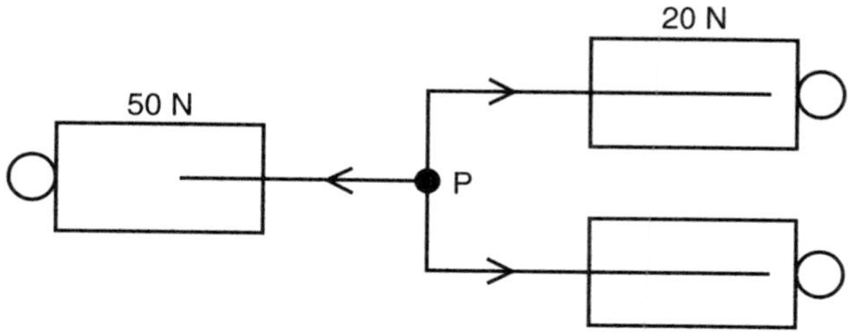

Fig. 12

P is at rest. The readings on two of the spring balances are given. What is the reading on the spring balance R? (1)

Chapter 5 (answers – page 199–200)

15 Fig. 13 shows a uniform METRE RULE of weight 3 N. The rule is pivoted 30 cm from one end and a force F keeps it balanced.

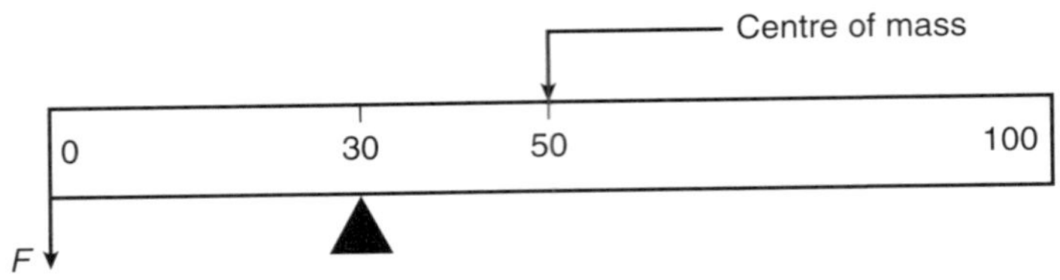

Fig. 13

What is the value of the force F? (2)

16 Fig. 14 shows a lever being used to lift the lid from a tin of paint.

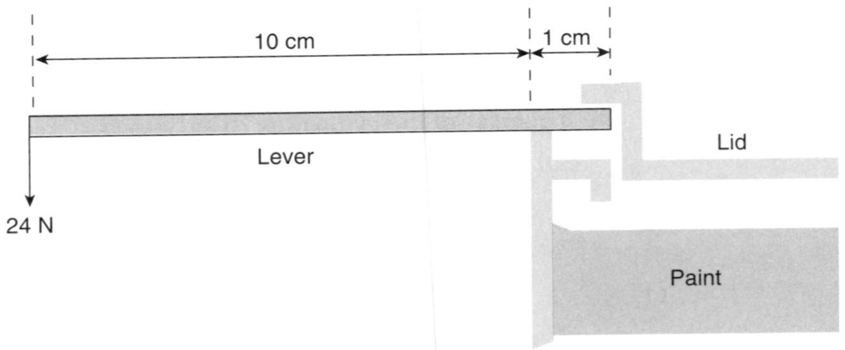

Fig. 14

(a) On the figure
  (i) mark the position of the pivot P. (1)
  (ii) draw an arrow to show the direction of the force F, which the lever exerts on the lid. (1)

(b) Calculate the moment of the force of 24 N about the pivot. (1)

(c) Calculate the value of the force F which the lever exerts on the lid. (2)

(d) What is the value of the force that the lever exerts on the pivot? (1)

(e) If the force F is too small to lift the lid, suggest two changes which you might make to increase the value of F. (2)

Chapter 6 (answers – page 200)

17 (a) Calculate the surface area of one face of a cube of side 2 cm. (1)

(b) Calculate the volume of the same cube. (1)

(c) Find its mass, if it has a density of 8 g/cm^3. (2)

18 A measuring cylinder contains 200 cm^3 of water. When a stone is added the level rises to 300 cm^3. If the density of the stone is 4 g/cm^3, calculate

(a) the volume of the stone. (1)

(b) the mass of the stone. (1)

Fig. 15

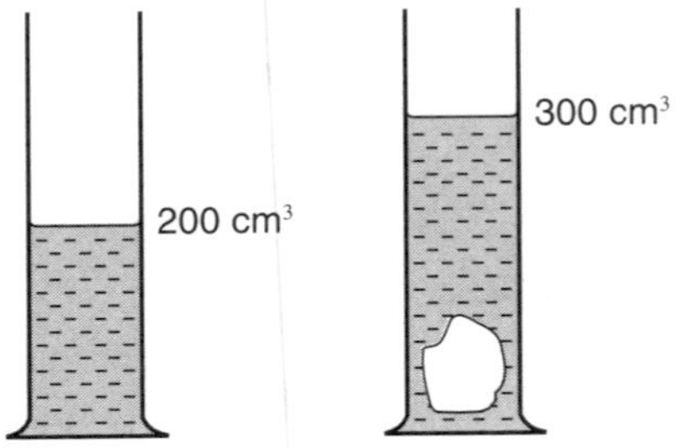

Chapter 7 (answers – page 200)

19 A hovercraft has a mass of 10 000 kg. It hovers at a constant height above the ground.

(a) Calculate the weight of the hovercraft. (1)

(b) What is the value of the upward force exerted by the air cushion? (1)

(c) The hovercraft has a rectangular shape of length 20 m and width 5 m. Calculate the pressure excess (above atmosphere) of the air in the cushion under the craft. (2)

(d) The hovercraft accelerates horizontally at 2.5 m/s^2. Calculate the horizontal force exerted by the driving propeller. You may ignore air resistance. (2)

20 Fig. 16 shows part of the hydraulic braking system of a motor car.

(a) Mark with an arrow on the diagram, the direction in which the piston in the slave cylinder moves when the driver presses down on the brake pedal. (1)

(b) Explain why the downward force on the brake pedal causes the piston in the slave cylinder to move. (1)

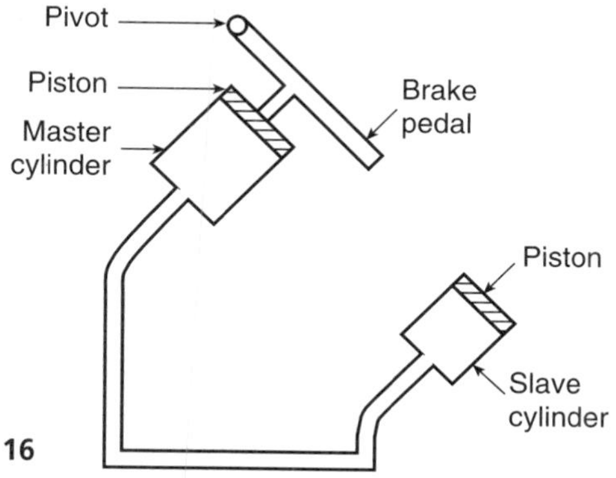

Fig. 16

(c) Why is it important that the brake fluid does not compress when the brake pedal is pushed down? (2)

(d) Find the pressure in Pascals in the brake fluid when the force on the master cylinder piston is 240 N. Show clearly how you obtain your answer. The master cylinder piston has an area of 16 cm^2. (3)

(e) The area of the piston in the slave cylinder is 2 cm^2. Calculate the force on this piston. (2)

Chapter 8 (answers – page 200)

21 (a) State Hooke's Law. (2)

(b) Fig. 17 shows how the length of a spring changes when various weights are hung from it.

Fig. 17

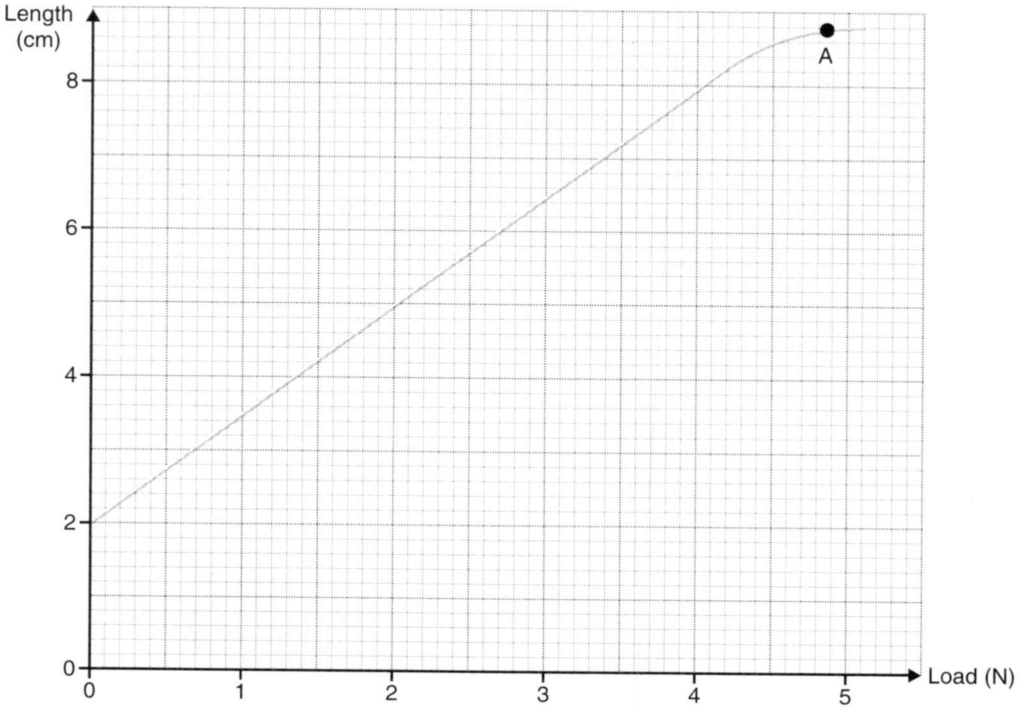

Use the graph to find:

(i) the length of the spring when load of 3.5 N is hung from it. (1)

(ii) the unloaded (unstretched) length of the spring. (1)

(iii) the change in length of the spring produced by increasing the load from 2 N to 3 N. (1)

(c) Explain what happens to the spring if it is unloaded before reaching point A on the graph. (2)

(d) Explain what happens to the spring if it is unloaded after reaching point A on the graph. (2)

Chapter 9 (answers – page 200)

22 The model shown in Fig. 18 is sometimes used to represent the arrangement of molecules in a solid.

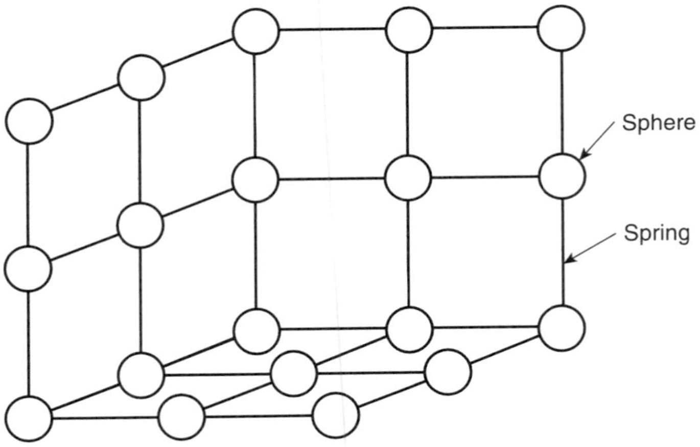

Fig. 18

(a) What do the springs represent? (1)

(b) How may the model be used to show what happens when a solid is heated? (2)

(c) State how the movement of molecules in a liquid differs from the movement of molecules in a solid. (2)

(d) Why is energy needed to melt a solid into a liquid at the same temperature? (2)

23 Fig. 19 shows apparatus used to show the behaviour of smoke particles in air.

(a) Why is light shone into the container? (1)

(b) Why are smoke particles suitable for use in this experiment? (2)

(c) Describe what you would see when looking through the microscope into the smoke cell. (1)

(d) What does this experiment tell you about the behaviour of the air molecules in the cell? (2)

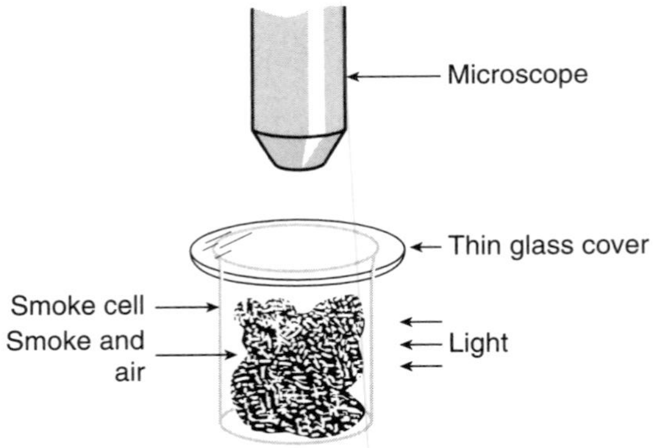

Fig. 19

Chapter 10 (answers – page 201)

24 Table 1 gives results obtained in an experiment to measure the volume of a fixed mass of gas when different pressures were applied to it without changing the temperature.

Table 1

p	*V*
23	10.0
43	5.26
63	
82	2.63
103	2.17
	1.85
139	1.61

(a) Fill in the two gaps in Table 1with suitable values. (2)

(b) On the grid provided in Fig. 20 plot a graph of the pressure (p) against 1/volume (V). (4)

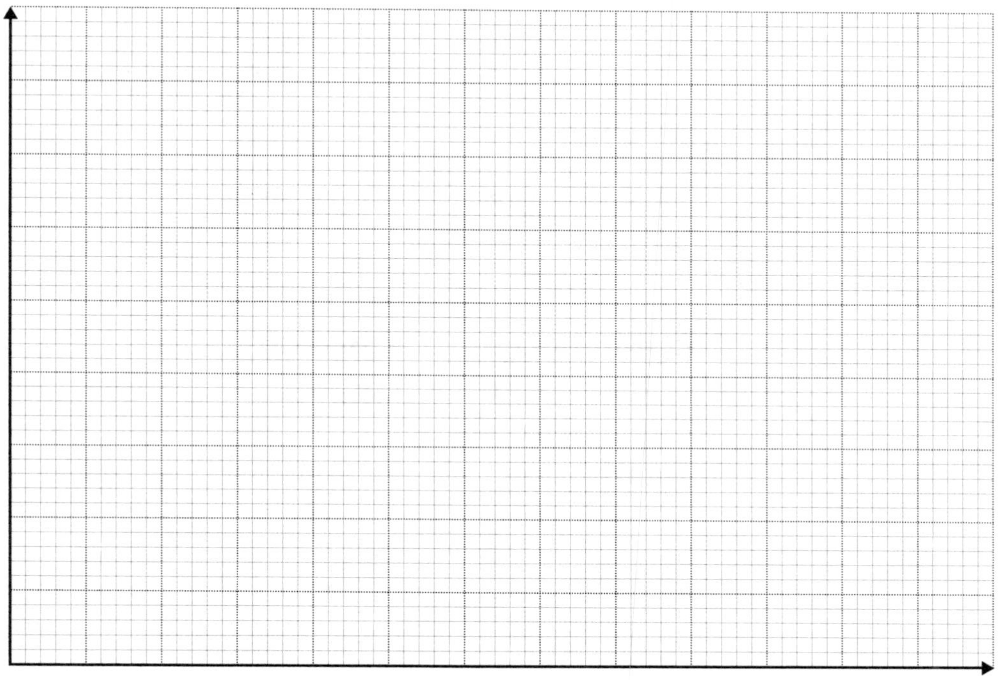

Fig. 20

(c) Draw a line on the graph that might have been obtained if the experiment had been repeated at a higher temperature for the same range of pressures. (2)

25 Some air at a pressure of 1 atmosphere and a temperature of 27 °C occupies a volume of 1 litre.

(a) The air is heated to 177 °C at constant pressure. What will be its new volume? (2)

(b) The air is now cooled to its original temperature keeping the volume constant. Calculate its final pressure. (2)

Chapter 11 (answers – page 201)

26 When 1 kg of water was heated for 5 minutes with an immersion heater the water's temperature rose by 30 °C.

To the questions that follow answer **either**; greater than 30 °C; **or** less than 30 °C; **or** equal to 30 °C.

What would be the temperature rise if the same heater heated

(a) 2 kg of water for 9 minutes? (1)

(b) 1 kg of paraffin for 5 minutes (given that the specific heat capacity of paraffin is less than that of water)? (1)

Chapter 12 (answers – page 201)

27 A beaker of water is heated, as in Fig. 21, and the movement of water is shown using a coloured dye.

(a) On the figure show the direction of movement of the water. (2)

(b) Explain why the hot water moves in this way. (2)

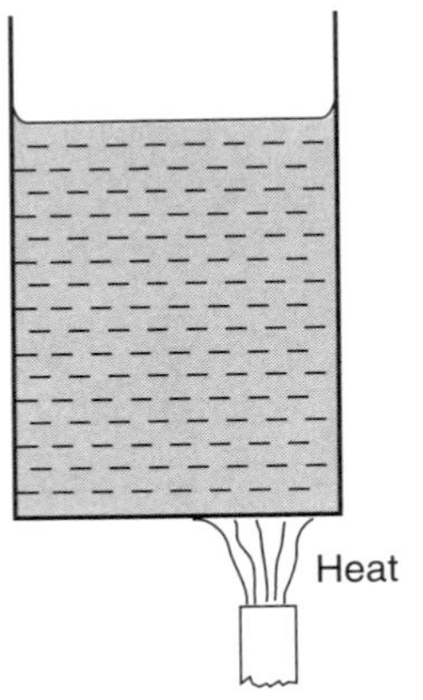

Fig. 21

28 On a hot day in Summer a cool breeze often sets in from the sea on to the land around midday.

(a) Explain how this breeze happens. (4)

(b) Could the reverse happen, i.e. a breeze from the land to the sea? If so, at what time is this most likely to happen? Explain how it happens. (3)

29 (a) Name three ways in which heat can escape from your home. (2)

(b) Choose **two** of these ways and explain how the amount of heat lost in each case could be reduced. (2)

Chapter 13 (answers – page 201–2)

30 (a) Waves may be either transverse or longitudinal. Why are longitudinal waves so named? (2)

(b) Which of the following are transverse waves and which are longitudinal?

Waves on water, sound waves, radio waves, light waves. (2)

31 A cork is floating in water. A stone is dropped into the water.

(a) After a short time the cork begins to move. Describe how the cork moves. (1)

Fig. 22 shows how the displacement of the cork from its original position varies with time.

(b) What is the amplitude and frequency of the water wave? (2)

(c) The water waves have a wavelength of 0.8 m. Calculate the velocity of the water waves. Show clearly how you obtain your answer. (3)

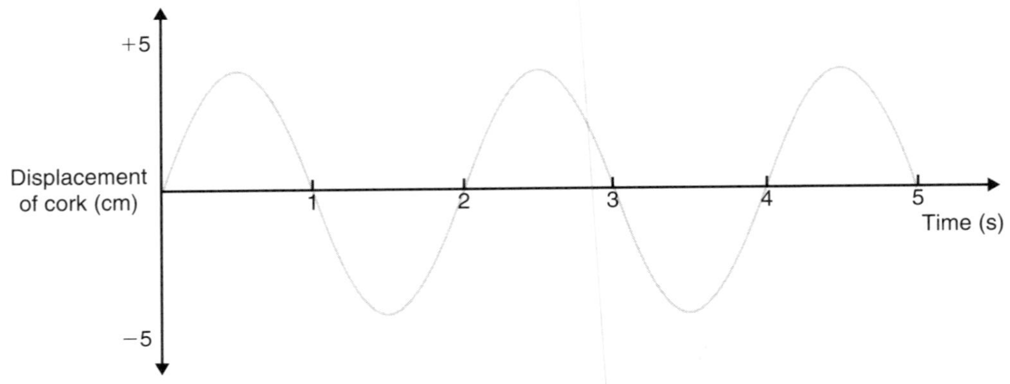

Fig. 22

32 A vibrating source in a ripple tank produces a series of equally spaced circular ripples which strike a straight reflector.

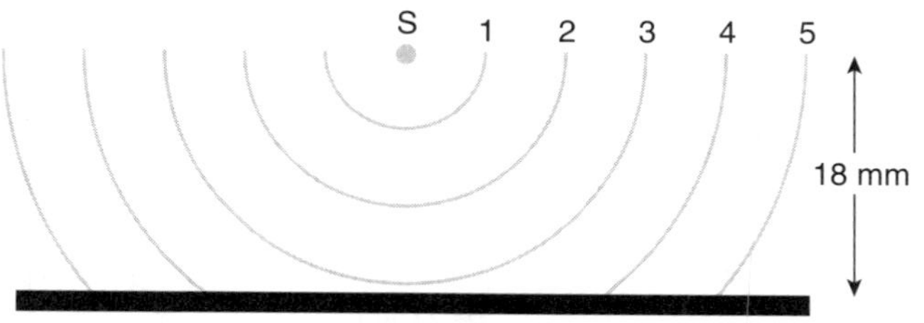

Fig. 23

(a) Complete Fig. 23 to show how crests 4 and 5 are reflected. (2)

(b) If the velocity of the waves is 48 mm/s and the source is 18 mm from the reflector, calculate

(i) the wavelength of the waves. (1)
(ii) the frequency of the waves. (2)

33 Fig. 24 shows wave crests just about to pass over a boundary between deep and shallow water. On the figure;

(a) draw in the position of three wave crests that are just crossing the boundary into the shallow water. (2)

(b) What is the name of this effect? (1)

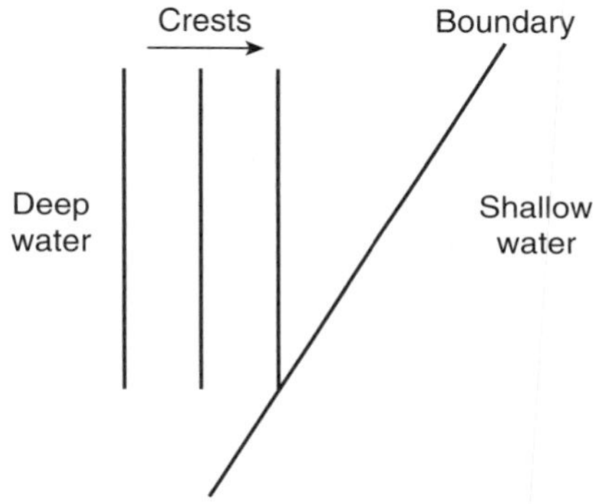

Fig. 24

Chapter 14 (answers – page 202)

34 A pinhole camera is used to view the image of a filament bulb.

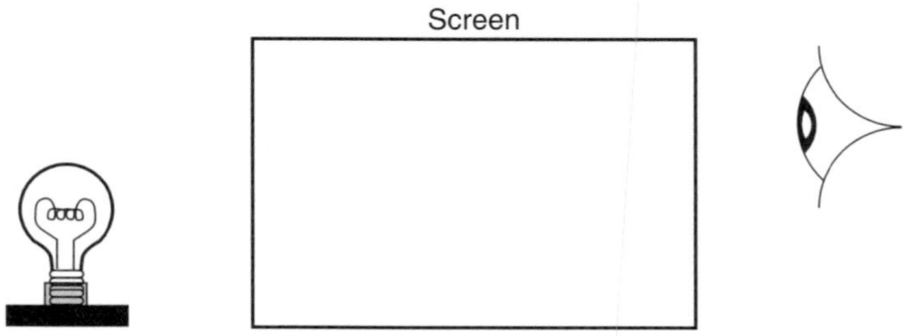

Fig. 25

(a) Draw a sketch of how the filament of the bulb appears on the screen of the pinhole camera. (1)

(b) What happens to the image as the bulb is moved **nearer to** the pinhole? (1)

35 Fig. 26 shows a periscope which may be used to see behind when towing a caravan. Only one mirror has been drawn in.

(a) Draw the second mirror in the correct position. (1)

(b) Draw a ray of light from the top of the object to the eye. (1)

(c) Draw a ray of light from the bottom of the object to the eye. (1)

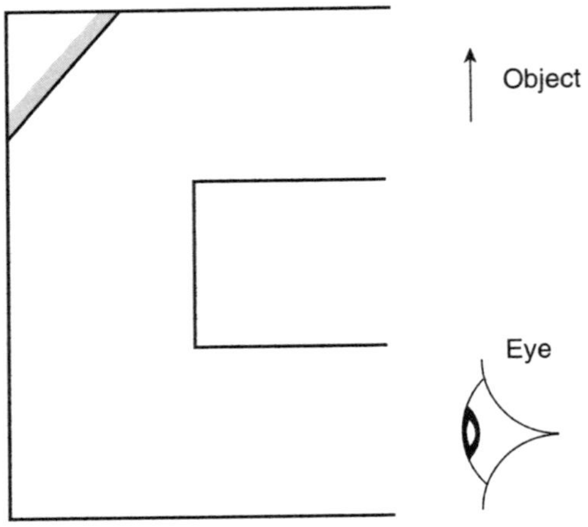

Fig. 26

(d) What is the main disadvantage of this type of periscope? (1)

Chapter 15 (answers – page 202–3)

36 (a) Fig. 27 shows a ray of light passing through a transparent material such as a block of glass or perspex. Name the angles marked X and Y. (2)

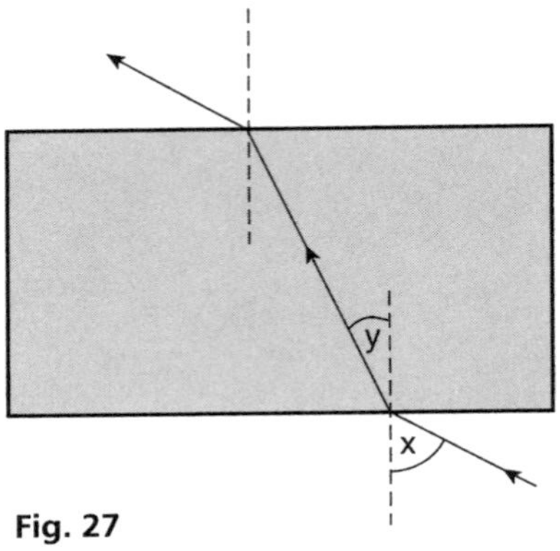

Fig. 27

(b) Figures 28(a) and 28(b) each show a ray of light entering and leaving a transparent block.

(i) In Figure 28(a) what is the name of angle Z? (1)

(ii) For Figure 28(b).

(A) name the type of reflection at point P. (1)

(B) explain why this reflection took place. (2)

(C) where is this effect used on a bicycle or car? (2)

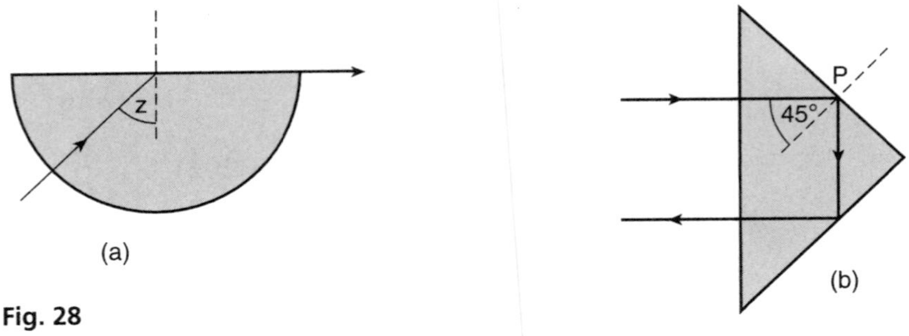

Fig. 28

(c) The type of reflection in Figure 28(b) is used to pass a beam of light along a solid glass fibre. This is shown in Fig. 29. Describe a practical application of a single flexible fibre or bundle of fibres. (2)

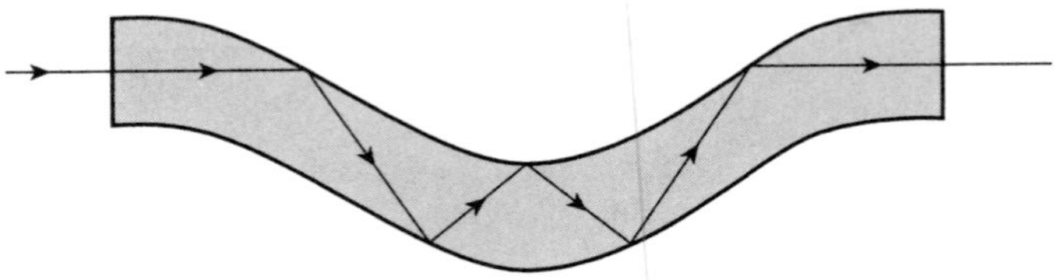

Fig. 29

37 In each of the scale diagrams in Fig. 30, rays of light are shown striking a lens. Copy the diagrams and show in each case possible directions of the rays when they come out of the lens. (3)

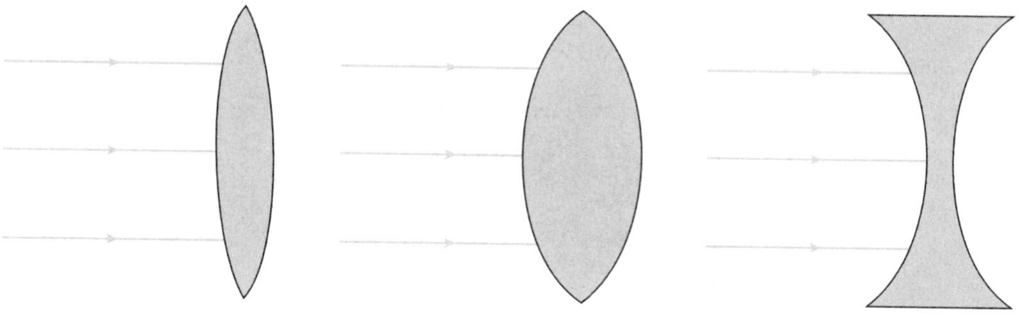

Fig. 30

38 Explain, in terms of waves, why blue light is refracted more than red light on entering a block of glass. (3)

39 (a) Use the words in the box to complete the sentences which follow

iris	lens	optic nerve	pupil	retina

(i) The light goes into the eye through the........................ .

(ii) The .... **controls** the amount of light getting into the eye.

(iii) The .... **focuses** the light.

(iv) An image forms on the ....

(v) The .... carries the message to the brain. (5)

(b) Fig. 31 shows a common sight defect.

(i) Name this defect.

(ii) In front of the eye, draw a lens which will correct this defect. (2)

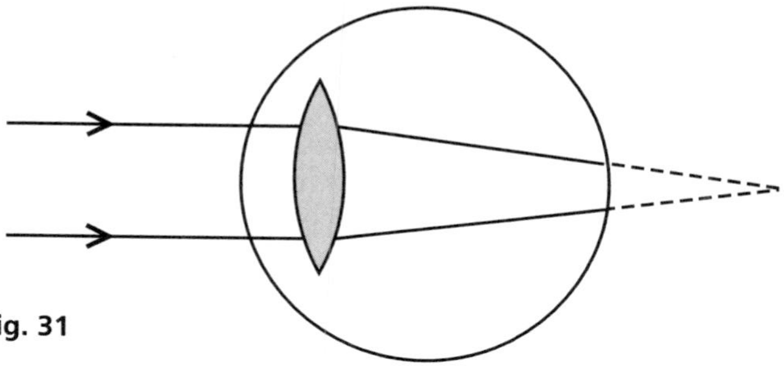

Fig. 31

40 Fill in the blank spaces with the correct word(s) in the following passage.

A person suffers from long sight because the eye lens is too .... When looking at a close object the image is brought to focus ....the retina. This fault may be remedied by using spectacles with a .... lens, so that the image is now formed .... the retina. (4)

Chapter 16 (answers – page 203)

41 Fig. 32 shows the diffraction of light waves passing through a narrow slit.

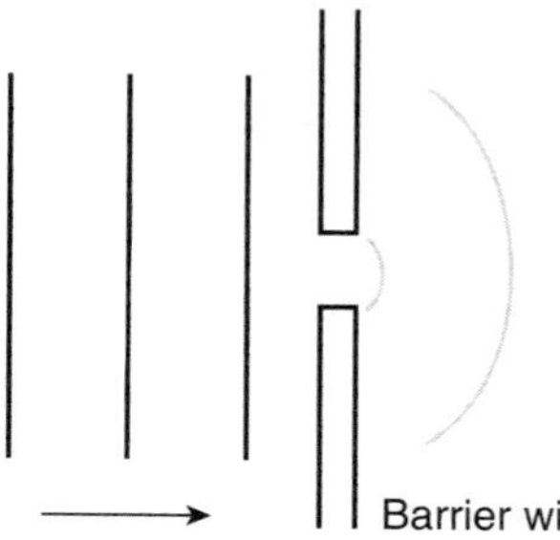

Fig. 32

(a) How could the spreading of the waves be increased? (1)

(b) Does the wavelength of the light increase, decrease or remain the same as the light passes through the slit? (1)

(c) What change, if any, would you notice in the diffraction caused by the slit, if the wavelength of the incoming light were greater? (1)

42 Microwaves are examples of electromagnetic waves and can be used for cooking (2500 MHz).

(a) Why are the walls of a microwave oven often made of steel? (1)

(b) Give a reason why microwave ovens are often considered to cook more efficiently than gas or electric ovens. (1)

(c) Water molecules inside food absorb the energy of microwaves. What is the microwave energy turned to inside the food? (1)

(d) Inside the food the speed of microwaves is reduced.

(i) What happens to the wavelength of the waves as a result of this change? (1)
(ii) What happens to their frequency? (1)

Chapter 17 (answers – page 203)

43 The speed of sound in air is 340 m/s.
The speed of light in air is 3×10^8 m/s.
In a thunderstorm a lightning flash and a thunderclap are made at the same time.

(a) Why do you see the lightning flash before you hear the thunderclap? (1)

(b) You see the flash 5 s before you hear the thunderclap. Calculate how far away the thunderstorm is. (3)

44 A fishing boat is using a sonar device which sends short pulses of sound vertically downwards. It receives an echo back after 0.6 s.

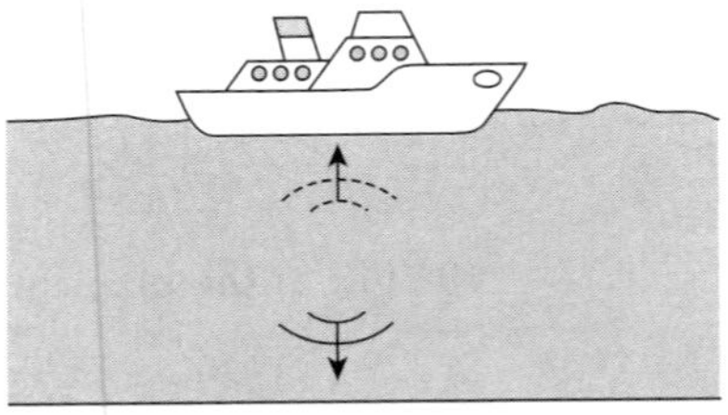

Fig. 33

(a) How is this echo produced? (1)

(b) Calculate how far the sound pulse travels in 0.6 s, assuming the speed of sound to be 1500 m/s. Show your working. (3)

(c) How deep is the water under the boat? (1)

45 A microphone is connected to an oscilloscope. Different frequencies and amplitudes of sound are picked up by the microphone and shown on the screen of the oscilloscope. In Fig. 34 which trace

(a) (i) has the highest frequency? (1)
(ii) has the lowest pitch? (1)
(iii) has the greatest amplitude? (1)
(iv) is made by the quietest sound? (1)

(b) Calculate the frequency of the sound made by the saxophone. (2)

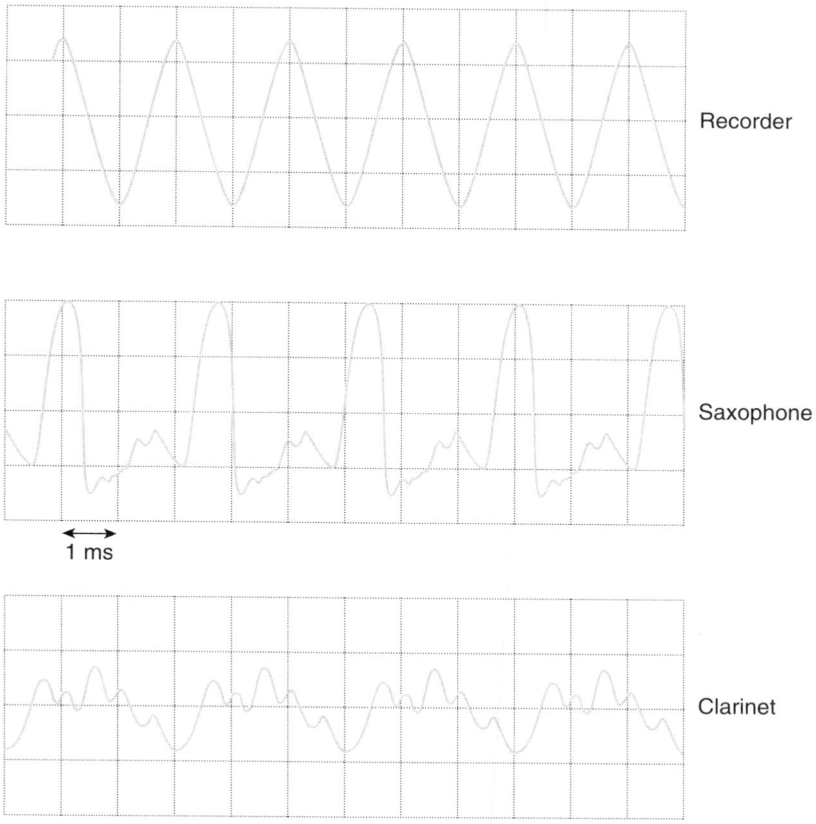

Fig. 34

46 (a) Explain what is meant by 'ultrasound'. (2)

(b) Briefly describe one medical use of ultrasound. (3)

(c) Briefly describe one non-medical use of ultrasound. (3)

Chapter 18 (answers – page 203)

47 Fig. 35 shows two bar magnets suspended by similar threads.

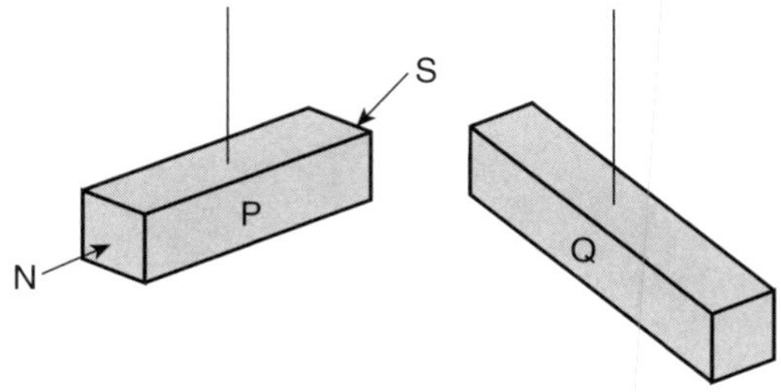

Fig. 35

(a) One end of magnet Q is brought near to the S pole of magnet P. The magnets attract. Label the S pole of magnet Q. (1)

(b) If the other end of magnet Q is brought near to the S pole of magnet P, what will happen? (1)

(c) State what you understand by the expression 'magnetic field'. (2)

48 Fig. 36 shows the top view of two bar magnets held on a smooth surface. The magnetic field has been drawn in.

(a) Describe the field at point X. (1)

(b) Y and Z are plotting compasses. Draw an arrow in each circle to show the direction in which the compass needle points. (2)

(c) What will happen to the magnets if they are released? (1)

(d) One of the magnets is turned round as shown in Fig. 37. Draw the magnetic field lines within the dotted boxes. (2)

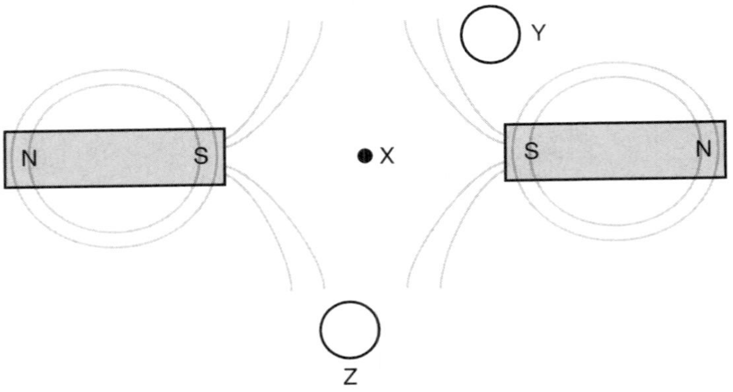

Fig. 36

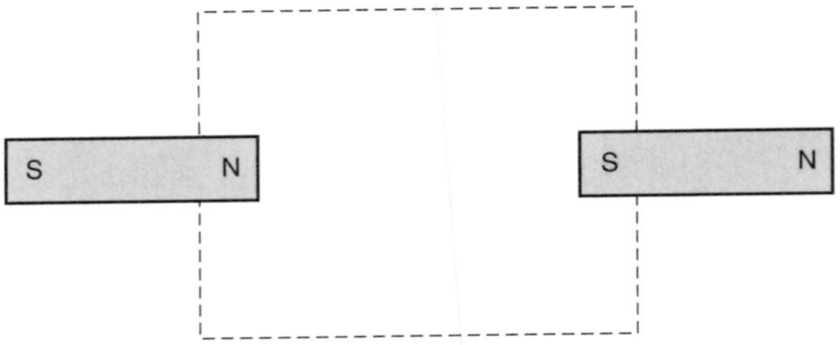

Fig. 37

Chapter 19 (answers – page 204)

49 Fig. 38 shows the inside of a factory chimney. The wires carry a large negative charge and the plate is positively charged.

(a) What happens when soot particles pass near to the wires? (1)

(b) Why is the plate charged positively? (2)

(c) What is the purpose of the whole arrangement? (2)

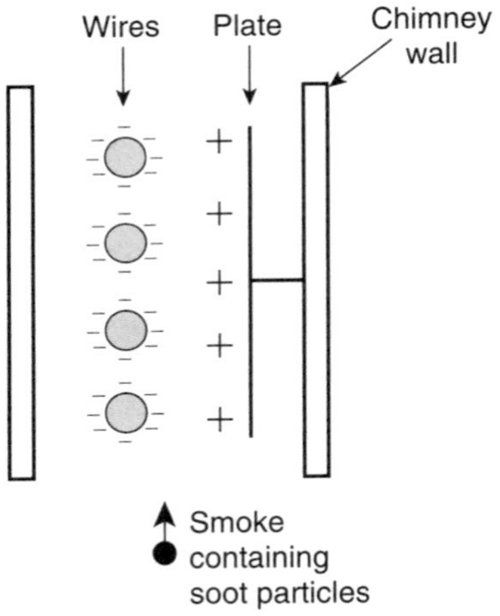

Fig. 38

Chapter 20 (answers – page 204)

50 Fig. 39 shows a circuit containing three identical ammeters A_1, A_2, A_3.

State whether the following statements are true or false.

(a) A_2 gives the reading of the current through the cell. (1)

(b) A_3 gives the reading of the current through the 6 Ω resistor. (1)

(c) The reading of A_1 is less than the reading of A_2. (1)

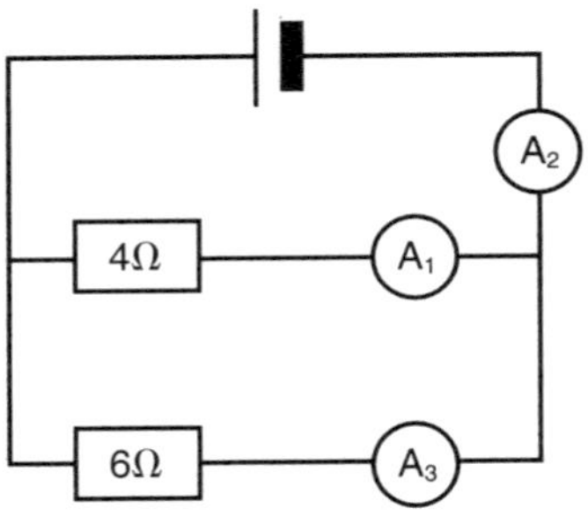

Fig. 39

(d) The reading of A_3 is equal to the reading of A_2 minus the reading of A_1. (1)

51 A pupil is doing an experiment to find the value of a resistor. The circuit he is using is shown in Fig. 40.

(a) What will the ammeter read? (1)

(b) Explain why the ammeter shows this reading (1)

(c) Using exactly the same components draw the circuit the pupil should have used to do this experiment successfully. (1)

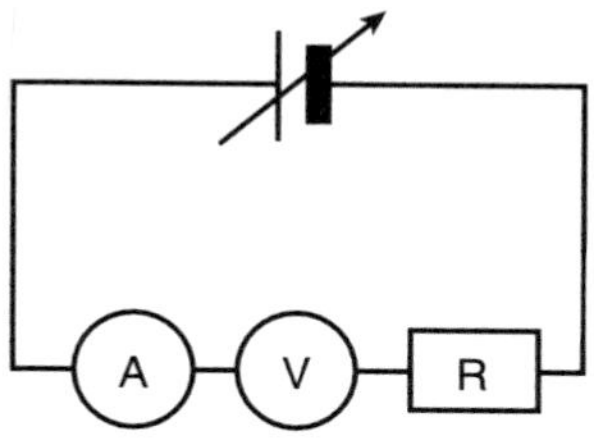

Fig. 40

52 Two resistors are in series with an ammeter and a 6 V battery. The ammeter reads 0.5 A.

(a) What is the value of the current through the 5 Ω resistor? (1)

(b) What is the value of the current through the 7 Ω resistor? (1)

(c) Calculate the p.d. across the 5 Ω resistor. (1)

(d) What is the p.d. across the 7 Ω resistor? (1)

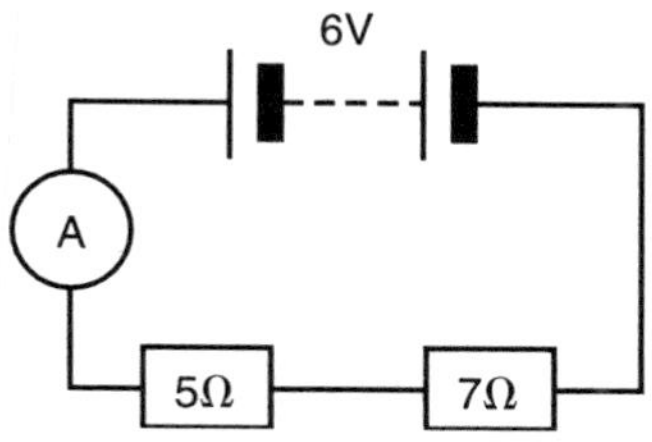

Fig. 41

53 A lamp and a resistor will both conduct electricity. Fig. 42 shows how the current through each component changes as the potential difference changes.

Fig. 42

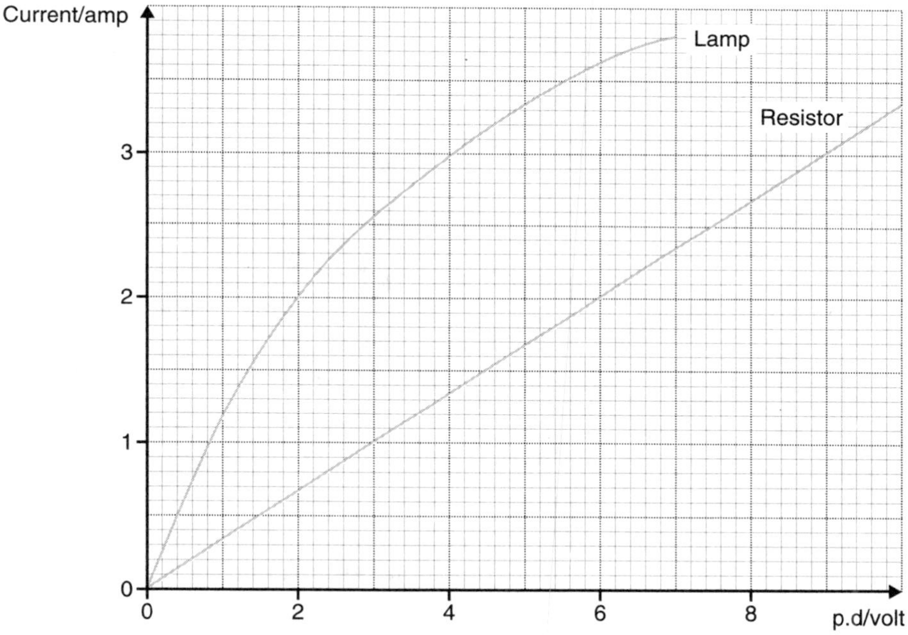

(a) Describe in your own words how the current through the lamp changes as the potential difference increases. (2)

(b) Use Fig. 42 to calculate the resistance of the resistor. (4)

(c) The lamp and resistor are now connected as shown in Fig. 43. The current in the circuit is 3.0 A.

What is the p.d. across

(i) the resistor? (2)

(ii) the lamp? (2)

(iii) the battery? (2)

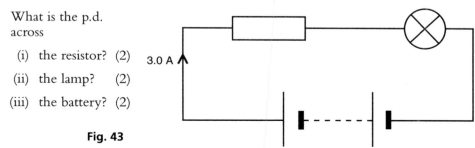

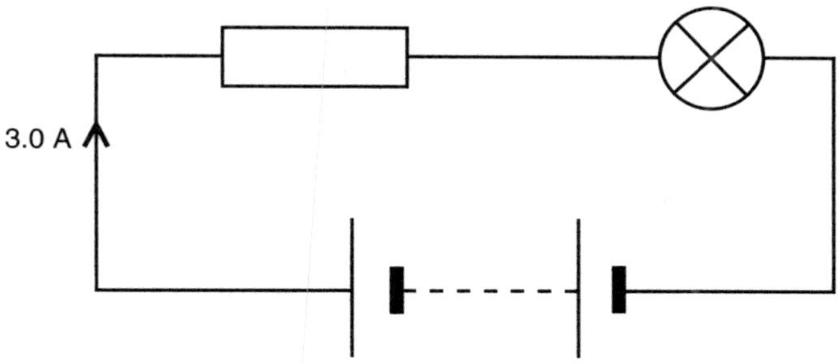

Fig. 43

(d) Calculate the resistance of the lamp when a current of 3.0 A flows through it. (2)

(e) The resistor and lamp are now connected in parallel to a 6 V battery as shown in Fig. 44.

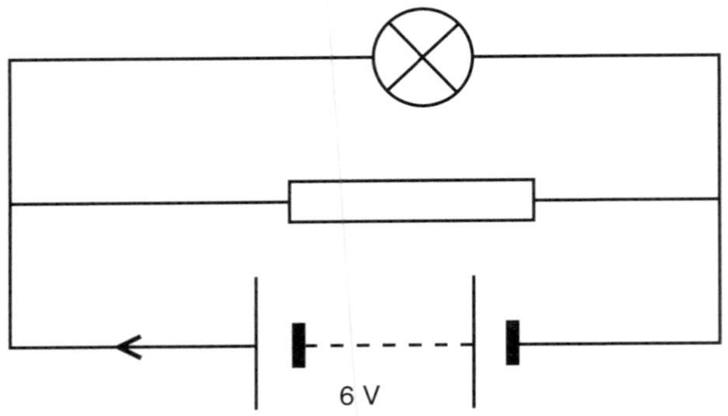

Fig. 44

Use Fig. 42 to find the current flowing through the battery. (2)

Chapter 21 (answers – page 204)

54 Fig. 43 shows a radiant electric fire for use on a 240 V mains supply. It has three heating elements, each rated at 1000 W.

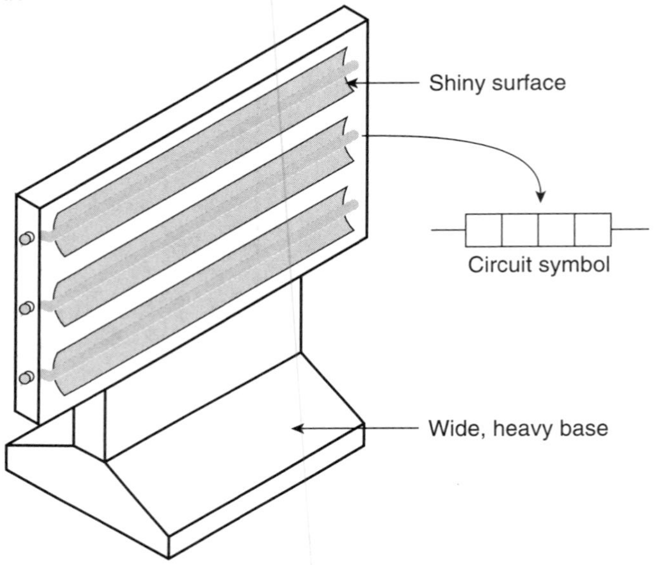

Fig. 43

(a) Two important features of the fire are the shiny surface and the wide, heavy base. Explain the purpose of these. (2)

(b) The three heating elements are controlled by two switches. One of these controls the top element, the other controls the bottom two elements together.

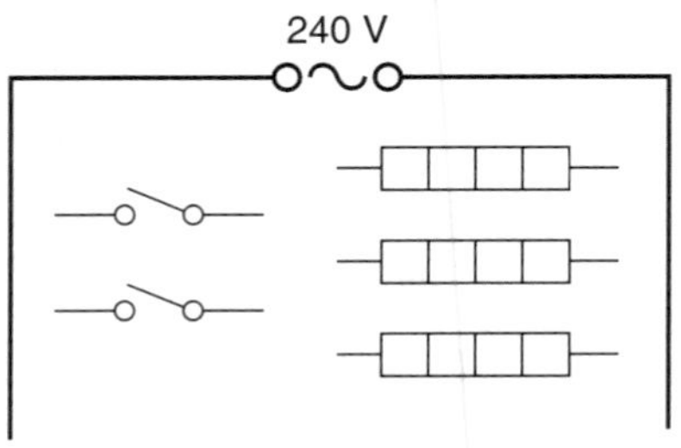

All three elements of the fire are switched on

(i) Complete the circuit diagram to show how this can be done. (2)
(ii) What is the total power rating of the fire? (1)

The electricity board charges 9 p for each kilowatt-hour of energy.

(iii) What is the cost of using all three bars continuously for 4 hours? (2)

Chapter 22 (answers – page 204–5)

55 Fig. 44 shows a plug wired by a pupil and connected to a hair dryer rated at 1000 W, 240 V a.c.

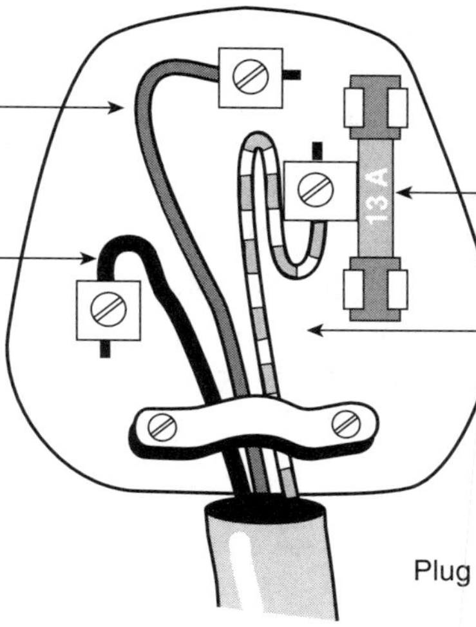

Fig. 44

(a) Several mistakes have been made. Name **four** of them. (4)

(b) The earth pin on a plug is longer than the other two pins. Explain why. (2)

56 Table 2 gives the power ratings of some common domestic appliances all of which work from the 'mains' (240 V).

Table 2

Appliance	*Power (W)*	*Current (A)*	*Fuse (A)*
Iron	1000		
Kettle	3000		
Television	60		

(a) Calculate the current used by each item and write the answers in the table. (3)

The standard value of fuses used in the home are 2 A, 5 A, 10 A and 13 A.

(b) Write suitable values of fuse for each item in the third column. (2)

Chapter 23 (answers – page 205)

57 Fig. 45 shows an electromagnet made by a pupil in the laboratory. The electromagnet is to pick up and release a metal object.

(a) Name a suitable material for part X. (1)

(b) Why is it made from this material? (2)

(c) The electromagnet will just lift a metal object of mass 0.15 kg. What will be the least force exerted by the magnet to do this? The strength of the gravitational field at the Earth's surface can be taken as 10 N/kg. (1)

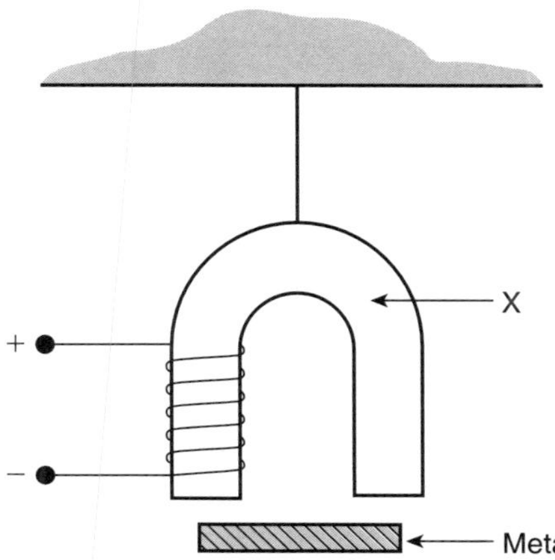

Fig. 45

58 Fig. 46 shows an electric bell.

(a) State and explain what happens to each of the following when the bell push switch is first pushed.

(i) The soft iron armature (2)
(ii) The contacts (1)
(iii) The hammer (1)

(b) What does the spring then do and what happens to the contacts as a result? (2)

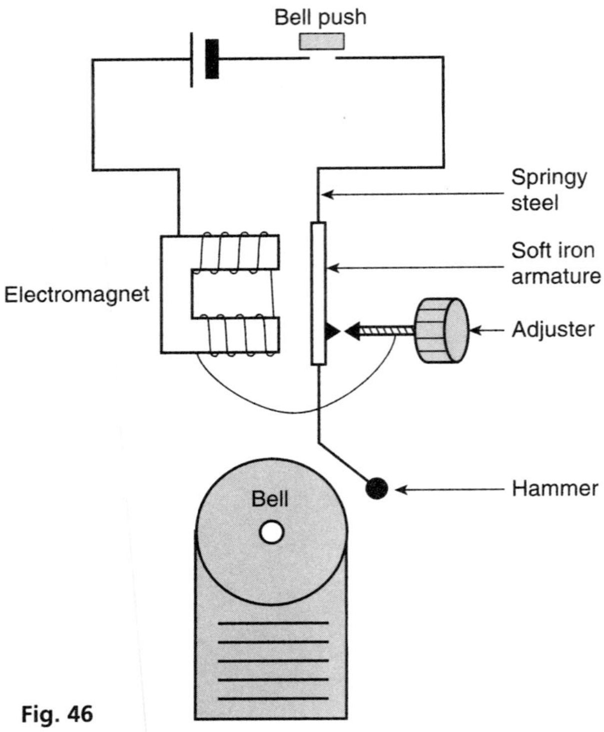

Fig. 46

59 A student set up the electric motor shown in Fig. 47.

(a) The motor did not work. What was wrong with it? (1)

(b) Why did this prevent the motor from working? (1)

(c) When the mistake was corrected the motor turned.

(i) Suggest **three** ways of making the coil turn faster. (3)
(ii) Suggest **two** ways of making the coil turn the other way. (2)

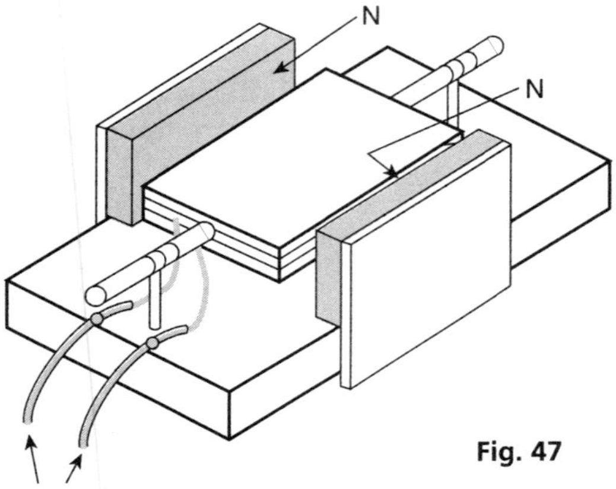

Fig. 47

Chapter 24 (answers – page 205)

60 Fig. 48 shows a simple generator connected to a lamp. The lamp lights normally when the coil is rotating at its maximum speed.

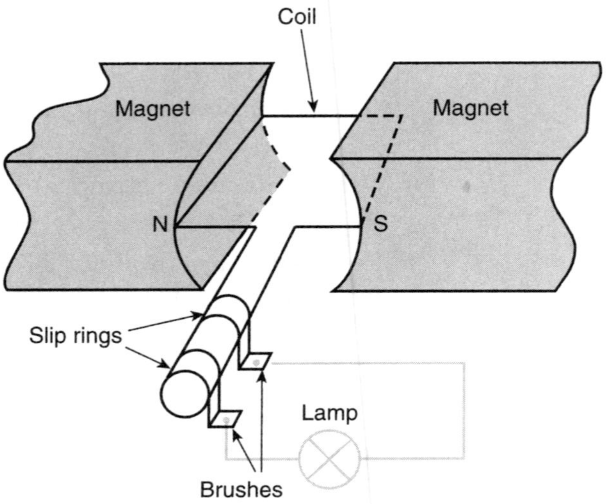

Fig. 48

(a) Describe what happens to the brightness of the lamp as the speed of the coil is increased from zero to its maximum speed. (1)

(b) What would be the effect on the lamp of reducing the number of turns on the coil which is rotating at maximum speed? (1)

(c) What would be the effect on the lamp of increasing the strength of the magnetic field, the coil having its original number of turns and rotating at maximum speed? (2)

61 Fig. 49 shows a simple form of transformer used for stepping down an alternating voltage supply.

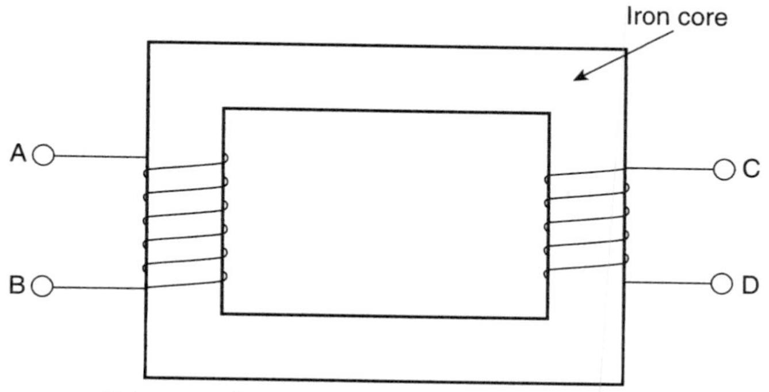

Fig. 49

(a) Explain in terms of magnetic fields how the transformer works. (3)

(b) A power line supplies electrical energy to a transformer in a factory.

The input voltage to the transformer is 11 000 V. The transformer changes this to 415 V for use in the factory. The power input to the transformer is 800 kW.

(i) Calculate the current in the secondary coil of the transformer. (3)
What assumptions have you made about the transformer? (1)

(ii) The power line to the factory is operated at as high a voltage as possible. Explain why this is so. (4)

62 Fig. 50 shows the beginning of the network of cables used to transmit electrical energy across the country.

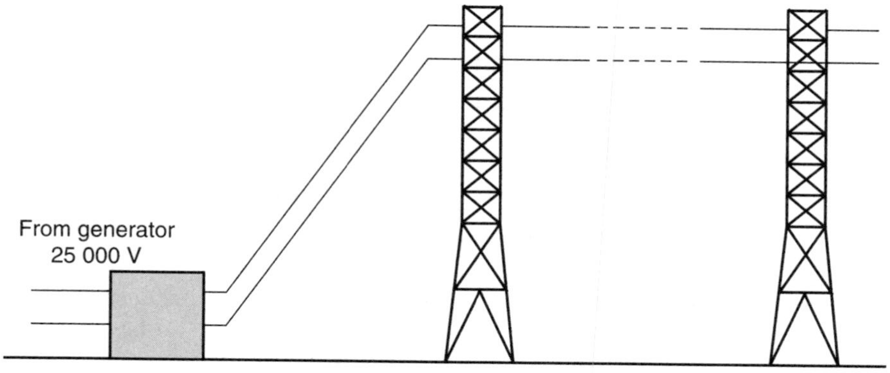

Fig. 50

(a) What is the name of this network of cables? (1)

The turns ratio of the transformer is: $\dfrac{\text{number of secondary turns}}{\text{number of primary turns}} = \dfrac{11}{1}$

(b) Calculate the output (secondary) voltage of the transformer. (2)

(c) Why is it called a step-up transformer? (1)

(d) Why is electrical energy transmitted at high voltage? (2)

(e) Why could it be dangerous to fly a kite near to a high voltage overhead cable? (2)

(f) Why is it safe for a bird to perch on a high voltage overhead cable? (1)

Chapter 25 (answers – page 205)

63 Fig. 51 shows parts of a cathode ray tube.

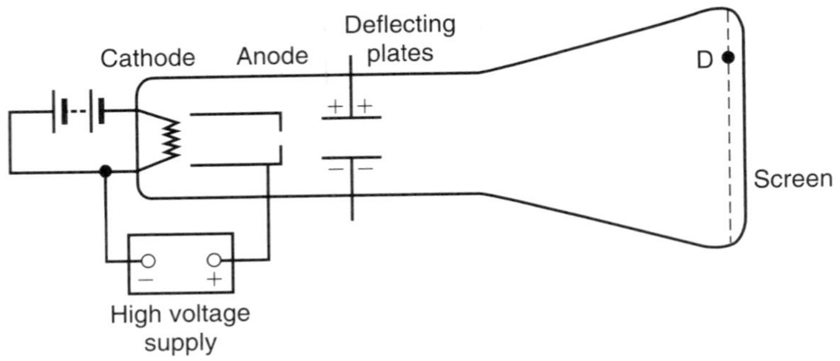

Fig. 51

(a) Why is a high voltage needed between cathode and anode? (2)

A spot is produced on the screen at D.

(b) On the figure draw the path of the cathode rays from the anode to D. (2)

(c) The connections to the high voltage supply are changed over so that the anode is now negative. What happens to the spot? Give a reason for your answer. (2)

Chapter 26 (answers – page 205)

64 The circuit diagram in Fig. 52 shows how a transistor may be used to operate a switch which makes a light come on when it gets dark.

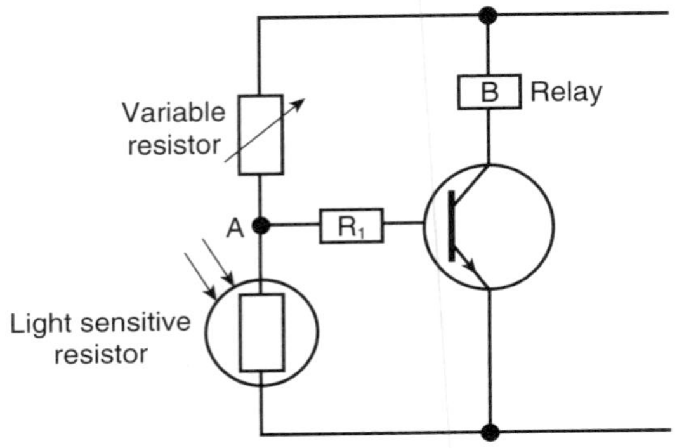

Fig. 52

(a) What happens to the resistance of the light sensitive resistor when it gets dark? (1)

(b) What effect does this change of resistance have on the collector current? (1)

(c) Why is a variable resistor preferred to a fixed resistor at A? (2)

(d) Why is it better to use a relay rather than to insert a bulb directly at B? (2)

(e) What is the purpose of the resistor R_1? (1)

65 A light beside the front door of a house is designed so that it will only go on when somebody is standing on the doormat, **and** it is dark. The control unit includes a pressure switch under the mat and a light sensor (which is ON in daylight and OFF at night).

(a) Where should the light sensor be placed so that it does not switch ON when the light comes ON? (1)

(b) The control circuit will need **two** logic gates, an AND gate and a NOT gate. Part of the circuit diagram is shown below. Complete Fig. 53 to show where the NOT gate should be placed. (1)

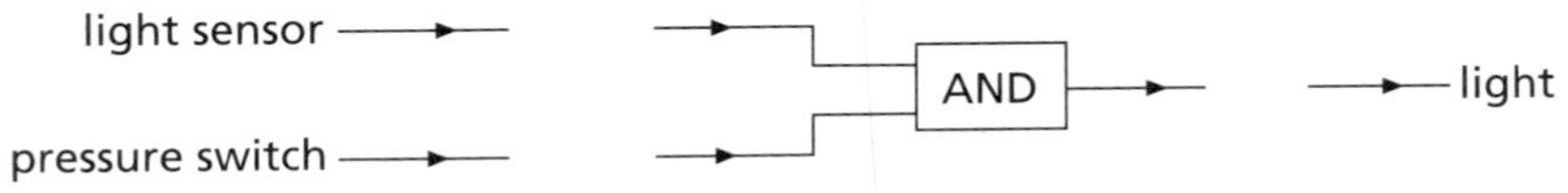

Fig. 53

(c) Complete the truth tables to show how each gate works.

(i) AND gate

Table 3

Input 1	Input 2	Output
OFF	OFF	
OFF	ON	
ON	OFF	
ON	ON	

(ii) NOT gate

Table 4

Input	Output
ON	
OFF	

(3)

Chapter 27 (answers – page 206)

66 Fig. 54 represents a neutral atom.

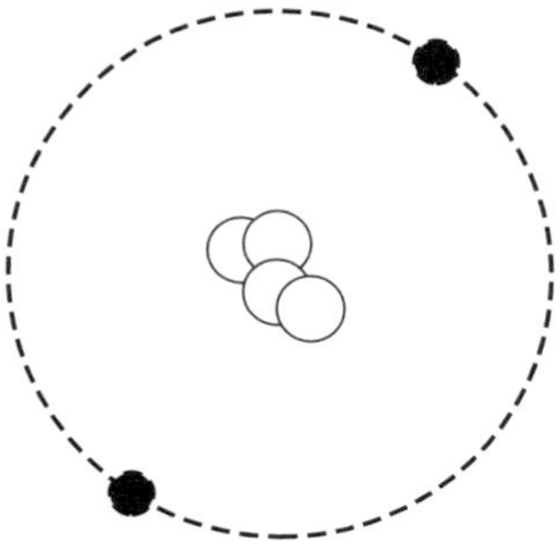

Fig. 54

(a) For this atom, fill in Table 5 below. (4)

Table 5

Number of electrons	
Atomic (proton) number	
Number of neutrons	
Nucleon (mass) number	

(b) Fig. 54 represents an atom of helium. In what way will an atom of another isotope of helium differ from this one? (1)

67 A detector shows that the activity of a radioactive sample falls from 160 units to 20 units in 15 minutes. Determine the half-life of the sample, explaining your calculation. (2)

68 The activity of a radioactive substance was measured using a counter.

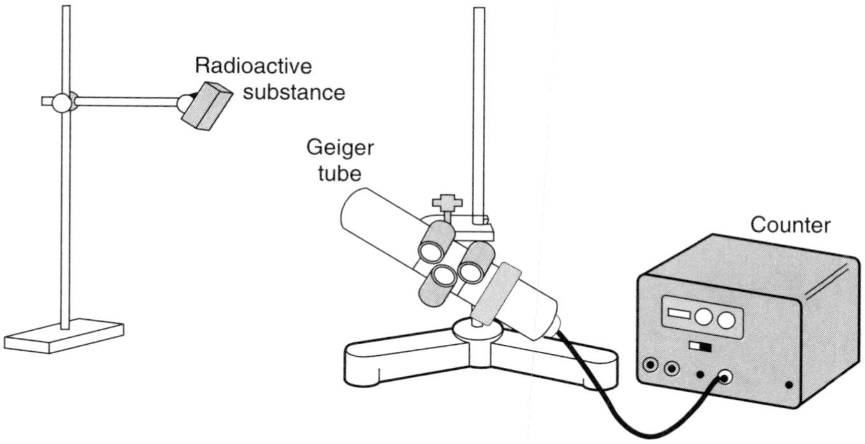

Fig. 55

The graph in Fig. 56 shows how this activity varied with time (the background count has already been deducted and can be ignored).

(a) Use the graph to find the activity after 15 hours. (1)

(b) Explain why the activity decreases with time. (2)

(c) Use the graph below to find out how long it takes for the activity to fall from 500 to 250 counts/minute. (1)

(d) On the graph, sketch another curve, starting at 500 counts/minute, for a different radioactive substance with a half-life twice as big. (2)

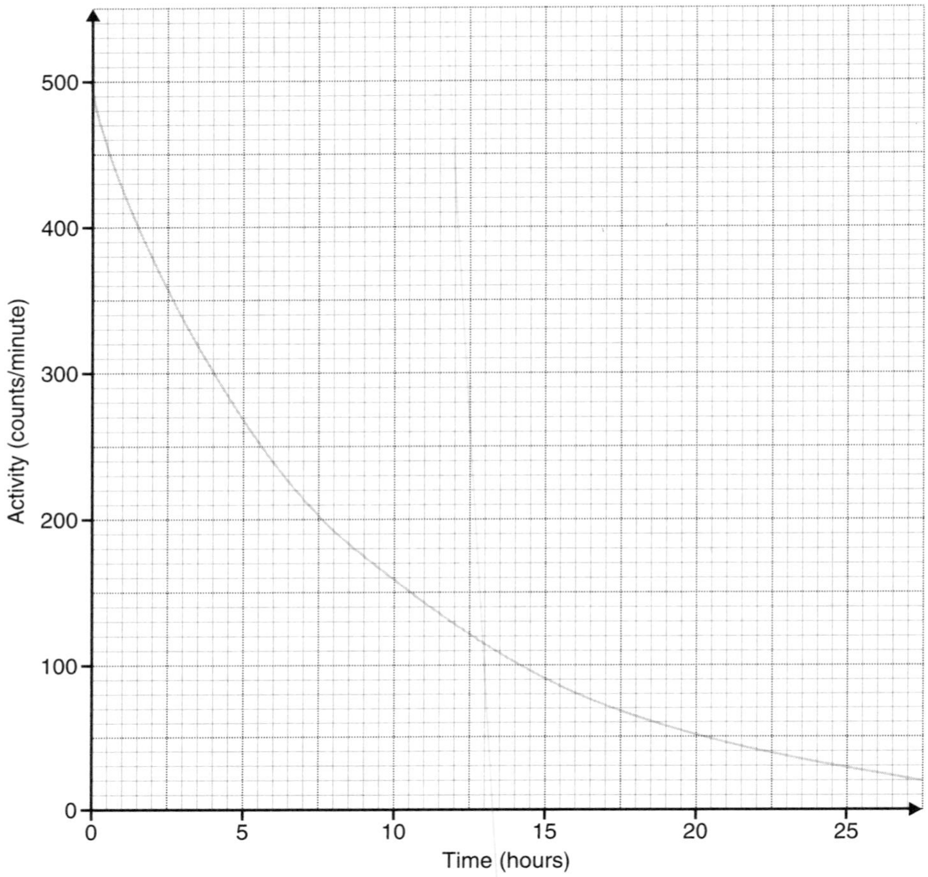

Fig. 56

69 The symbol in Fig. 57 is on a cupboard door to warn of danger.

(a) What sort of materials would you expect to find inside the cupboard? (1)

(b) Why are the materials dangerous? (2)

(c) Name three precautions you would take in using the materials in the cupboard. (2)

Fig. 57

70 Fig. 58 shows nuclear fission of uranium 235 in a nuclear reactor.

(a) Describe the process shown in the figure. Explain how it can lead to a chain reaction. (5)

(b) After the reactor has been running for a few years the uranium fuel rods in the reactor are removed and taken to Sellafield. There the waste products are separated and put into large cans which are then sealed.

The cans are then kept in water.

Give **two** reasons why the waste products are kept in sealed cans, under water. (2)

(c) When Uranium 235 absorbs a neutron it undergoes fission (break up). The equation below shows one way in which this can happen.

$$^{235}_{92}U + ^{1}_{0}n \rightarrow ^{144}_{56}Ba + ^{90}_{36}Kr + \text{neutrons}$$

(i) How many neutrons are released by this fission? (1)

(ii) In addition to the many particles released in this fission what else is released? (1)

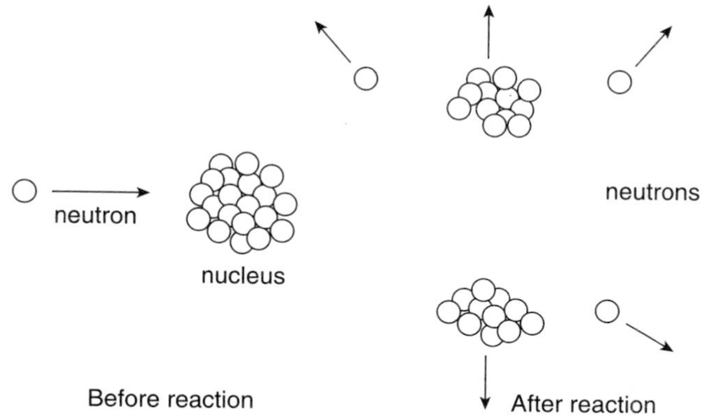

Fig. 58

Chapter 28 (answers – page 207)

71 Every object attracts every other object with a force.

(a) What type of force is acting between the Earth and the Moon? (1)

(b) What **two** factors does this force depend on? (2)

(c) What evidence is there on Earth to show the force of the Moon? (1)

72 (a) The Earth has a layered structure. On Fig. 59 label the layers indicated by the arrows. (2)

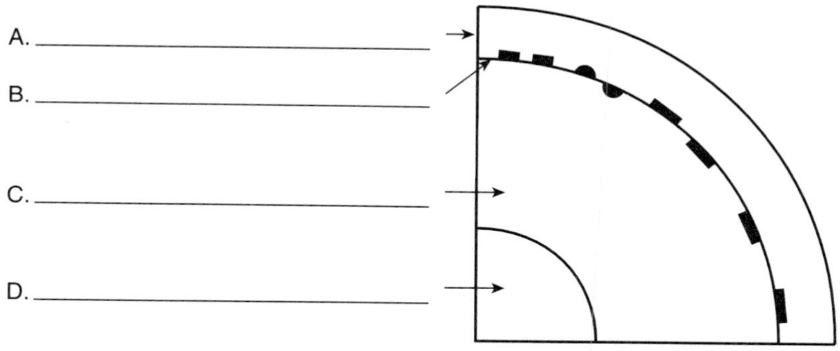

Fig. 59

When an earthquake takes place waves are sent out through the earth and can be detected thousands of kilometres from the place at which the quake occurs. Two types of wave are sent out; P and S.

(b) Explain how P and S waves differ in the way they are transmitted through the earth. (2)

(c) The trace in Fig, 60 is from a seismometer which detects earthquake waves. Calculate the ratio of the average speed of P waves to those of S waves. The first P wave arrives at the seismometer 7 minutes after the quake. (5)

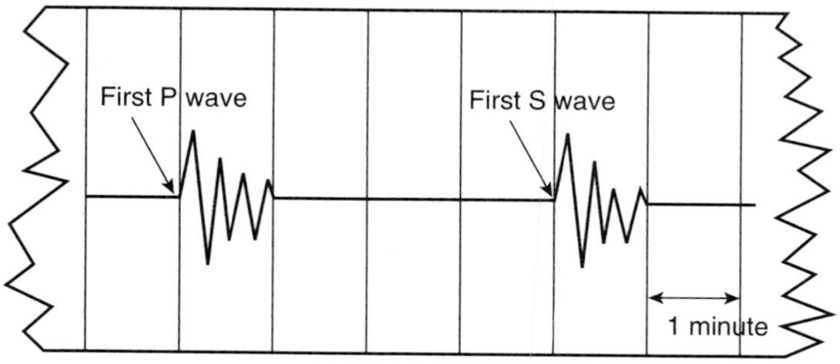

Fig. 60

(d) Explain, with the help of Fig. 61, what is meant by the Shadow Zone in the detection of earthquakes' waves. What does the existence of this zone tell us about the composition of the Earth? (3)

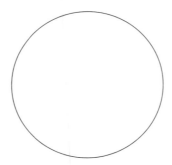

Fig. 61

73 Some information about planets in the Solar System is given in Table 6.

Table 6

planet	*length of day*	*length of year*
Earth	24 hours	365 days
Mars	24 hours 40 min	686 'Earth' days
Venus	2808 hours	225 'Earth' days
X	10 hours	10753 'Earth' days
Y	4224 hours	88 'Earth' days

(a) In terms of the movement of a planet, explain what is meant by

(i) a day (2)

(ii) a year (2)

(b) Which of the planets X, or Y, would you expect to be furthest from the Sun? Explain your answer. (3)

(c) On each planet, a day is divided into so many hours of darkness, and so many hours of light. Explain why, in Summer in Britain, it is light for more than 12 hours each day, whereas in Winter it is light for less than 12 hours each day. (3)

Chapter 29 (answers – page 207)

74 Morse Code is gradually being abandoned worldwide as a means of sending distress signals from shipping. The replacement system uses digital signals and satellite positioning which enables the exact position of a ship to be transmitted automatically.

(a) What was the advantage of Morse Code? (2)

(b) What might be the advantage of using an automatically transmitted digital signal? (3)

(c) Why are digital signals used rather than analogue? (1)

75 A loudspeaker is a transducer.

(a) What is meant by a transducer? (1)

(b) Explain how a loudspeaker acts as a transducer. (4)

76 Optical fibres are often used in communication systems.

(a) Use a diagram to show how light pulses are passed along the fibre. (2)

(b) A semiconductor laser is used to send the light pulses along an optical fibre.

(i) Why is a laser used? (4)

(ii) What sort of code is used to send information along the fibre? (1)

(iii) What is the carrier wave? (1)

(iv) Is the carrier wave amplitude or frequency modulated? (1)

Chapter 30 (answers – page 207–8)

77 A record stores a signal in analogue form, a CD stores a signal in digital form.

(a) What is the varying property that stores the signal information on a record? (1)

(b) A record player can have difficulty in reproducing high notes. Suggest a reason for this. (2)

(c) Some notes can sometimes sound louder than others or be distorted or noisy. This is due to the method of playing back the signal. Suggest reasons for these problems. (3)

(d) A CD player generally avoids the problems given in (c). What are the features that allow it to avoid these problems? (2)

Chapter 31 (answers – page 208)

78 Listeners to short wave radio broadcasts in this country can often hear signals transmitted from the other side of the world.

(a) A particular part of the earth's atmosphere is responsible for this. What is its name? (1)

(b) Draw a simple diagram to show how the signal could be getting around the world. (2)

(c) Some receivers in between the original transmitter and receiver will be able to hear the signal, others will not. Explain why. (2)

79 A typical radio station transmits a FM signal on a frequency of 100 MHz. The speed of radio waves is 3×10^8 m/s.

(a) Calculate the wavelength of the carrier wave? (2)

(b) Why do local radio stations use carrier wave frequencies of about 100 MHz? (2)

Chapter 32 (answers – page 208)

80 Three geostationary satellites could provide worldwide communications.

(a) On a diagram show how these satellites should be positioned. (2)

(b) A transmitter is at one position on the equator and a receiver at another position, also on the equator. Assume that the height of a geostationary satellite is about 36 000 km and that the distance between the transmitter and the receiver is twice this distance.

(i) Calculate how long it takes a signal to travel from the transmitter to the receiver via the satellite. The speed of radio waves is 3×10^8 m/s. (3)

(ii) If this signal were carrying a telephone conversation, would there be a noticeable delay between speaking and hearing the reply? (2)

(iii) Give a possible frequency for the carrier wave used to transmit the signal to the satellite. Explain your choice.(2)

(c) Is the satellite likely to be an active or a passive satellite? Give a reason. (2)

Further invaluable question practice can be found in *Letts GCSE Questions and Answers Physics*.

Answers to exam questions

1 (a) gradient of graph A near 200 s is 2/50 = 0.04 m/s = 144 km/hr (2)
(b) travelling with increasing speed (1)
(c) at constant speed (1)
(d) when the two graphs have the same gradient, i.e at about 150 s (2)
(e) area under graph B = $\frac{1}{2}(200 \times 4) = 400$ m (2)

2 (a) (i) $a = \dfrac{20 - 0}{4.7 - 0.7} = 5.0$ m/s^2 *(penalise more than 3 sig. figs.)* (2)
(ignore negative sign for acceleration)
(ii) distance = speed × time = 20 × 0.7 = 14 m
(iii) distance travelled = area under curve (1)
$= \dfrac{(4.7 - 0.7) \times 20}{2}$ (1)
= 40 m (1)
(allow methods using constant acceleration formulae)
(iv) total stopping distance = 54 m (1)
(b) (i) deceleration less
(ii) distance travelled is the same
(iii) distance travelled is greater

3 (a) A air resistance (1)
B weight (1)
(b) (i) terminal velocity (1)
(ii) balanced (1)
(c) (i) 1.5 s (1)
(ii) 15 m/s (1)
(iii) distance = speed × time (1)
= 7.5 m/s × 2 s
= 15 m (1)

4 (a) (i) 75 or 76 m/s (2)
(ii) acceleration = slope (tangent) at $t = 0$
$= 60/9 = 6.7$ m/s^2 (3)
(b) The thrust from the engines is constant but air resistance increases as the speed of the aeroplane increases. Thus, the resultant force gets less. (3)
(c) The length of the runway equals the area under the graph up to $t = 25$ s, which is about 1300 m. (2)

5 (a) 500 N. As the car is travelling at a constant speed, there is no total force acting on it. Therefore, the force exerted by the tow rope must be equal and opposite to the force of friction. (1)
(b) The extra force which accelerates the car is 1000 – 500 = 500 N
Use $F = ma$ to calculate $a = \dfrac{500}{1000} = 0.5$ m/s^2. (3)

6 (a) (i) the gravitational force between the two (1)
(ii) the tension in the string (1)
(iii) the frictional force between the tyre and the road (1)
(b) inwards (1)

7 (a) Conservation of momentum states that, when two objects interact, their total momentum remains constant, providing no external force is acting on them. (2)

(b) The gain in momentum of the rocket is equal and opposite to the momentum of the ejected hot gases. (2)

(c) $(m \times v)$ spaceship + $(m \times v)$ gases = 0
$(50\,000 \times v) + (20 \times 10\,000) = 0$
$v = -4$ m/s (increase in velocity) (3)

(d) (i) momentum = $m \times v$
= 1500 × 10 = 15 000 kg m/s (2)

(ii) 15 000 kg m/s (2)

(iii) $900 \times v = 15000$
$v = 16.7$ m/s (2)

8 (a) work done = force × distance moved (in direction of force) (1)
= 1000 N × 15 m/s × 20 s (1)
= 300 000 J (2)

(b) efficiency = useful output energy/total input energy
= 300 000/1 000 000) × 100 % (1)
= 30 % (or 0.30) (1)

9 (a) reaction time = 12 m/15 m/s = 0.8 s (1)

(b) (i) $\frac{1}{2} \times 1000 \times 15^2 = 112\,500$ J (2)

(ii) 112 500 J (1)

(iii) $Fs = 112\,500$
$F = 5625$ N (2)

(iv) converted to heat/thermal energy in brakes (1)

(c) When a car is turning the passengers tend to go on in a straight line. *Relative to the car* the passengers feel they are being forced outwards. The car has to exert an inward force on the passengers to get them round the corner. (4)

(d) The crumple zones increase the time it takes to stop the car and its passengers, thus *decreasing* the force acting on them. (4)

10 (a) (i) being pushed up by the trampoline (1) non-uniform acceleration (1)

(ii) rising above trampoline (1) with uniform deceleration (1)

(b) C (1)

(c) acceleration = $\frac{\text{change in speed}}{\text{time taken}} = \frac{8}{0.8} = 10$ m/s^2 (2)

(d) (i) K.E. $= \frac{1}{2}mv^2$ (1)
$= \frac{1}{2} \times 70 \times 8^2$
= 2240 J (1)

(ii) P.E. $= mgh$ (1)
$= 70 \times 10 \times 3.2$
= 2240 J (1)

∴ same (1)

11 (a) It is increasing. (1)

(b) The gravitational potential energy of the rocket increases as it moves from the Earth to the Moon. Work has to be done to achieve this and thus fuel has to be used. (3)

(c) astronaut + spacecraft in free-fall
no reaction possible with floor of craft
no sensation of weight (3)

12 (a) (i) 32 J (ii) 32 J (iii) 4 W (5)

(b) (i) 24.5 J (ii) 7 m/s (3)

13 (a) A vector quantity has direction as well as size.
A scalar quantity has size only. (2)

(b) vector – e.g. momentum, force, velocity. scalar – e.g. mass, volume. (2)

14 $R = 30$ N (1)

15 2 N (1)

16 (a) (2)

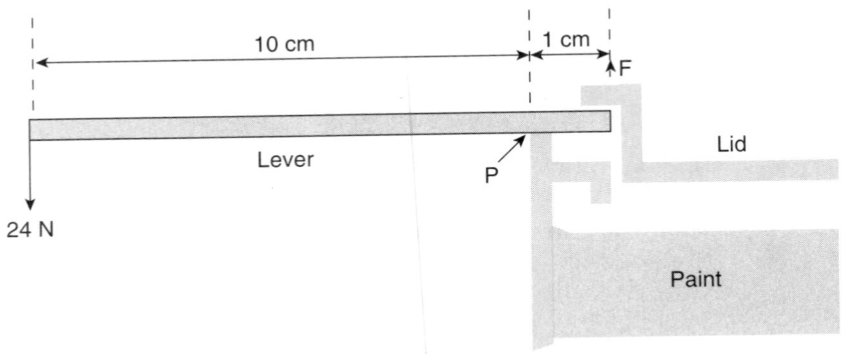

(b) 2.4 Nm or 240 N cm (c) 240 N (d) 264 N (4)
(e) increase the size of the force applied to the end of the lever or increase the length of the lever (2)

17 (a) 4 cm^2 (b) 8 cm^3 (c) 64 g (4)

18 (a) 100 cm^3 (b) 400 g (2)

19 (a) 100 000 N (b) 100 000 N (c) 1000 Pa (N/m^2) (d) 25 000 N (6)

20 (a) arrow on diagram near slave cylinder pointing UPWARDS (1)
(b) The liquid transmits pressure from master cylinder to slave cylinder. (1)
(c) if the brake fluid compressed, the pressure applied at the brake pedal would not be transmitted to the slave cylinder and the brakes would not operate effectively (2)
(d) $P = F/A$
$= 240/16$ (1)
$= 15\ N/cm^2$ (1)
$= 15 \times 10\ 000\ N/m^2$
$= 150\ 000$ Pascals (1)
(e) $F = P \times A$
$= 15 \times 2$ (1)
$= 30$ N (1)

21 (a) The deformation (e.g. increase in length) of a material is proportional to the force applied to it, provided the elastic limit is not exceeded. (2)
(b) (i) 7.2 or 7.3 N (ii) 2 N (iii) 1.5 N (3)
(c) As the weights are taken off the readings will return along the line of the original graph. (2)
(d) As the weights are removed the readings will return along a line below the original graph and parallel to it. (2)

22 (a) The springs represent the forces between molecules. (1)
(b) When a solid is heated the molecules vibrate about their average position with greater amplitude. The spheres in the model should be made to vibrate with greater amplitude. (2)
(c) In a liquid the molecules move throughout the liquid. In a solid molecules stay in the same average position. (2)
(d) Energy is needed to overcome the forces holding the molecules together. (2)

23 (a) The smoke particles reflect some of the light and can therefore be seen. (1)
(b) They have small enough mass to move slightly when buffeted by molecules, but are large enough to be seen under a microscope. (2)
(c) the smoke particles 'jiggling' about in a random way (1)
(d) They are very small and moving very fast. (2)

24 (a) about 3.6, about 123

(b) (6)

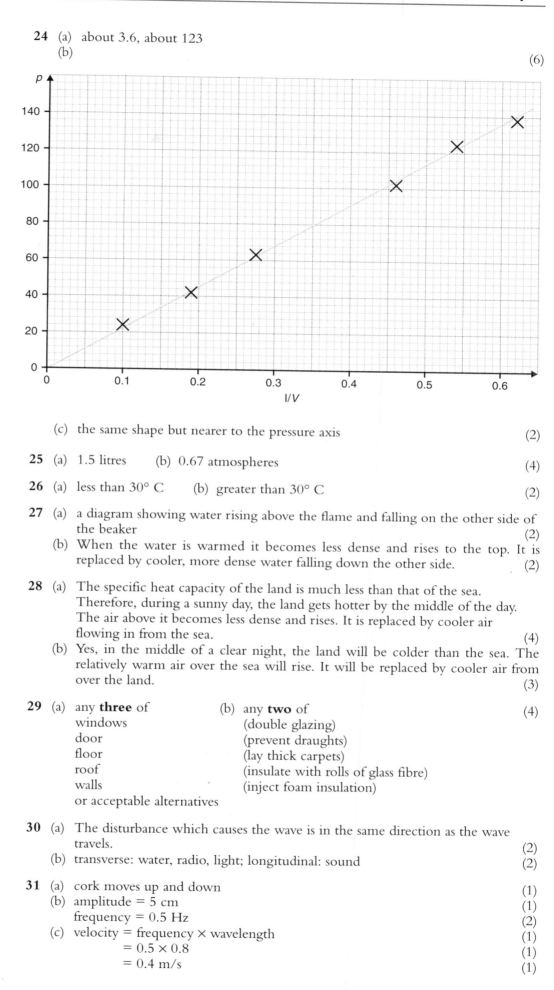

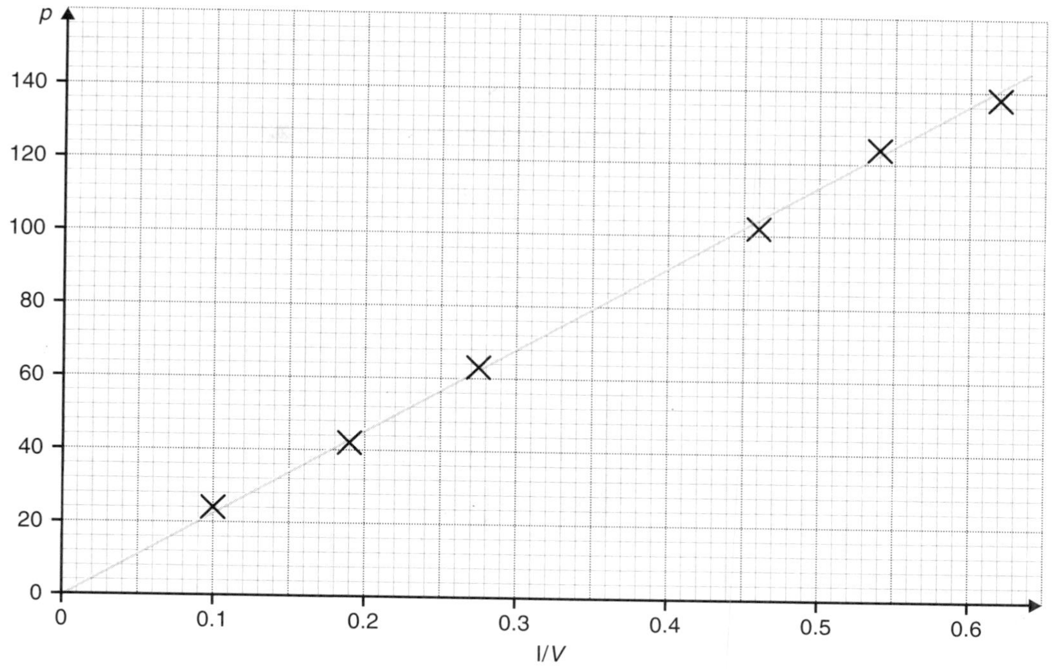

(c) the same shape but nearer to the pressure axis (2)

25 (a) 1.5 litres (b) 0.67 atmospheres (4)

26 (a) less than 30° C (b) greater than 30° C (2)

27 (a) a diagram showing water rising above the flame and falling on the other side of the beaker (2)

(b) When the water is warmed it becomes less dense and rises to the top. It is replaced by cooler, more dense water falling down the other side. (2)

28 (a) The specific heat capacity of the land is much less than that of the sea. Therefore, during a sunny day, the land gets hotter by the middle of the day. The air above it becomes less dense and rises. It is replaced by cooler air flowing in from the sea. (4)

(b) Yes, in the middle of a clear night, the land will be colder than the sea. The relatively warm air over the sea will rise. It will be replaced by cooler air from over the land. (3)

29 (a) any **three** of
windows
door
floor
roof
walls
or acceptable alternatives

(b) any **two** of (4)
(double glazing)
(prevent draughts)
(lay thick carpets)
(insulate with rolls of glass fibre)
(inject foam insulation)

30 (a) The disturbance which causes the wave is in the same direction as the wave travels. (2)

(b) transverse: water, radio, light; longitudinal: sound (2)

31 (a) cork moves up and down (1)

(b) amplitude = 5 cm (1)
frequency = 0.5 Hz (2)

(c) velocity = frequency × wavelength (1)
= 0.5 × 0.8 (1)
= 0.4 m/s (1)

32 (a) (2)

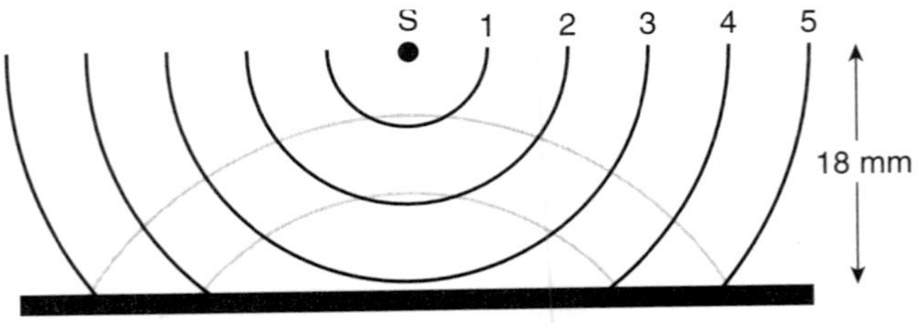

(b) (i) 6 mm (ii) 8 Hz (3)

33 (a) (2)

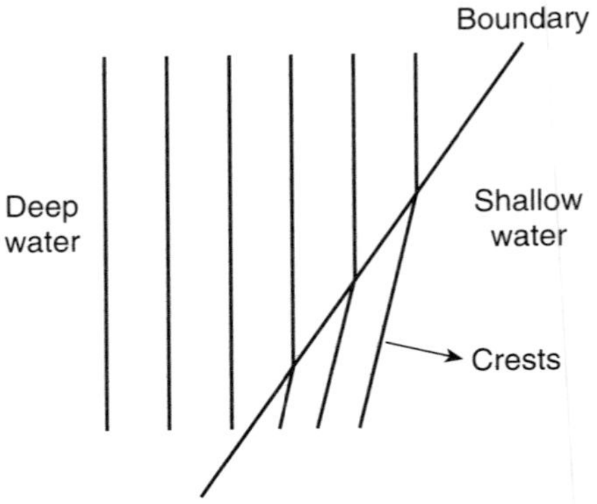

(b) refraction (1)

34 (a) inverted (b) gets larger (2)

35 (a), (b), (c) (3)

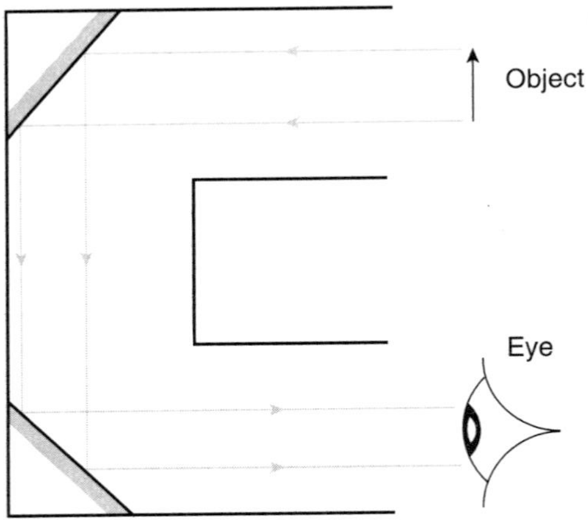

(d) The image is inverted. (1)

36 (a) X is the angle of incidence; Y is the angle of refraction (2)
(b) (i) Z is the angle of incidence (or critical angle) (1)
(ii) (A) total internal reflection (1)
(B) The incident angle is too large for refraction to take place. (2)
(C) in reflectors (2)
(c) the transmission of telephone conversations by passing light along fibre optics (2)

37 (3)

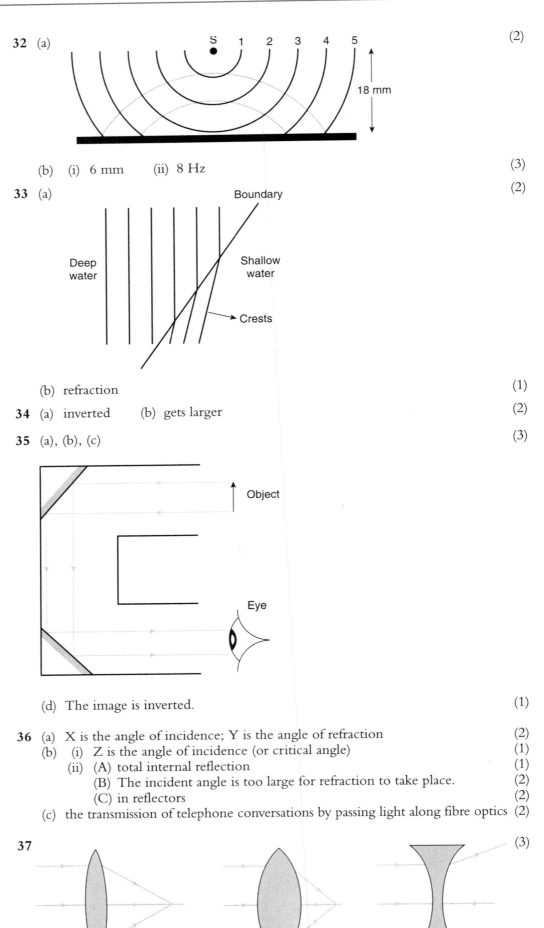

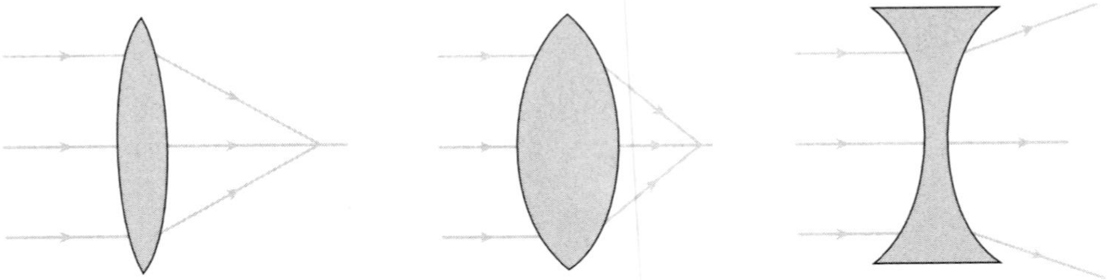

38 Blue light slows more than red light on entering a glass block. Therefore, if it enters obliquely, it will bend more than red light. (3)

39 (a) (i) pupil (1) (ii) iris (1) (iii) lens (1) (iv) retina (1)
(v) optic nerve (1)
(b) (i) long sight (1) (ii) convex lens (1)

40 thin or weak; behind; converging (convex); on (4)

41 (a) The spreading could be increased by making the slit narrower. (1)
(b) The wavelength remains the same. (1)
(c) The diffraction (spreading out) would be greater. (1)

42 (a) To prevent microwaves getting out of the oven and irradiating people. Energy would also be 'lost'. (1)
(b) In a microwave oven only the food is heated. In a conventional oven energy is wasted in heating the air surrounding the food. (1)
(c) heat (1)
(d) (i) The wavelength is smaller. (1)
(ii) The frequency remains the same. (1)

43 (a) Light travels faster than sound. (1)
(b) distance = speed × time (1)
distance = 340 m/s × 5 s (1)
= 1700 m (1)

44 (a) by reflection off the sea bed or an object (e.g. fish) (1)
(b) 900 m (c) 450 m (4)

45 (a) (i) recorder (ii) clarinet (2)
(iii) saxophone (iv) clarinet (2)
(b) about 384 Hz (2)

46 (a) sound waves with a frequency above that heard by humans (2)
(b) e.g. scanning the womb to monitor the development of a human embryo (3)
(c) dog whistle – the frequency is too high to be heard (or to annoy) but can be heard by dogs (3)

47 (a) The S pole of magnet Q is the furthest one from the magnet P. (1)
(b) They will repel. (1)
(c) The region in which magnetic forces are experienced. (2)

48 (a) There is no field at X. It is a neutral point. (1)
(b) (2)

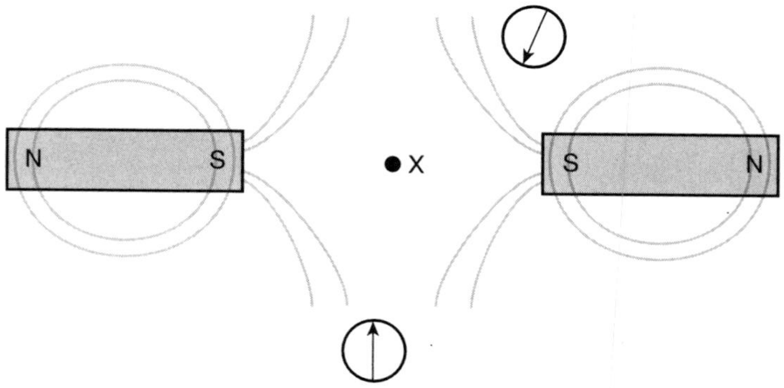

(c) They will repel. (1)
(d) (2)

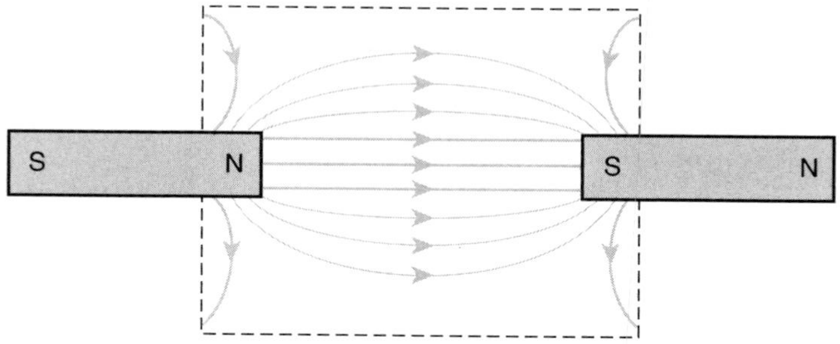

49 (a) They become negatively charged. (1)
(b) to attract the negatively charged soot particles and remove them from the 'smoke' (2)
(c) to remove soot from the 'smoke' so that the discharge to the atmosphere is 'clean' (2)

50 (a) true (b) true (2)
(c) true (d) true (2)

51 (a) zero (1)
(b) The voltmeter, which has a very large resistance, has been placed in series with the resistor rather than in parallel. (1)
(c) (1)

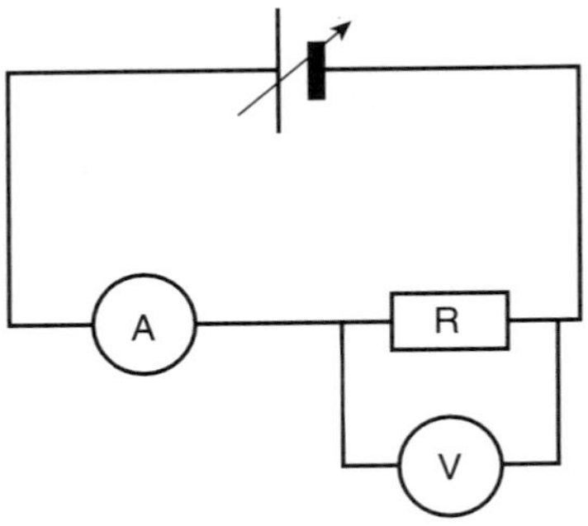

52 (a) 0.5 A (b) 0.5 A (2)
(c) 2.5 V (d) 3.5 V (2)

53 (a) current increases rapidly at first (1) then more slowly (1) (2)
(b) recall of formula (1)
reading of p.d. (1)
reading of current (1)
calculation of 3 ohms (1)
(c) (i) 9.0 V (ii) 4.0 V (4)
(iii) 13.0 V (2)
(d) $R = V/I = 4/3 = 1.33\ \Omega$ (2)
(e) 2 amp + 3.5 amp = 5.5 amp (2)

54 (a) to reflect radiant heat into the room
to make it very difficult to accidentally kick over the fire (2)
(b) (i) (2)

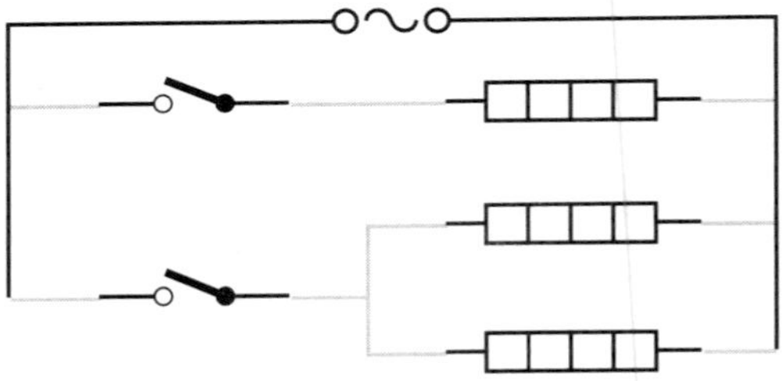

(ii) 3000 W (1)
(iii) 12 kW cost £1.08 (2)

55 (a) Four of the following:
The brown wire is connected to the neutral terminal – it should be connected to the live one.
The blue wire is connected to earth – it should be connected to the neutral terminal.
The green/yellow wire is connected to the live terminal – It should be connected to earth.
The outside cable insulation has been cut back too far, so that the cable is not properly clamped by the clench and all the strain comes on the terminals.
There is a sharp kink in the green/yellow wire. (4)
(b) When the plug is pushed into a socket, the longer earth pin opens gates to the live and neutral connections. (2)

56 (a) iron 4.16 A, kettle 12.5 A, t.v. 0.25 A, (3)
(b) iron 5 A kettle 13 A t.v. 2 A (2)

57 (a) soft iron (1)
(b) It is easily magnetized and demagnetized. (2)
(c) 1.5 N (1)

58 (a) (i) It becomes magnetized and is attracted towards the electromagnet. (2)
(ii) They get pulled apart. (1)
(iii) It strikes the bell. (1)
(b) The current having stopped, the spring pulls the soft iron armature away from the electromagnet. The contacts close, the current flows again and the whole process repeats itself. (2)

59 (a) The two magnets both have the same pole facing inwards. (1)
(b) This means that there is a very weak magnetic field between the magnets, and therefore very little force on the sides of the coil. (1)
(c) (i) stronger magnets, more turns on the coil, a larger current (3)
(ii) interchange the two magnets, reverse the direction of current flow (2)

60 (a) The lamp will be out or very dim for slow speeds. As the speed increases the brightness of the lamp will increase until it reaches its normal brightness when the coil is rotating at its maximum speed. (1)
(b) The lamp would become less bright. (1)
(c) The lamp would become brighter. (2)

61 (a) primary current produces a magnetic field in iron (1)
magnetic field passes through secondary coil (1)
magnetic field changes (1)
(b) (i) power out = power in (1)
$415 \times I$ = 800 000 (1)
I = 1930 A *(penalise more than 3 sig. figs.)* (1)
assumed 100% efficiency (1)
(ii) for high efficiency/to reduce energy loss (1)
high voltage means low current, for given power (1)
low current means low heating effect (1)
heating effect proportional to I^2 (1)

62 (a) the National Grid (b) 275 000 V (3)
(c) The voltage is increased. (1)
(d) to reduce the current flowing and hence the energy lost due to heating the cables (2)
(e) the kite might touch the cables and thus connect the person flying it to the high voltage (2)
(f) The whole of the bird is on the wire, i.e. at only one voltage – there is no potential difference across the bird. (1)

63 (a) to accelerate the electrons (2)
(b) The negatively charged electrons are attracted upwards by the positively charged plate. (2)
(c) The anode now repels all the electrons back to the cathode so the spot is no longer seen. (2)

64 (a) The resistance increases. (1)
(b) The collector current increases. (1)
(c) The variable resistor is used to alter the potential of point A. If the potential of A increases, the base current increases. This then increases the collector current. (2)
(d) The relay requires less current to operate it than the bulb does to make it bright. (2)
(e) Resistor R_1 limits the current through the base of the transistor and prevents damage. (1)

65 (a) on top of the light shade (or other place where light does not shine on it) (1)
(b) in series with the light sensor (1)
(c) (i) outputs are: OFF, OFF, OFF (1 mark if all 3 correct) (1)
ON (1)
(ii) outputs are: OFF, ON (both must be correct to earn mark) (1)

66 (a) 2 electrons, atomic number 2, 2 neutrons, nucleon number 4 (4)
(b) It will have the same number of protons (atomic number) but a different number of neutrons. (1)

67 5 minutes. The activity falls to one-eighth of its original value. Therefore three half-lives have elapsed in 15 minutes. (2)

68 (a) 90 counts per minute (1)
(b) Atoms are decaying all the time. As time passes there are fewer and fewer left to decay. Therefore the count rate falls. (2)
(c) 6 hours (1)
(d) (2)

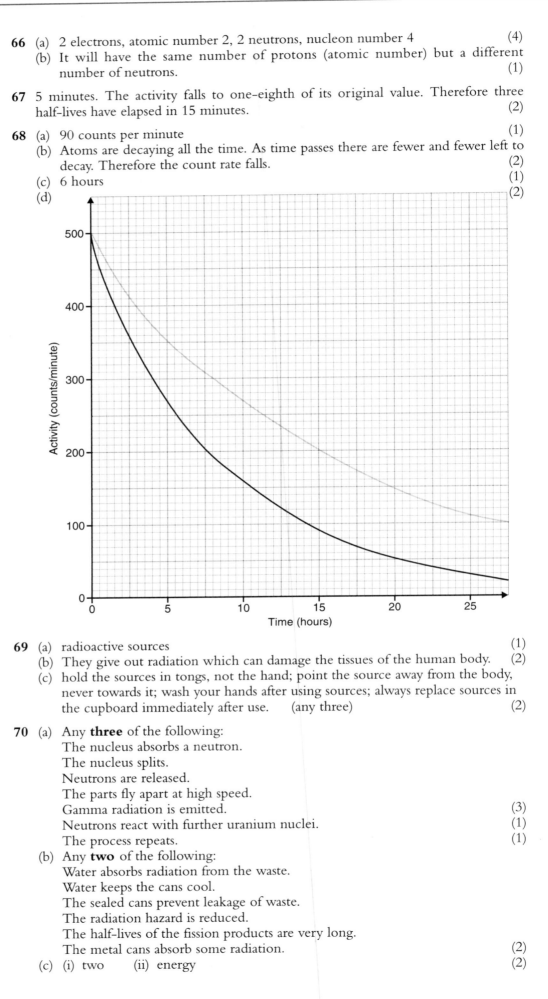

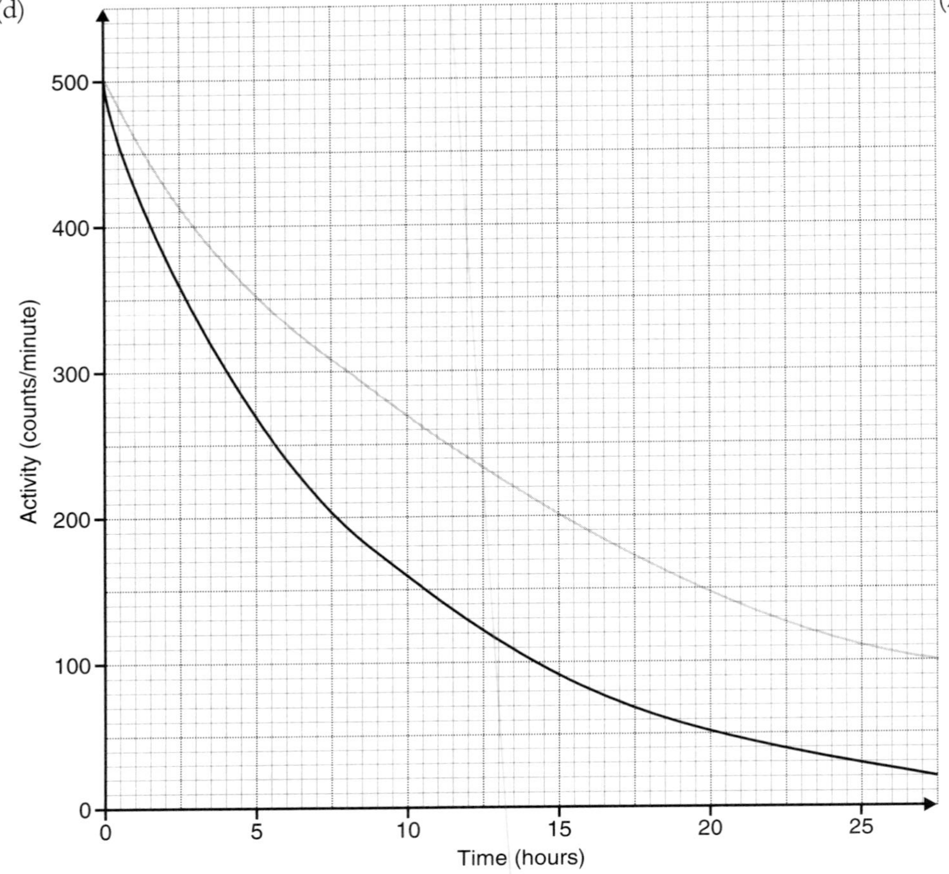

69 (a) radioactive sources (1)
(b) They give out radiation which can damage the tissues of the human body. (2)
(c) hold the sources in tongs, not the hand; point the source away from the body, never towards it; wash your hands after using sources; always replace sources in the cupboard immediately after use. (any three) (2)

70 (a) Any **three** of the following:
The nucleus absorbs a neutron.
The nucleus splits.
Neutrons are released.
The parts fly apart at high speed.
Gamma radiation is emitted. (3)
Neutrons react with further uranium nuclei. (1)
The process repeats. (1)
(b) Any **two** of the following:
Water absorbs radiation from the waste.
Water keeps the cans cool.
The sealed cans prevent leakage of waste.
The radiation hazard is reduced.
The half-lives of the fission products are very long.
The metal cans absorb some radiation. (2)
(c) (i) two (ii) energy (2)

71 (a) gravitational (1)
(b) mass of objects (1) distance apart (1)
(c) tides (1)

72 (a) A = atmosphere B = crust C = mantle D = core (2)
(b) P waves longitudinal, material oscillates in same plane as wave direction. (1)
S waves transverse, material oscillates at right angles to plane (1)
(c) D = distance to quake
7 minutes = time for P waves to arrive (1)
speed of P waves = $D/7$ (1)
7 + 5 = time for S waves to arrive (1)
speed of S waves = $D/12$ (1)
Ratio = 12/7 (1)
(d) shadow zone – a region where P or S waves are NOT detected (1)
evidence for the core/mantle structure (2)

73 (a) (i) one complete revolution of the planet (1) about its own axis (1)
(ii) one complete orbit of the planet (1) about the Sun (1)
(b) X (1)
longer year (1)
larger orbits take more time/general pattern is greater distance, greater time (1)
(c) Earth's axis tilted (1) toward Sun in Summer (1) away from Sun in Winter (1)

74 (a) The advantage of Morse Code was that it assigned the shortest codes to the most frequently used letters and therefore made the sending of messages faster and more efficient. (2)
(b) An automatically transmitted signal can contain all the necessary information about the ship. It can also transmit the exact position of the ship and can be operated by anyone, not just a skilled radio operator. (3)
(c) Digital signals are used as there is less chance of a mistake being made in reading the signal. (1)

75 (a) A transducer is a device that changes a signal or message from one form of energy into another form (1)
(b) An electrical signal is fed to a loudspeaker. This changing voltage causes a changing current in the coil of the loudspeaker. The changing current in the coil causes a changing magnetic field which interacts with the field of the permanent magnet to produce a changing force on the coil. As the coil is attached to the cone of the speaker, the changing force causes the cone to move in and out and to produce a sound wave (see Unit 29.3) (4)

76 (a)

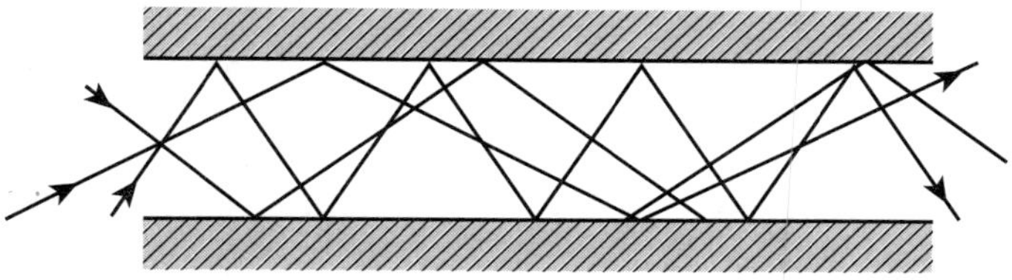

(2)

(b) (i) A laser is used as it emits an intense beam of one wavelength and can be switched on and off millions of times per second. A source of one wavelength is important as light of different wavelengths travels at different speeds in glass (that is what causes dispersion in a prism). If a pulse of light contained light of different frequencies, those frequencies would travel at different speeds down the fibre and the pulse would be 'spread out'. The pulses at the other end of the fibre would overlap and the signal could not be distinguished. (4)
(ii) usually digital code (1)
(iii) The carrier wave is light. (1)
(iv) The light is amplitude modulated. (1)

77 (a) The varying property on a record is the shape of the side of the groove. (1)
(b) High notes have a high frequency. That means that the variations of shape of the side of the groove are close together. If the stylus is too large to follow the changing pattern or has too great an inertia to follow the pattern, the note will not be reproduced. (2)

(c) If the resonant frequency of the stylus is in the range of the notes being reproduced, the stylus will have maximum amplitude of oscillations at that frequency. These large amplitude oscillations can cause distortion. Dirt in the record groove or a damaged stylus can cause additional signals which are amplified by the record player and heard as noise (3)

(d) A CD player detects a digital signal. The signal is read by a light beam and so the problem of speed of response is not encountered. Also, since the signal is a series of '0' and '1' which are then decoded, there is not the problem of picking up noise and amplifying it. (2)

78 (a) The ionosphere is responsible for the radio signal being reflected back down to earth. (1)

(b)

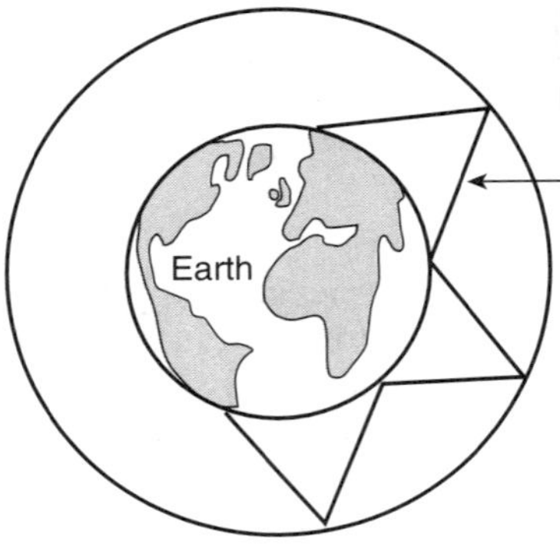

(2)

(c) As the signal is reflected back up to the ionosphere, receivers in between the points of reflection do not detect any signal. Any receivers around the points of reflection will be able to receive the signal. (2)

79 (a) The speed of radio waves is 3×10^8 m/s.

since $v = fl$, $l = \frac{v}{f} = \frac{3 \times 10^8 \text{ m/s}}{100 \times 10^6 \text{ Hz}} = 3 \text{ m}$ (2)

(b) Waves of 100 MHz are sky waves which means that line of sight communication is needed. This means that the broadcast will only be received in the immediate vicinity of the transmitter. Thus the radio station can remain 'local'. (2)

80 (a)

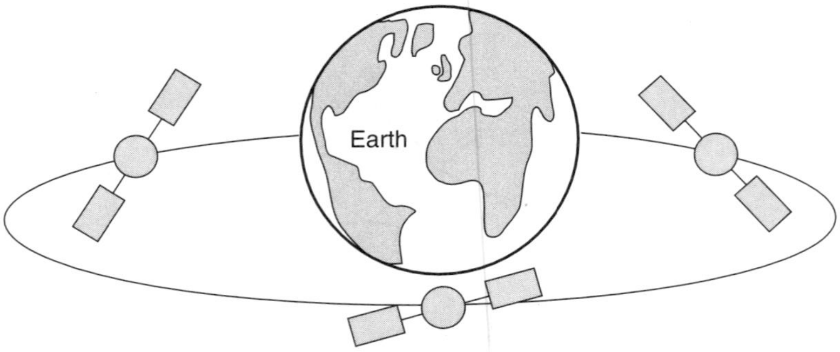

(2)

(b) (i) assume the signal has to travel $2 \times 36\,000$ km $= 72\,000$ km

$speed = \frac{distance}{time}$ and so $time = \frac{distance}{speed}$ (1)

therefore, $time = \frac{72\,000\,000}{3 \times 10^8} = 0.24$ s (2)

(ii) In a two way telephone conversation, the delay would be 0.48 s, nearly half a second which would probably be noticeable. (2)

(iii) The frequency will be higher than 30 MHz (it is actually about 4000 MHz). This is because it is important that the signal is not reflected by the ionosphere. (2)

(c) The satellite is likely to be an active satellite so that it can retransmit the signal in a narrow beam to a receiving station. Passive satellites are no longer used. (2)

Answers to quick tests

Quick test 2

1

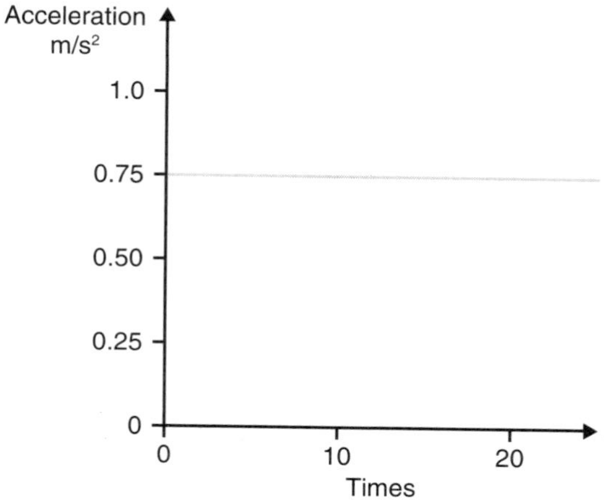

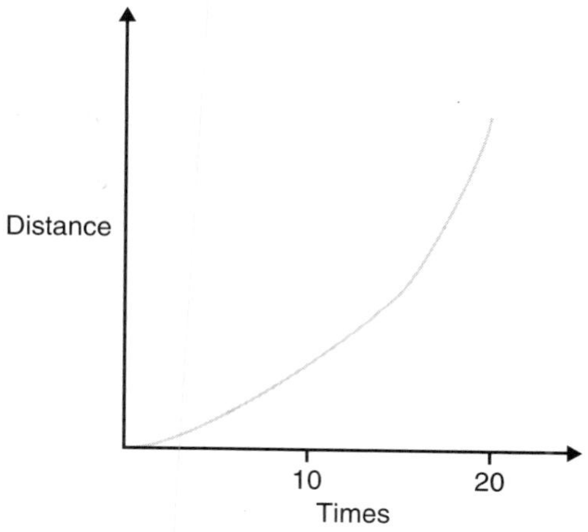

2 m/s^2 or cm/s^2

3 13 m/s

4 (a) 50 m (b) 10 m/s

5 (a) 6 s (b) 600 m

Quick test 3

1 Newton (N), kgm/s.

2 See Unit 3.1.

3 (a) $2\ m/s^2$ (b) $1.5\ m/s^2$

4 When a car stops suddenly, the belt stops the passenger, thus reducing the chance of him or her hitting the windsceen or steering column. There is some 'give' in the belt, so that the passenger stops less suddenly than the car. This avoids the passenger's chest or abdomen being crushed.

5 50 kg

6 9 N inwards.

7 400 kgm/s

8 See Unit 3.8.

9 The dingy moves in the opposite direction to the boy at a speed of 12 m/s.

Quick test 4

1 Any four from chemical, electrical, light, nuclear, sound and thermal.

2 See Unit 4.2.

3 It is no longer in a form which can be used easily, i.e. it is no longer 'useful'. Usually 'lost' energy is in the form of thermal energy in the atmosphere.

4 (a) 15 J (b) 5.5 m/s

5 4:1
6 Watt (W)
7 12 W
8 (a) any two from velocity, momentum and force
(b) any other two quantities, e.g. mass and speed

Quick test 5

1 See Unit 5.1.
2 400 N
3 See Unit 5.3.
4 See Unit 5.5. When a 'stable' object is displaced slightly from its rest position, it tends to return to that position. An 'unstable' object tends to topple over.
5 60 %

Quick test 6

1 See beginning of Chapter 6.
2 mass, length, breadth and height
3 64 g
4 3 g/cm^3

Quick test 7

1 See the beginning of Chapter 7.
2 25 N/cm^3
3 80 N/cm^3
4 in all directions
5 2 MPa

Quick test 8

1 See Unit 8.1.
2 See Unit 8.1.
3 See Unit 8.1.
4 175 mm
5 1 cm
6 elastic potential energy

Quick test 9

1 A gas has neither a fixed volume nor a fixed shape. Its volume depends on its temperature and the surrounding pressure. It takes the shape of the vessel containing it.
2 the intermolecular bonds
3 1000
4 See Unit 9.1.
5 See Unit 9.2.

Quick test 10

1 See Unit 10.1
2 It doubles.
3 1500 cm^3
4 133 333 Pa
5 4 times

Quick test 11

1 See beginning of Chapter 11.
2 2000 J/kgK
3 Tea is mainly water which has a very high specific heat capacity.

Quick test 12

1 See Unit 12.1.
2 by radiation
3 See Unit 12.3.
4 See Unit 12.3.
5 See Unit 12.4.
6 See Unit 12.4.

Quick test 13

1 See Unit 13.1
2 sound
3 5 Hz
4 See Unit 13.4.
5 See Unit 13.5.

Quick test 14

1 shadows and eclipses
2 See Unit 14.1.
3

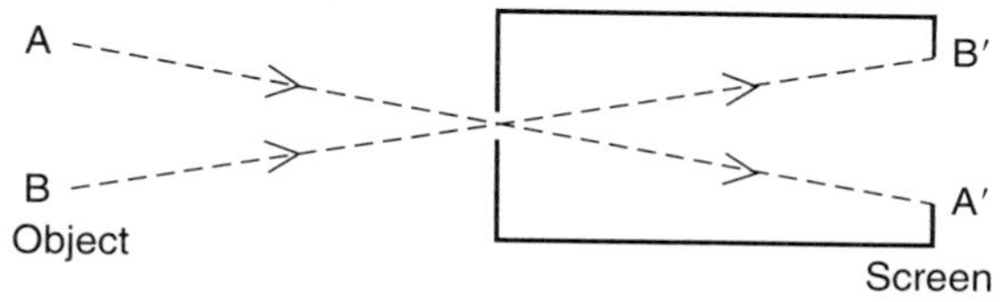

4 It gets larger and brighter.
5 See Unit 14.2.
6 The image is virtual and as far behind the mirror as you are in front of it.

Quick test 15

1 Light travels more slowly in glass than air. The part of the wavefront which first enters the glass slows down first, i.e. it travels more slowly for longer. This results in the direction of travel of the wavefront changing.
2 See Unit 15.2.
3 See unit 15.2.
4 See Unit 15.3.
5 A real image is formed by rays actually crossing. Such an image can be seen on a screen placed where the rays cross.
A virtual image exists where rays of light appear to have come from. Such an image can never be seen on a screen.
6 See Unit 15.6.
7 In order to focus light from objects at different distances, the lens of an eye automatically alters its thickness by means of the ciliary muscles, whereas the lens of a camera has to be moved forward or back to achieve the same result.
The amount of light entering an eye is controlled automatically by the iris increasing or decreasing the diameter of the hole at its centre (pupil). To achieve the same result with a camera, the size of the hole (aperture) has to be adjusted manually or electronically.
In an eye the image is formed on the retina and the information transmitted to the brain whereas the camera requires a film to act as the screen.

Quick test 16

1 See Unit 16.1.
2 radio waves, infrared rays, yellow light, ultraviolet rays, gamma rays
3 infrared radiation
4 about 1500 m
5 γ-rays are high frequency radiation which occur naturally. X-rays are man-made rays of similar frequency.

Quick test 17

1 Sound waves are longitudinal waves which require a material (medium) through which to travel. Electromagnetic waves are transverse waves which can travel through space (a vacuum).
2 3 m
3 300 m/s
4 reflection
5 See Unit 17.3.
6 See Unit 17.6.

Quick test 18

1 N-pole means a **north-seeking** pole.
2 See Unit 18.2.
3 See Unit 18.2.

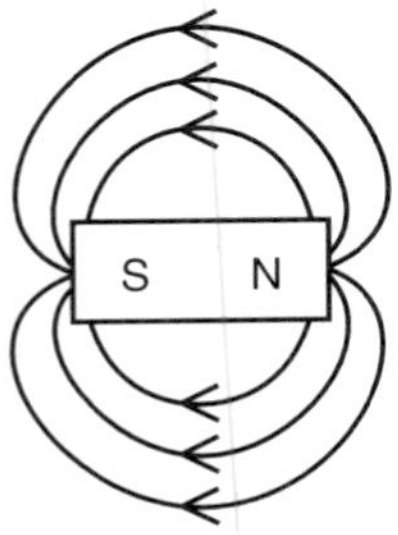

Quick test 19

1 See the beginning of Chapter 19.
2 See Unit 19.1.
3 See Unit 19.1.
4 See Unit 19.3.
5 See Unit 19.3.

Quick test 20

1 2.5 A
2 6 Ω
3 6 V
4 It should have a low resistance so that it does not significantly reduce the current that it is placed in the circuit to measure.
5 (a) 6 Ω (b) 0.55 Ω
6 0.1 A, 0.15 A approx.

Quick test 21

1 2.07 MJ or 0.56 kWh
2 3.125 A
3 40 W

4 electric lamp, iron, 2 kW fire
5 2 A
6 35 p

Quick test 22

1 See Unit 22.2.
2 10 A
3 See Unit 22.3.
4 It draws more than 13 A which is the maximum current that should be taken from a power socket. The cable to the cooker is thick and therefore can carry a larger current without over-heating.
5 See Unit 22.4.

Quick test 23

1 As the current is increased the domains of the electromagnet become more aligned. Once they are perfectly aligned a further increase in current will have no effect.
2 See Unit 23.2.
3 sound, electrical
4 electrical to sound
5 The strength of the field, the size of the current and the length of wire at right angles to the magnetic field.
6 See Unit 23.7.
7 Increasing the current, using stronger magnets and increasing the number of turns on the armature (coil).

Quick test 24

1 The speed at which the wire is moved, the strength of the magnetic field.
2 True. When the coil of an electric motor is rotated, the turns of wire on it cut through the field of the magnets and induce an e.m.f. (voltage) in themselves.
3 (a) 40 V (b) 50 Hz
4 For an e.m.f. to be induced in the secondary the magnetic field in the iron core must be changing. The magnetic field in the iron core is due to the current in the primary which must therefore be changing.
5 See Unit 24.4.

Quick test 25

1 See Unit 25.1.
2 See Unit 25.2.
3 For a current to flow, the anode must be positive in order to attract the electrons away from the cathode. If the anode is negative, the electrons are kept near the the cathode by repulsion.
4 The sharp shadow cast by a Maltese Cross tube – see Unit 25.3.
5 (a) because the lower plate is positive with respect to the upper one
(b) increase the voltage between the horizontal plates
(c) reverse the voltage between the horizontal plates
6 electrical (current in filament), heat (hot cathode), kinetic (moving electrons), light (picture on screen)

Quick test 26

1 Their conducting properties are between good conductors and good insulators.
2 See Unit 26.1.

3 See Unit 26.1.
4 to permit current to flow in one direction only
5 See Unit 26.3.
6 The current coming out of the amplifier is greater than the current put in.
7 The circuit has two stable states and will stay in whichever one it is put.
8 All information is processed in the form of digits only, not continuous numbers (analogue).
9 (a)

IN		OUT
A	B	
0	0	1
0	1	0
1	0	0
1	1	0

(b)

IN	OUT	
0	1	
1	0	

(c)

IN		OUT
A	B	
0	0	0
0	1	0
1	0	0
1	1	1

Quick test 27

1 See Unit 27.1.
2 proton
3 (a) a helium nucleus (b) high frequency electromagnetic radiation
4 atoms of the same element which have a different mass **or**
atoms with the same number of protons but a different number of neutrons
5 See Unit 27.4.
6 See Unit 27.5.
7 one hour
8 alpha particles
9 See Unit 27.6.
10 The moderator slows down neutrons to reduce the probability of their capture by uranium-238 nuclei.

Quick test 28

1 See Unit 28.3.
2 See Unit 28.3.
3 *F*
4 detecting earth tremors – see Unit 28.6
5 See Unit 28.8.
6 (a) The Moon and Sun are on opposite sides of the Earth.
(b) The Moon and Sun are on the same side of the Earth.
7 See Unit 28.12.

Quick test 29

1 The resistance of the transatlantic cable caused the signal to lose energy.

2

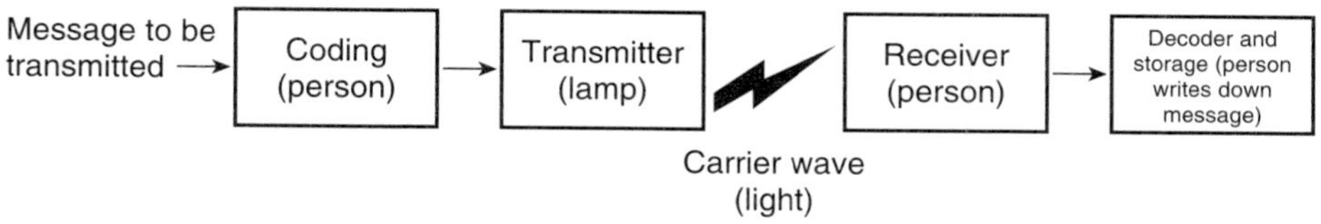

3 an analogue signal – see Unit 29.4 and Fig. 29.3
a digital signal – see Unit 29.4 and Fig. 29.4

4 Digital codes are used increasingly for communications because this code is more secure than analogue code and is almost immune from interference and noise (see Unit 29.4).

5 amplitude modulation – see Unit 29.5 and Fig. 29.6

Quick test 30

1 The analogue signal is stored on a record by changing the shape of the sides of a groove cut into the surface of the record. The right and left channels are stored separately as the different shapes of the two sides of the groove.

2 Dirt can easily get into the groove on a record. As the stylus passes over the dirt, additional signals are generated. These signals are amplified and sound like noise.

The magnetic pattern on a tape is stored by many very small magnetic particles. Not only is it difficult to store a perfect magnetic copy of the signal but the imperfections in the particles, as well as the size of the particles, all introduce additional noise.

Because the final signal output is an amplified copy of the signal obtained from the record or from the tape, any additional signals generated by the recording or playback process are amplified as much as the wanted signal and can usually be heard.

3 The signal is fed to the recording head, which is a small electromagnet with a gap in it (see Fig. 30.2). The varying magnetic field caused by the varying signal causes the magnetic particles on the tape to be magnetized by a varying amount. The pattern of the signal is therefore stored as a varying magnetic pattern.

4 Because digital recording only has to record the difference between a '0' and a '1', it is much easier to ensure that the digits are recorded correctly and are read correctly when played back. To ensure that the digital signal is played back correctly, error correction digits are included which check that a digital sequence is likely to be correct and instructs the playback equipment to re-read or ignore the sequence if it is not correct.

Quick test 31

1 1500 m

2 Because the wavelength of the wave is long compared with most obstacles, the wave diffracts significantly around hills and bridges and is able to be received (see Unit 16.1).

3 The local stations can use the same frequency if they ensure that their signal strength is low enough for the York transmission not to be able to be picked up in Newcastle and the other way round.

4 Because the waves are reflected off the ground and the ionosphere, there will be places between reflections where no signal is received.

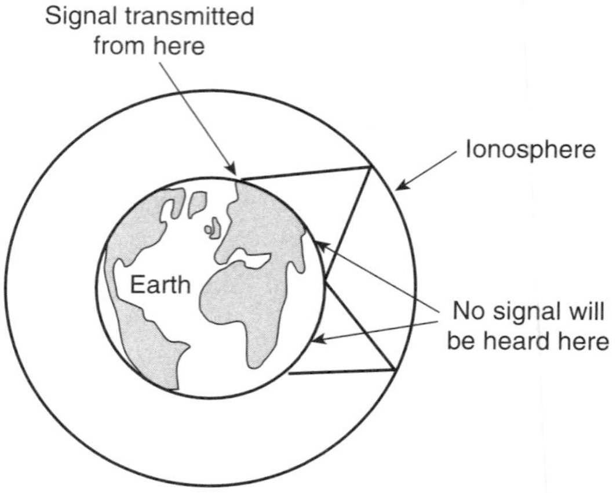

Quick test 32

1 A geostationary satellite has to be above the equator as the centre of the orbit must coincide with the centre of the Earth. An orbit that allows the satellite to pass over London will also have to be centred on the centre of the Earth and the result would be a path rather like that described in Fig. 32.2.

2 Since television satellites are geostationary, they are positioned over the equator. This is in a southerly direction from this country, the exact direction depending on the position of the satellite in the orbit. In Australia, satellite dishes will have to point roughly North.

3 The advantage of a polar orbiting satellite is that it can cover the entire surface of the Earth. The disadvantage is that it is only over one particular place for a short time and so can only download the information it gathers for a short time each day.

4 4 hours

Coursework

From 1998 there is a new coursework system for all GCSE Science courses. The same system applies to all GCSE Examination Boards.

During your Physics course you will be expected to complete a coursework assessment that includes a **whole investigation**.

A whole investigation involves you scoring marks in four separate skill areas. These are:

- Skill Area P – Planning experimental procedures
- Skill Area O – Obtaining evidence
- Skill Area A – Analysing evidence and drawing conclusions
- Skill Area E – Evaluating evidence

In addition you can score marks by carrying out assessments which test only one or two of these skill areas. Your final mark must include **at least two pieces of work** of which **one must be a whole investigation**.

For each of skill areas P, O and A, there is a maximum of eight marks and skill area E has a maximum of six marks.

A single final total mark out of 63 is obtained. This mark of 63 includes three marks allocated for your spelling, punctuation and grammar (SPaG). This mark out of 63 is calculated by adding together the best marks awarded for each of the four skill areas, doubling the total, and then adding a further mark of up to three for spelling, punctuation and grammar.

For example, if you are awarded six marks for skill areas P and O, five for skill area A, four for skill area E and two for SPaG, your overall mark is

$$2 \times (6 + 6 + 5 + 4) + 2$$

A total of 44 is obtained for the coursework assessment.

The marks awarded by your teacher, and samples of the work from your school or college will be checked (moderated) by an expert from outside your school to make sure the marking is the same as in all other schools and colleges. The moderator may add marks to your total, if your teacher has been harsh, or deduct marks, if your teacher has been generous in the marking. He will alter marks for your school as a whole but will not normally alter the order of candidates within your school.

Some advice on each of the skill areas P, A, O and E follows. This should help you get the highest marks in each of the skill areas. One word of warning at this stage: sometimes the maximum mark you can achieve in a skill area is limited by the complexity of the task set.

Skill Area P Planning experimental procedures

The following table shows the Programme of Study requirements.

The first point to make about this skill area is perhaps a very obvious one. If you are being entered for a Physics examination, the subject of your coursework must be physical. You cannot use coursework which is about rates of reaction, even though it has been marked using the same criteria. However, you might use an investigation about electrolysis in Physics and Chemistry.

Programme of Study Requirements
You should have been taught: ● To use scientific knowledge and understanding, drawing on secondary sources where appropriate, to turn ideas suggested to you, and your own ideas, into a form that can be investigated. ● To carry out preliminary work where this helps to clarify what you have to do. ● To make predictions where it is appropriate to do so. ● To consider the key factors in contexts involving a number of factors. ● To plan how to vary or control key variables. ● To consider the number and range of observations or measurements to be made. ● To recognize contexts where variables cannot readily be controlled and to make judgements about the amount of evidence needed in these contexts. ● To select apparatus, equipment and techniques, taking into account safety.

Your investigation should use your factual knowledge of Physics. If your investigation involves a prediction, this should be based upon factual knowledge. You need to write something like:

I think .... will happen because ....

To help you get a suitable 'because', it may be best to include a section of theory which you consider relevant. You do not have to remember this as you do have access to books, etc.

At this stage we must consider the topic of **variables**. Suppose you are measuring the resistance, at room temperature, of different lengths of wire taken from the same reel. Clearly the resistance of the wire is related to its length. The longer the wire, the greater is its resistance. The length of wire is the **independent variable**. This means that it can have any value you choose. The resistance of the wire is the **dependent variable**. This is because it depends on the length of the wire used.

There are other variables in this investigation which you have fixed:

1 The diameter (area) of the wire.
2 The temperature – room temperature.
3 The material of the wire.

When you are planning, it is important to identify all your variables and decide which ones you are going to vary and which ones you are going to keep constant (unchanged). It is very unwise to vary more than one independent variable at the same time. You should also state how many values of each independent variable you will need to use. When you start changing a fresh variable, compare the new results with your previous ones. If you are making predictions about the effects of different variables, try to predict the effect before you start and try to give a scientific reason why. It does not matter if you are wrong.

Ensure that your planning is clearly written in a form which your teacher and the external moderator can follow. Usually drawing a diagram will help in this. Remember marks can only be given for what is written down.

At this stage your teacher may look at your plan and may even make suggestions, especially for your safety!

Skill Area O Obtaining evidence

The following table shows the Programme of Study requirements.

Programme of Study Requirements
You should have been taught: • To use a range of apparatus and equipment safely and with skill. • To make observations and measurements to a degree of precision appropriate to the context. • To make sufficient relevant observations and measurements for reliable evidence. • To consider uncertainties in measurements and observations. • To repeat measurements and observations where appropriate. • To record evidence clearly and appropriately as you carry out the work.

In this skill area you carry out the plan you made. As you do this you will make detailed observations and/or measurements. If you are aiming for high marks, it is best to include some measurements.

Make sure you write down your observations straight away. Use a suitable table or tables for this. There are two reasons why you should record your observations and measurements immediately:

1 In case you lose them – it does happen
2 It enables you to see possible errors or gaps in your results and helps you to see patterns that exist in them.

Make sure your observations are detailed. If you are observing the colour of something, record it accurately, for example, as dark green rather than just green.

If you are taking measurements, are you taking them to the right degree of accuracy? For example, when measuring the diameter of a length of wire, a ruler is not accurate enough; a micrometer screw gauge should be used instead. Also, the diameter should be measured at several different points along the length of the wire and an average taken.

If you get the following results:

$$0.25\ mm^2 \qquad 0.25\ mm^2 \qquad 0.25\ mm^2 \qquad 0.27\ mm^2$$

is it right to work out an average of 0.255 mm^2? No, it is wrong for two reasons:

1 It is likely that the 0.27 mm^2 is wrong and you should check it.
2 Quoting an average to three decimal places, suggests a degree of accuracy which you cannot justify. Your measurements were accurate to only two decimal places.

Do not be afraid to modify or change your plan. You may wish to repeat readings, increase the temperature range in an investigation or take additional measurements.

Skill Area A Analysing evidence and drawing conclusions

The following table shows the Programme of Study requirements.

Programme of Study Requirements
You should have been taught: • To present qualitative and quantitative data clearly. • To present data as graphs, using lines of best fit where appropriate. • To identify patterns or trends in results. • To use graphs to identify relationships between variables. • To present numerical results to an appropriate degree of accuracy. • To check that conclusions drawn are consistent with the evidence. • To explain how results support or undermine the original prediction when one has been made. • To try to explain conclusions in the light of your knowledge and understanding of science.

This skill area follows on from Skill Area O. If you fail to get satisfactory results for Skill Area O, your teacher can give you other results to analyse to enable you to score marks in this skill area. Having got all your observations and measurements, now is the time to try to make sense of them. Go back and remind yourself of your original plan and any prediction you made. Look objectively at your results. Do they support your prediction?

If you have altered two or more variables, what effect does each one have on your experiment? You may find that altering one variable has much more effect than varying others. If your prediction is not right, try to see why not.

Your measurements are usually best displayed in some kind of graph. You can use a computer to help you plot the graph, providing it is your own work.

If you draw a graph on a piece of graph paper, choose your scales and axes carefully. Try to fill the piece of graph paper and use simple scales, e.g. 1 small square represents 1 °C, rather than a complicated scale, e.g. three small squares represent 2 °C. Label each of the axes with both quantity and unit and draw a line of 'best-fit'. This may not go through all the points plotted. Put an appropriate title on your graph.

Draw a conclusion from your results. Comment on whether it supports or disagrees with your original prediction and try to explain it using your scientific knowledge and understanding.

Skill Area E Evaluating evidence

The following table shows the Programme of Study requirements

Programme of Study Requirements
You should have been taught: • To consider whether the evidence is sufficient to enable firm conclusions to be drawn. • To consider reasons for anomalous results and to reject such results where appropriate. • To consider the reliability of results in terms of the uncertainty of the measurements and observations. • To propose improvements to the methods that have been used. • To propose further investigation to test their conclusions.

This is the most difficult skill area for candidates. You have to look at your evidence and comment upon its reliability and whether it is sufficient to enable a firm conclusion to be made. You should also look at any anomalous results.

If you collected three results and plotted them on a graph, it is unlikely that you will be able to justify a straight line graph, for example. You need a minimum of five results to justify drawing a line of any shape.

Points which lie well away from the 'best-fit' line may be anomalous results. Either check them or explain why you think they are unreliable, e.g. because you misread a meter or you think the wire got hot due to the current flow.

Finally you should suggest changes you would make, if you were repeating the experiment, in order to get more valid results. This could involve improvements to existing experiments or further work.

Getting the best marks in your coursework

The following criteria have been written to help you judge your performance in Sc 1.

It illustrates what is required in each skill area for two marks, four marks, six marks and eight marks (*Note:* six marks is the maximum for Skill Area E). If your performance is between two and four, you can be given three marks. In order to score eight marks in Skill Area P, you have to have met the requirements for two, four and six marks also.

Remember that coursework makes up 25% of the total marks for your Physics examination. These marks, earned before you take the written examination, can make a difference to your final grade.

	P: Planning Planning my work	**O: Obtaining evidence**	**A: Analysing and concluding**	**E: Evaluating**	
2 marks	I can plan something to investigate.	I can use equipment safely and take some readings or measurements.	I can show what I have found out.	I can say something about how well my plan has worked.	**2 marks**
4 marks	**plus...** I know that my plan is a fair test, and can choose the right equipment to use.	**plus...** I can take a series of useful readings or measurements and I can record them carefully.	**plus...** I can show if there is a pattern in what I have found out by using diagrams, charts or simple graphs.	**plus...** I can say how accurate my results are and if my experiment can be improved.	**4 marks**
6 marks	**plus...** Using scientific ideas I can decide which are the most important factors. I can say what readings I will need to take, and how many of them I will need.	**plus...** I can make careful and accurate readings or measurements and record them clearly. I can repeat my observations and measurements if this will help.	**plus...** I can use my scientific knowledge and the information from my diagrams, charts or graphs to help me make a conclusion.	**plus...** I can explain if my evidence is good enough to support my conclusion. I can suggest improvements to obtain better results.	**6 marks**
8 marks	**plus...** I can use detailed scientific ideas in my plan to help me to get reliable results. I have used details of any information which helped me to plan.	**plus:** I can use equipment skilfully to obtain high quality results.	**plus...** I can use detailed scientific ideas to explain my conclusion. I can say how my results link back to my planning.		**8 marks**

Index